Arrival

1941 – 1952

Lilian Forshaw was born in Brighton, Sussex and studied at Brighton Art College, where she specialised in painting and Industrial pottery before spending some time painting and working in Venice. In her final year she trained to be an art teacher, and has continued to explore new techniques and media throughout her life, most recently becoming an award winning portrait painter.

Encouraged by her daughter to, 'write down all the family stories her grandmother and mother had told her' she made a start when she retired and surprised herself when, in less than two years she had written four books, covering the years from 1887 to 1952. Arrival is the third book in a trilogy of books about family life in Brighton. Lilian now lives near Battle, East Sussex.

Find out more about Lilian and her writing:
www.singletobrighton.co.uk

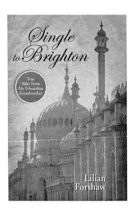

Clara's richly illuminated story makes me wish I could chart my own grandmother's life with such depth and clarity. I could not put *Single to Brighton* down. Nor can I wait to hear, in the second volume, what happened next to the intrepid Clara.

**The Eminent Historian
Professor Lisa Jardine CBE**

Dolly's story has all the narrative excitement of the roaring twenties. It is full of the sights and sounds of the period, and shot through with the emotions of the age.

**The Eminent Historian
Professor Lisa Jardine CBE**

Arrival

1941 – 1952

My memoir based on true stories

Lilian Forshaw

First published in 2016 by Deerfold Press

Copyright © Lilian Forshaw 2016

www.singletobrighton.co.uk

Typesetting in Garamond by
Lilian Forshaw

All Illustrations and Photographs © Lilian Forshaw
Printed in Great Britain by
Berforts South West Ltd, Hastings
A catalogue record of this book is available from
The British Library
ISBN 978-0-9954979-0-0

List of author's own drawings and photos

As a child of the nineteen forties, my aim has been to capture
the true stories of the lives and events that surrounded
my early years, before they are lost forever.

I have always loved books with pictures they make me feel
I am really inside the story. As this is my book I have included
quite a few pictures. I hope they make you feel you are
inside the story too.

Author's notes
While the stories told to me by my Grandmother,
Mother our wider family and neighbours, recorded here are true,
some of the names and places have been changed to
preserve anonymity

My special thanks to Ollie Wardle
who typed my original manuscript and
helped me through my battles with wayward computers.
Ollie you are a star.

Paul, Galia and Adrian
Chris, Alexander and Sebastian
Thank you all for your help and support.
This truly is a family affair.

Now, before I go any further I should tell my readers, who have not read books one and two of my Grandmother Clara's life, that some of the time the Willow pattern china, owned by our family members, and now sit on our dresser here at Deerfold Cottage in East Sussex, will add their memories of our family life, which will, to avoid confusion, be printed in italic font.

When I realised they had been among us longer than any single living member of our human family, I thought, they must have some stories to tell.

To aid the understanding of new readers I will note, in the early pages, who and where these pieces of china came from.

I know many of you enjoy reading the Willow's contributions, but as there were fewer of them in daily use during the 1940s they have less input into this time of our lives. However, it is the smallest item in my Willow pattern family, a place setting named Mispah, which opened book one in Granma Clara Ann's youth that features on the front cover of this book.

You will find a list of family and Willow characters on the back pages

Map of 1940s Brighton included at reader's request

Clara in 1938, finally retired aged 70

Preface to bring you up to date with events in book two.

September 1940

Clara was taking a moment of quiet contemplation sitting on
the widow seat looking back into the now empty room, that was,
until an hour ago, her snug little flat overlooking the stable yard in
Porthall Mews; all the comings and goings of the day had ceased,
only the odd motor vehicle could be heard passing along the nearby
Dyke road. She had hoped for a peaceful retirement; a room of
her own and just herself to look after. It hadn't lasted long. The
soft spring and lovely summer of '39 were absolute bliss. No bells
summoning her upstairs carrying the usual laden trays followed by
the inevitable request, 'Oh and would you be a dear Clara and just
bring some more of this - or - another that.'

Brighton had been where she had lived and worked since she
had fled her childhood home on Pevensey Levels in 1887. Taking
the train to Brighton on that hopeful day, everything she saw was
new. Turning left outside the station she'd met a street teeming with
people, and close packed with cottages, where, as she walked down
the hill, she found herself constantly in near collision with women
carrying baskets barging in and out from narrow passages stinking
of steamy boilers. Her ears felt assaulted by sharp barking clipped
voices calling their wares, when she was so fresh from soft burrs and
jingling sheep bells. In contrast, turning her steps right, toward the
sea, the vision of soaring sky pointing pinnacles and dumpy onion
shaped domes of the Royal Pavilion, took her breath away. While
sails scudding over the sea were a familiar sight; the pier with its
swooping chain linked great arches thrusting out to the horizon,
surprised her eyes. Her sister Rose had said she would see some rare
sights; but these sights, these were astonishing. Looking back to
those days she was still a country girl, now, four lifetimes had gone
by.

When, in 1938 her employer died, Clara would have been made
homeless, but for the coincidence that her 70th birthday fell in the
same month making her eligible to claim the weekly 10 shillings,

(50p) old age Pension. By managing her small savings along with this pension she decided she could retire from being on call 24 hours a day, apart from the regulation one half day off in seven. Those first few months had been lovely; she could plan her own day and even change her own mind. The only regular arrangements she had, and looked forward to each week, was to make a steamed steak and kidney pudding for her daughter and son in law, Dolly and Art, taking it the short walk along to their house in Coventry Street, where she joined them for Saturday lunch. Then, if she didn't feel too tired after they had eaten and cleared away, she walked along to the Seven Dials, arm in arm with Dolly, to catch the number 38 bus down to West street where Dolly treated her to a shilling (5p) seat at the Academy Cinema.

On Sundays she took the bus across town to her son and daughter in law, Jimmie and Hilda, in Picton Street for tea. It was nice to join in the family fireside with her bit of knitting she'd been doing for the Grandchildren. Clara never outstayed her welcome, just enough to know she was part of their lives. When the weather was fine a walk over the road from Porthall into Dyke Road Park where she could sit on a bench and look out to the sea beyond the tree lined horizon. Well that too was lovely.

Now every passing day brought news in the papers and on the wireless that caused her an ever rising agitation. The gardeners over in Dyke Road Park had started stripping the turf off the back playing field to make allotments where the locals could grow vegetables. It was all so unsettling.

Bad news had struck close to home when a friend's son was killed in a flying training accident and in consequence his mother took her own life; her third sister Fanny was trapped in Paris; Jimmie had gone overseas with the Territorial's, nobody knew where. And on top of it all her grandson had been evacuated far away to a farm in Yorkshire. Even her sister Nancy's husband, Valentino, who everybody said was more English than the English themselves, was interned as an enemy alien, 'How could they be such hypocrites,' Nancy wrote to Clara, 'when half the Government Ministers had eaten Valentino's food at our Italian restaurant in Soho for all these years.' The tensions were becoming unbearable.

Artie, having passed his medical as A1, expected to be called up, but had been told, as he was 38 years old and a healthy Plumber, he was in a 'Reserved Occupation,' to keep things going at home. Now Dolly was pressing her Mother to give up her comfy little domain and move into their spare room. She would be safer, they said. But Clara said she would be no safer living in Coventry Street than she was up the road in Porthall Mews. Although for practical purposes, the thought had not escaped her notice, that if Dolly and Artie's spare room was occupied it would avoid having another awkward evacuee. It was for the whole family's peace of mind they all said. She wasn't convinced. Until the Saturday lunchtime she set her basket down on Dolly's kitchen table, lifted the tea towel and found she had brought her old jerry in the basket instead of the basin of steak and kidney pudding wrapped in its' cloth. Clara had sunk onto a kitchen chair all of a heap thinking she must be going out of her mind. That's when she relented. Well, perhaps it was for the best. And, after all, she had to admit, the Ack-Ack guns, set up just a few hundred yards away from her flat in Porthall Mews, were disturbing her nights much more often.

Standing up with a sigh she fastened the top button on her black Astrakhan coat, (the one her employer, AHP, had given her in the last winter she had worked for him.) Yet again, here she was giving up her own private little hideaway. The very thought brought those passed times rushing back into her mind –

Way back in 1887 it had been heart breaking to leave her little room up in the eaves at her Grandparent's Inn on Pevensey Marsh all those years ago when she was nineteen and forced to part from Frank. She was sorry to have to leave dear old Mr Luckins to his fate in Brighton's workhouse and so sad that Miss Crimmins had to close the Blue Tearooms by the Clock Tower, putting an end to that happy company of women. It was a very unhappy, let alone the heart wrenching time, in 1919, when she and the children were evicted from their home in St George's Mews, and an awful blow in 1930 to be spirited away from such a good position, after her AHP died in such awkward circumstances. In the whole of her 72 years the only time she had left one place for another in a happy state, and that was when she left her job in Adelaide Crescent at the

Whitesides, to be married. Although they were such lovely people, she had thoroughly enjoyed being their family cook.

Oh stop all this looking back in regret, she told herself as she pulled on her gloves. Come on Clara Cowley, you've always before been determined to look upon the best side of life. Ah, but now what would another war bring?

Book Three 1941 - 1952

BOOK THREE: 1941 – 1952

Part One

1

Clara's Safe Haven

Past midnight and now the snow was hardening on the roads when Doctor John pulled his bicycle down the front steps from the family house where he and his wife, Doctor Grace, had their surgery in Richmond Terrace opposite the Level in the centre of Brighton. Most of their patients lived up the steep hills, to Hanover and Prestonville either side of this, the Steine Valley.

The night was quiet, and the sky looked like clearing.

Artie had 'phoned the surgery at tea time to say Dolly's waters had broken before he made a second call from the 'phone in the kiosk at the top of Stanford road to exchange his fire watch duty with a workmate for the coming night. Since Christmas the bombing had lessened. On the way back home he dropped in to his sister Hetty Levett, in Upper Hamilton Road, to tell her the news and warn her to be ready to come and help with the birthing after she'd given her husband Arthur his tea.

By the time he walked back along Coventry Street the snow had turned from a fine breadcrumb spattering to floaty feathers covering the pavement and roadway.

It took the Doctor over an hour slipping and sliding his way on the unlit road with his heavily laden old bike across the London Road and up Old Shoreham. Seeing a toiling shadowy figure down the hill Alfie Allen the ARP Warden hurried towards the Doctor to give a push up the steep gradient. Negotiating the turn on to Stanford Road the two men stopped for a short breather.

"Hope it's an A and not a D tonight Doc?"

"Just along Cov." the doctor answered.

"Aha, then it'll be an arrival. The wife said young Dolly looked near her time. Good luck then Sir. Goodnight to you."

"Goodnight Alf."

Scrubbing off his boots on the front door mat Doctor John hung his bicycle clips on the handlebar of his machine, propping it against the wall on the newspaper protected linoleum floor, before following the prospective father through to the downstairs back room where his glasses immediately steamed opal white. The room was much too hot, a good fire had settled since midnight and as if for a long haul the kettles sat lazily steaming in the hearth. Hetty stood up to greet their family doctor. He smiled and nodded, slipped his glasses low on his nose to see his way to the bed, set his bag down and deposited a half bottle of whisky underneath the foot of the bed.

Sitting down beside his patient he took his glasses off and proceeded to dry them clean whilst smiling down at the young woman he had last seen six months ago.

"There we are then, second week in January it is." he said with a knowing chuckle. A man of few words all kind and full of good humour.

After his examination the anxious mother enquired,

"Will it take much longer Doctor?"

"A while yet my dear, you just settle back. I'll be with you, do as I say as the time comes. Have no fear, all's well."

It had been a long haul for Dolly, she'd worn herself out. Her crying and shouts had woken Clara in the room above bringing her mother out onto the landing to ask what all the noise was about. Artie called up the stairs to her to say all was well, she was not needed yet. So she returned to bed where over the last month she had finally been able to sleep through the nights.

At 10 to 4 a.m. Doctor John said,

"Well done, a lovely healthy girl Mrs Smith." He didn't rush away, not Doctor John. He and Hetty cleaned and cleared together while he was watchful of his patient. Artie made a cup of tea for his wife and all four sat together the two men drinking tea laced with John's own reviver. He did not leave until the baby was washed and put to the breast staying until he was satisfied all was going well. Both John and Grace Vance knew the families in their care. Whatever home either Doctor was in, they became part of that family and loved as a cherished member.

As he helped the Doctor on with his coat Art said,

"Thank you Doctor. What do I owe you?"

"Call in to the surgery next week sometime. I'll leave a bill on the hall table." Outside on the front doorstep both surveyed the lightening sky, "Been a quiet night up there." he observed looking at the blue starry dawn. Turning to Artie, "Finish that bottle for me and get some sleep old chap. Call me if you need me." He advised, pulling his scarf up over his face. The snow crunched under his boots as he set off on foot astride his old wheels towards the long steep curve that is Hamilton Road.

"Just look at those pretty blue eyes Artie." Hetty said. She got no answer. Her brother hadn't needed the whisky. Sitting beside the bed his head on the pillow next to his wife and new baby Artie was asleep.

Taking the baby from Dolly's arms Hetty quietly left the room. Upstairs Clara lay in her bed propped up surrounded by pillows, a quilt pulled up to her chin. Beside her the flame flickered on the candle in a little Willow pattern nightstick sitting on the table under the window. A fire still glowed low in the tiny arched bedroom grate.

"Here she is Clara." Hetty laid the baby in Clara's arms. "Dolly's fast asleep."

"Pull open the curtains Hetty dear, will you? We'll see the sunrise together this little one and I'"

Hetty looked down at the baby snuggled against her white haired Grandmother as she snuffed out the candle flame and drew back the curtains. Across towards the Race Hill she could just see a plane patrolling across the pale sky out over the Channel. As she was leaving the room she heard the old lady whispering to the baby,

"I was born on a cold winter night too – I've got so much to tell you –."

It was there in that terraced house in Brighton, Sussex at dawn on a cold January in 1941, my Grandma Clara Ann's stories began.

Dolly's eyes flickered open as Hetty was collecting her coat ready to leave,

"You won't believe what Clara was telling that babe when I left the room."

"Oh I do," answered Dolly sleepily. "Lily will soon know all about our family back to 1065."

"Don't you mean 1066?"

"No," laughed Dolly, "Oh don't make me laugh it hurts. No my mother can tell family stories going back to 1065. Just you believe it."

"Well… I suppose I've got to if you say so."

But Dolly had already fallen into that special deep sleep.

The Willows on the dresser at Deerfold Cottage

'We know. We've heard all those stories too,' said Tubby, the short blue and white Willow pattern nightstick, 'I was there that night. Laura and Bea, Clara's cup and tea dish, were on Clara's old bamboo table over by the fireplace and Ol' Po, well, he was under the bed of course, and Mispah the tiny place setting, was watching from the mantelpiece alongside Frank's last letter that arrived back in 1940.'

'Frank had written telling Clara about his travels through the Rockies and Yosemite National Park before he returned to his island again,' Mispah said, 'he had explained how he was rearing sheep and was planning to sell the farm island to the family who were looking after the place while he had been away. They had a growing family to support and it would be ideal for him to retire and move on.'

'Pity Clara had such a sad letter to write when she replied, sending the Newspaper Article about young Toby's death in that flying accident, and another telling about Petronella's suicide.' Sighed Mrs P, 'You know I think you five in Clara's room, were the only Willow pattern at the house in Coventry Street, Dolly never had any Willows of her own to use during the war years.'

'Bloomin' well out of date that's us lot.' called out Big Pol with her big laughing voice. She was the jug Clara's Grandfather, John Pilbeam used to serve his ale from at the Lamb Inn on Pevensey Levels.

'Back in and back out of fashion more like.' said Uncle Bert. A ripple of laughter went round the kitchen. Uncle Bert, a large tureen, dated 1880, had been found in an Antique shop in Goudhurst by Lily and Paul back in the 1980s

'Everything's out of date here,' remarked the Trumpet vase, 'even this house. It's the oldest place I've lived in,' and before any of the other Willows could have their say, the vase went on, 'Although I feel more at home here at Deerfold Cottage, between friends, than I've felt before.'

'Thanks for that my lovurly.' answered Ol' Po. 'You are our latest addition you know?'

'And your story telling brings us all together. Our memories mingle don't they?'

'Well put,' answered Uncle Bert, 'but now let's get back to 1941. Clara lay with the new baby in her arms listening to the world.'

'A very different world to the one our Clara was born into in 1868,' remarked Laura.

'Yes,' went on Bea, 'hers was a time of real quiet, a time when Grandfather John was her own storyteller. He used to say, "Listen to the world at dawn children," wouldn't he Bea?'

'"When that first wind whispers across the land, you'll see the old sun peep up over the horizon." ' Uncle Bert interrupted, laughing, as he repeated John's well remembered words. 'In hilly ol' Brighton it had to come off the wide sweeping bay and' up across the fish market and the railway works.'

'Ow'd you know Bert, you weren't there.' butted in Ol' Po.

'Ha, ha!' chuckled Uncle Bert in a tap the side of your nose sort of way. 'You'd be surprised to know where I was in Brighton in those days!'

'An' when there's been a stormy night yer can smell the sea water and weed right up over the Downs.' Laura joined in.

'Sometimes on hot days the air smelled of tar and salty rope an' wood.' added Mispah, keeping the happy thoughts rolling.

'Mm, an' when my flame was blown out, and the blackout curtains were drawn back, the smell of a boiling kettle an' tea brewing.' mm lovely, mused Tubby.

'Oh yes an' fried bread done in drippin', crisp 'n' hot.' added Ol' Po.

'Nevertheless,' came back Bea's quiet voice, 'on the day Lily was born ...'

'Yes she was Clara's last Grandchild.' Laura reminded the listeners.

'Clara began to relive the happiest times of her life,' went on Bea, 'telling the baby her stories.'

'Her own epilogue maybe.' offered Mispah

Here is a poignant story
to touch your hearts.

You may recall that towards the end of book two, in 1939, I began
to weave the lives of the Forshaw family into my own.

In the late spring of 1941 the twins' Mum, Joyce Forshaw, had
her own story, one she kept close to her heart, in sadness, for the
young man who she went out with before she met her husband and
who might have asked for her hand, had he not been piped at the
post by Alex Forshaw.

In her apron pocket she had a letter from that young man's
mother, – *'just to say he went down with HMS Hood.'*

BOOK THREE: 1941 – 1952

2

Lily

I am told that on the morning of my birth snow still laid on the ground. The school playground, that runs along behind the gardens on our side of Coventry Street, was a smooth and white as a newly spread bed sheet. A pale sun shone across the hard white expanse reflecting the voices of the early arrivals, squealing and piping with children's delight to be the first to make their marks in the snow. A fresh nip in the air and crunch underfoot revealed underlying ice; a great source of good sliding from the sloping high corner down towards the tall red brick school building. Irritated loud adult voices brought the instigators to a stand-still to prevent the whole playground being turned into a skating rink. In the school lavs muffled voices could be heard between the sound of slamming wood on wood doors preceding urgent voices calling out, "hold the door for me," and "go away." Feet running, skid, ouch, cry. A whistle blew, bleep bleeeep, causing a sort of hush then a final high pitch blast, it's sound giving a longer squawk gained quiet; followed by the sound of feet, dragging reluctantly one behind the other drained away, ending in a vibrating bang as heavy doors clicked shut. I can visualise exactly what I was told, for young children living in Coventry Street these were the sounds of our early years, before we took our part in the life of that playground.

Of course I don't remember anything of those days. I only know from Dad's sister, my Aunty Hetty, telling how I drifted off to sleep in the deep feather bed with Gran telling me where she was born. It was the first of many tales I heard, when later I was able to creep up onto her family quilt to hear more stories, amongst what Gran called, 'geejaws;' all the little items secreted between the pillows and blankets. Each item had its own family story to tell. They may be the tiny jellies she called jujubes, or a pretty sweety paper, always the odd small crab apple – anything that started a story. From then on those stories have gradually returned to my conscious memory.

Later, after the war was over, Gran told me about the time when my mother refused to put me into the cradle style gas mask. My Mother thought the nasty black rubber thing was as big a hazard to shut me in, than to keep me out. It had to be pumped all the time the baby was inside. What would happen if she was rendered unable to carry on pumping? She said, surely the baby inside would suffocate.

When I finally made my first notes for this book I was seven years younger than Clara would have been when I was born, already my hair was as white as hers was then. Snuggled down beside her in her bed she told me her stories, the stories she couldn't contain any longer. Granma's tales have been seeds set to germinate a huge gathering of characters and places in my visual memory.

Now I am a Grandmother I can no longer contain her stories.

Grandma often had a faraway look and I think by then she was already losing her sight. I noticed her fingers gently tracing across the patches in her quilt; a counterpane made of pieces of fabric from old family dressmaking off cuts, full of lives whose memories remained close, keeping her company. Sometimes, hardly audible words told me Granny was falling asleep, until her hand moved onto a patch evoking a memory of a little incident that sparked another tale to keep me thrilled through grey winter afternoons. Between stories we snoozed, she recovering from nights broken by the noise of bombing and the distant booming from the great anti-aircraft guns situated nearby on the Dyke Road

Over the years little by little, in her soft Sussex burr, Granma painted word pictures about her own childhood.

I was full of wonder when she said she had twelve brothers and sisters, I couldn't imagine that many children in one house. "Oh no she chuckled, we were all born at St Leonards just along the coast from Hastings but I spent most of my early years living with our Grandparents, John and Ann Pilbeam at their Inn on the Pevensey Levels." Her mother, she said, was John and Annie's third daughter, Emily. Gran said, her mum produced each new addition about two years apart, and we all lived. "Yes, dear ol' mum, she lost more than one tooth for every child she bore." For years I pictured this poor woman whose teeth fell out every time she had a baby! I have to laugh at how my childish mind took her words so literally. Granma said, that looking back on those times her Granny and Granfer were wonderful the way they had all their Grandchildren staying at one time or another at the Inn, every summer and ever so many winter weeks.

By the time Clara Ann arrived at the Inn in 1870 Grandfather John Pilbeam was as well known for the cattle he reared on the Marshland as he was for being an Innkeeper.

It was her world I inhabited for the first years of my life.

3

This is Clara Ann's voice telling her stories.

"I could only have been a little tot, not much more than two years old, when I remember being carried in Granny Ann's arms looking down at her vegetable garden at the back of the Lamb Inn. I can't tell what she said to me that time because I was too young but as the years went by Gran would explain about the vegetables she mingled with flowers and herbs. Oh, she knew which plants enjoyed each other's company. She only had a small area of garden but most of what she wanted for her kitchen was there. Granny particularly loved Gilly flowers which she grew along the edges of her vegetable plot. In the evenings their perfume was softly lovely.

Since my first introduction to her garden I watched her carry my brothers and sisters around, each in their turn, with us all trailing along hearing her story again and again, the same as she did for me, that first time, only then I'd had her all to myself.

Walking along the brick path to the far end where Gooseberry bushes and late sweet fruiting raspberry canes grew, were two woven reed Skeps. Granfer had made those for Grannie's Bees. She would always stop a little ways back and call,

"Hallo my dears come and meet our new baby." The odd Bee would often be hovering nearby so it looked as if a Bee or two came out to meet her and settle on her somewhere. She'd tell the Bee the new babe's name.

"Meet Rose– or John," she'd say,

"John this is one of our workmen. He visits the flowers to introduce them to each other, he collects their pollen and takes it home to his factory, then the family in there, look," – pointing to the Skep, – "makes honey for us all. Mr Bee will come to say Hallo to you once in a while, just let him sit for a breather then he'll be off back to work again. Try not to move suddenly or touch him, he's very delicate." She told one of my brothers, "careful Harry, keep still, Mr Bee is carrying heavy shopping bags those big yellow ones on his back legs see." She made these little chats a routine we each heard – it was a good way to learn.

Along with the Bee Skeps a big clump of cherry rhubarb grew beside the gate where it opened into a small orchard, just enough space for a few trees. On the northern side behind the pigsty Granny's father James had planted a Walnut tree. It was a sapling from one of the group of Walnut trees his father, Will Hartshorn, cultivated years back nearby his Carpentry shop, because Walnut produces a good carving timber. Gran's Walnut tree stood to the north a little away from the fruiting trees because James had said it would grow tall and he didn't want it to overshadow the fruit trees in the orchard. The tree gave us lovely fresh Walnuts, such a clean creamy flavour. I did love them.

What other fruits were there now? Well, certainly a Bramley apple and a lovely sweet eater I think it's name was something like Ole Turner's Orange or gold – something like that because the flesh was a peachy gold colour. The Quince tree had the prettiest colour leaves in the orchard and its bone hard fruits gave us Marmalade better than any Oranges made. There were two Pear trees and a big sprawling Medler tree. They're funny looking ol' things, bit like little overripe Crab apples. Gran made jelly with them to go with cold meat. The old folks enjoyed their Medler relish. When the windfalls were down the piggy was allowed in to clear up; other times of the year any orphaned lambs Granny hand reared were put to the orchard to keep the growth down under the trees.

Now there was one Lamb all my sisters and brothers must remember I'm sure. We called her Silly Dilly. Granny had her in a box by the range because her mother died in a deep cold winter so she was a January baby. Granny bottle fed Dilly and of course she thought Gran was her mummy. Dilly followed Granny everywhere but one day burned her nose on the oven door so she had to be kept out of the kitchen. Silly Dilly made such a fuss when Gran shut her out in the orchard. Ah! Mmm silly little Dilly pretty little thing.

As one memory faded Granma's voice lowered, often into a sweet chuckle and another vision took its place.

* * * *

Our Grandparents were both born in the 1820's. So they started their lives as Georgians. Cheeky ol' George IV was still king then, 'e lived along at Brighthelmst'ne in those days. No concerns about ol' Boney fetchin' up on these shores in their childhood times. I know they both talked about King William more than George. I still have the silver Groat Grandma Ann gave me; it was minted in the last year of King William's life. It says 1837 on the back and I'm told it was a fourpenny piece, (2p today) she used to keep it in an old leather purse in her apron pocket.

Granny Ann was a Miss Hartshorn. The Hartshorn's were Carpenters and Blacksmiths back up inland ter'wards Win'mill hill way. At the time Granma Ann was born her father James worked with his two unmarried brothers, Joe and Edwin, in their Father Tom's Carpenter's shop. Next door, the Blacksmith's belonged to their half brother George, he were Tom's son by his first wife Molly who died in childbirth. Originally the Blacksmiths had been Molly's father's place so George inherited the business. George, 'e got well known for his elegant wrought iron gates 'n' fire irons. Granfer John had a set of grand fire dogs at the Lamb Inn that

George made. He fashioned real lively looking animal's heads on his work. Grandmother Annie, she was a highly respected Wheelwright before she married John Pilbeam, her father James said he, 'couldn't keep the young wench out of his workshop she was so keen to join him and his brothers,' so they helped her learn the Wheelwrighting craft and set her up in her own workshop and she became so thundering good her products were much saught after by folks from miles around.'

Robert Pilbeam owned the Lamb Inn where Granfer John was born in 1823. The Pilbeams' came from farming families across the eastern end of the Marsh, none of them had owned the land they worked, Robert was the first in the family to own property

Before Granfer and Gran took over the Lamb Inn from Granfer's Father, Robert, in the late 1850s, Beer, Bread and a Bed, BBB, were all there was to be had by wayfarers and locals. Since those early days Grandfather John had become well known for his 'thumping good Ales, grand songs and story-telling.' And his wife Annie's cooking, especially the Hams she smoked up in the inglenook, 'were to die for.' That's what they said.

Oh, dear Great Grandfather Robert, now 'e was a case 'e was. Granfer told how 'is father liked a bit o' music especially when they sang the Psalms in church along with all their musicians.

When they were young boys Granfer and his three brothers always had their working dogs with them. They walked miles checking on the beasts across the Levels and along the seashore but, their Dad made sure they found themselves near the village church when it was the time for the Psalmody service. In they'd all troop, Grandfather, the boys and their 'workers.' That's what Granfer's father called their dogs. Barney and Meg belonged to their Father. I don't recall the names of the three pups owned by Granfer John and his brothers. Howsoever, they all made themselves at home in their usual back pew, the dogs lying in their own comfortable fug round their masters' feet during the service. Robert would join in with the musicians and singers at the top o' 'is voice. Together, the violin, viola and squeeze box could create a huge emotional sound. On festival days, cymbals and a drum often accompanied the congregation and Robert's contribution helped fill the old stone building to the rafters.

"Aw the old vicar daren'st 'tut' 'im tho'. Aw no. A visiting young vicar did comment on, 'is loud singing,' just the once. Father gave 'im such a look," said Granfer John, then said that, his Father told the young vicar, 'I'm a singing to our Lord not to you young man. I've got ter get me innings right up high. He ain't always close by as you says he is.' 'Hah, young parson 'e didn't like that. But church, they got their own back, they didn't like all the noisy instruments so as them new organs were put in the churches and the clergy had local orphans to pump the bellows, well, that put paid to folks airing their lungs' with quite the same vigour."

"Sad really," Granfer said, "Father did enjoy 'is singing." Granfer said that after he'd witnessed his Father's summary dismissal for showing his open and honest joy in raising his voice to the Lord, he for himself lost all interest, he just felt only contempt for them and their religion; especially when they expected to extract a tithe from poor folks and gave nothing in return themselves.

* * * *

"That wasn't only time the family 'ad a set to with vicar. When John and Ann got married in 1844 John was recorded in the register as a 'Farm Labourer' and Ann Hartshorn, 'Spinster.' James wanted, 'Wheel-wright' after his daughter's name.

'We can't have that in the Register,' the vicar said, 'that would be most improper.' He was new to the village and 'e were shocked that a young woman worked at a man's job. Ann's father, James, told vicar,

'Then you'd best not 'av us 'ere at all if you're not respectful to my daughter's skill.'

'Oh, 'e changed 'is tune pretty quick. Well, never knew when 'e might want his own carriage wheels seen to, did 'e?'

By the time I was growing to understand what that was all about Granny Ann hadn't done any Wheel-wrighting for a few years so when Granfer pointed out the wheels on, (Granma Annie's oldest friend Henrietta) Aunt Hetta's pony trap, it was the first time I'd really noticed. Granfer and I were giving Dora, Hetta's pony, a bit of a rub down whilst she were waiting for her Mistress – she, Hetta, was upstairs takin' tay with Granny. Granfer drew my attention to the wheels on the trap saying,

"Look ther', them's pretty wheels. Must have been the last pair your Granny made a'fore she passed the Wheel-Wrighting business on to 'er Apprentice. Hetta's 'kept 'em well tended."

They really were beautiful lightweight and painted a dark red with fine outlining. Well, I thought to myself, my Granny can do so many things; bake, cook, sew her lovely quilts and grow lines of vegetables and flowers, oh so much – now I'm seeing another of her skills. I felt a bit silly, for I couldn't think of anything to say – but stand there admiring them wheels.

Granfer said, "I first saw my Ann was when I were but a 12 year old lad, standin' there beside my father while he and James Hartshorn were discussing a job Dad wanted done for the Inn. I noticed this little gal, she were planing off a piece of wood. Struck me how expertly she seemed to be handlin' the job. Never forgot that sight. When my brother Robbie dragged me along to one o' them village socials I saw 'er again – I must 'ave bin a bit more'n twenty years by then. Oh my goodness the lads were round Annie all evenin'. Beautiful long chestnut coloured ringlets she had. I'd not seen her without a work cap on before, there and then I knew she were for me, so as soon as I could, I called at her parent's house. Her Mother gave me a look 'n' left me outside the door. I didn't know p'raps she'd 'ad enough of all them young men a comin' to court her daughter. Anyways, round the house came a lovely sight, her skirts all brushin' the lavender hedge. Her Ma, Rosanna was 'er name, grew low hedges of lavender and rosemary all along the pathways, said it brought the perfume into the house on their skirts. Lovely it was."

Little nosegays of that lavender found their way into Granny's scrap book. Granny Ann became known in our family as a Magpie for the little titbits of life she tucked into her scrapbook.

"Ann were surprised to see me a standin' there hat in hand. Well, she walked towards me carryin' a basket with 'er pickins of tiny tips o' herbs and straight way took my elbow guiding me into the cottage, callin',

'Ma, can I bring 'im in?'

'Yes, orl right then.' Her Mother says,

Sat me at the kitchen table and makes me a dish o' tea. First time I tasted tea that was. Very proud she was of the neat tea box her father made. O' course her Mother, she hovered around us all the while; small woman, Mrs Hartshorn, deep dark eyes and almost black hair. They say she came from Spanish folks. When I asked if I could call again Ann said,

'Of course you can John.' As if I hadn't needed to ask. That's all we said, didn't 'ave to say no more. Tuh! I wondered how such a lovely little woman could be my gal, an' me such a galumpin' great fella. She mixed me many more dishes of tea with her little herbal tips. 'O' corse now I use one of Granny Hartshorn's mugs with a Greyhound handle, but my Annie keeps to 'er dainty tea dish."

"Did the vicar give in and allow Gran's trade to be entered into the marriage certificate then, Gramps?" I asked.

"Oh yes o' course her father James wouldn't 'ear of it any other way. He told me how her being the only gal in a family of all they brothers, there were no keeping the inquisitive little wench out of the workshop."

"So they did the best thing and trained her to Carpenter. And she it was who decided a Wheel-Wright was needed hereabouts. And there she was," he said, "between the carpenter's workshop and her uncle's smithy. Damn fine job she did too." Granfer stood there quietly smiling at his memories.

"There's many a time tho' your Granny Ann has had to laugh at them men who'd come and stand a waitin' for attention outside her workshop, then starts a callin' out.

'Maister where are' yer?'

'Here, says Ann, that's me.'

'The looks on their faces were a treat.' Annie said.

'You'll not lift that 'eavy wheel me gal.' They'd say,

Ah but she did, for her Uncles made a lifting gear, it took all the strain yer see."

* * * *

"Granny and Granfer Pilbeam started their married life together at Hill House. Granfer said he worked for other farmers but he was a very young chap when he rented land to start breeding his own small flock of sheep before adding beef cattle, all on his own account. Then he took on fattening animals for other farmers. Part of the acres he rented, oh it were a large area, belonged to Franklin Anderson.

From a very young man our Granfer was well known. Hah! You wouldn't miss him, he was an unusually tall big chap was Grandfather John. Aw, he was over six feet tall with broad shoulders, and strong, my goodness I knew neighbours who said, 'e 'ad an arm that could fell an Ox. I can hear him now he had a voice like thunder. Yes, all who knew him thought a lot to 'im. Mm, but for all his mighty size 'e was a kindly man, full of humour. He just loved to see others joyful.

The Lamb Inn, built in the 15th Century is a two storey building of brick and tile set where the ground rises up away from the salt marsh and seashore. Standing at the meeting of two lanes well frequented by passing farm traffic and long distance provisions wagons. Although he did say in winter, days, even weeks could go by without a wheeled vehicle or a horse and rider passing by.

When Grandfather took over the licence from his father Robert in 1858 he and Granny attracted many more travellers to their

Bar Parlour. I overheard customers say John was rollicking good company. As they entered the bar locals would call out, '*Whatcheer* John,' and John would reply, '*Holloa Meddy*.' Meaning, 'me dear,' and there would be greetings all round. The Mrs they'd say, 'well she were 'a right welcoming woman.'

Besides all the Willow pattern china John and Annie brought with them from Old Granny Hartshorn's wedding present, there was already a large Blue and White Willow jug in residence, even had a name, she was known as 'Big Pol,' short for Polly. Great Grandfather Robert had used the jug to bring ale up from the barrels in the cellar and she held the privileged position all those years sitting on the end of the bar at the Lamb Inn. She remained in use through Granfer John's time too. The locals said, 'That ol' jug must have heard all the old stories over and over again.'

Now when John and Ann first come to the Inn old Maister Robert he used ter 'ave chopped rushes on bar room floor 'cos customers all smoked pipes an' the men would spit on the floor. Robert, 'e smoked a long old church warden but he never spat, no, that long ol' pipe didn't cause spittle like the little clays the ol' men an' wimmin puffed on. They kept to the tiny bowl pipes 'cos they'm couldn't afford the baccy in their young days, in the early 1800s. Jolly ol' crowd they were suppin' at their gills. Ale was strong in them times. Any ways they loved it when young Johnny came into bar he always brought gales of laughter then. Yes, he was the natural one to take over from 'is father; so patient with the customers; cared for them he did. Everybody liked John an' when he found Annie, well, he couldn't have made a luckier choice in a bride. "Oh dear me, 'lucky the folks 'oo find a compatible bonding."

However there was one thing Granny told me she would not tolerate in her place and that were men spittin' on the floor. The bar room had a well worn flagstone floor. It was easy to flush down and mop off but Granny said spittin' was a dirty dangerous habit. She hadn't allowed spittin' in 'er Wheel-Wrighting workshop. The men could go outside if they wanted to do that. Let them spit in the Blacksmith's fire or the Carpenter's shop but not in here, an' she told 'em so.

Many more men chewed baccy in those days an' even the pipe tobacco was of the sort that made lots o' spittle. Well Grandfather said you couldn't stop the men doin' it. But Gran said she could. She said if they really had to spit they could spit in the fire, she wasn't going to clean out no spittoons.

The locals soon got used to her ways but newcomers had to get to know it wasn't allowed. So she did what she had done in her own workshop. She put up a notice, not in words of course because not all men could read; it was a picture, well two pictures really.

Her father James carved them for her. One had a man's head facing away from the inglenook spitting with a cross a few inches from his face stopping a splatter of fluid, and the other facing towards the fire with a head spitting towards the flames. Grandfather had to laugh at that. Anyway it worked or'l right, so Granny got her way.

Men folk around already knew both of them well, Ann for her Wheel-Wrighting and John as a Shepherd regularly driving his animals to the markets at Hailsham, Pevensey and Battle; Farmers and Breeders came from a good wide distance to buy Grandfather's prize winning cattle and sheep. Old Wattie at the Abattoir was keen to tell his customers his meat came from prized animals off the Levels. Yes, when I worked at the Anderson's their Cook, Mrs Charlish, would tell the visiting butcher to - 'Be sure you're bringing me Mr Pilbeam's beasts, I'll know if they're not mind.' And she did too.

Over the years John and Annie not only built a welcoming reputation at The Lamb, the substance grew with them, quite a cluster of buildings rose around a stable yard with Botheys for the lads, workshops and barn. Granny had her pigpen and her hen house, she herself developed a garden producing an abundance of vegetables and fruit orchard including two happy hives of Bees.

* * * *

When I was old enough I was allowed to join the Drovers, I must have been nine perhaps. I loved going with Granfer and the Gaffers. The evening before market day Granfer and the collies would round up and pen the flock near a gate in the Drovers lane, so's to make an early start.

Granfer's call to his animals was, 'Cum On Boiz n Gals, Cum On Boiz n Gals.' That's all, whether sheep or cattle they'd soon arrive around him, but from then on while he was in their company he never uttered another human word. Young Bull calves would push and shov 'n' nip each other an' skip about, but from Grandfather's throat came only a grunt or growl. The animals understood and like jostling schoolboys got in line through a gateway. If one were bumping the others he would just lean against the beast, be they big or small they knew who led the herd. Then he counted them through the gate with a, 'Den,' at a notch on his Crook for every five pairs.

I'll never forget the first time I went out before dawn. Our steaming breath hanging on the morning air, the moon in a black sky was sending shards of light through the branches beside the lane. High grasses splashed dew up my legs; Mmm, it felt lovely fresh and clean. I was taken by surprise at the way the light suddenly happened. Then so slowly the hedges and fields around took on colour. The thought of that first time does still take my breath away.

My sister Rose came next after me in the family line, she never went along on a Drove. The boys did when they were old enough but Rose, when she was over at the Inn always stayed back looking after the toddlers and a babe or two that might be there. She preferred to get on with her lace knotting, sitting at the back door on a low nursing chair with the cushion on her knees, all the better if it were sunny, because it helped her see all those tiny loops. Our Rose, she had such nimble fingers with any intricate work. We girls wore Rose's pretty lace bonnets for Sundays, Granny too. But I liked the wild outdoors in those days, the wind and the weather just thrilled me. The animal sales could be exciting to watch. At first I thought the Auctioneer was funny but soon I got to understand what he was sayin'. I felt very proud to be with Granfer b'cos everybody knew Johnnie Pilbeam. He stood out taller than all around. 'Hearty good company,' somebody said, and a reporter on the local paper wrote, 'The epitome of a great Inn Keeper.'

Best of all I liked our journeys back home after the market was done. Sometimes we had new young stock to drive, and they needed close watching. The dogs were kept busy those evenings. But mostly we were alone, Granfer, me and my young brothers.

Until we got back down onto the Levels our path wended along the ridge of hills between stands of tall beech trees, less and less light spilt through their leafy canopy until the darkness closed in. We children would pretend we were frightened and walk close to Grandfather then when we approached clearings where the rising moon oozed through to the laneway we'd stop and dance whirling each other round and hollerin' atop our voices. Granfer would keep up his regular pace sometimes getting ahead of us giving a chuckle at our antics but once down out onto the Levels moving through the murmuring reeds Granfer would say,

"Now stand quite still and look, see up above, the sky is like a huge dome overhead. Watch how the star constellations wheel." He'd talk quiet and slow when he told us to look and watch.

"The stars tell us stories. It's goin' ter rain by mornin', the Dipper, 'es not holdin' water ter'night. Listen, you can 'ear the sound of the stars," Yes, you could hear a faint high pitched crackle, "and they have their own shapes and those bright colours, them's are planets. So if you watch all your lives you'll see their positions change across the year. Stars tell us the weather and the moon tells us when to plant seeds.

"Which ones Granfer?" we would whisper as if it was a secret.

"You ask your Granny about that, you'll see when she does her sowings." We often saw him sniff and taste the air listening to the wind hearing the way it rolled across the land.

"Like waves in the sea," he'd say, "when the sea is steep the reeds lay away from its pressure." He said how life was wondrous, full, surrounded by sky, sunsets and the aurora flowing so silent and wide across the winter sky. He'd stand tall and very erect dressed in his sage green tweeds: every day a clean white cotton neckerchief, long waistcoat and on these return journeys in the cool of an evening a heavy caped coat, the usual leather boots and a long crook in his hand.

Come to think of it, in twenty years he must have worn the same rumpled old tweed hat. It was elderly when I was a babe. Over his shoulders a roomy canvas bag went everywhere with him. In summer his colours were camouflaged, the grey green more yellow buff, rough collared shirt and darker trousers. The shirt of course made by Granny. No 'e never stood out on the Marshland, it took an instinctive eye to catch sight of him at any distance. Those were peaceful times.

The breed of sheep Granfer favoured were deep in the girth, men in those days liked their breakfast chops big with plenty of fat and because the beasts gave birth out on the Levels the sheep he bred had small heads to make their birthing easier.

We only ever went to the three closest markets. They'd no need to go further 'cos the longer drive would lose too much fat off the beasts. Ah, though I do remember Granfer telling us about the time when he took his flock on a Drove to Smithfield. This is how he told it."

* * * *

"It were late spring of 1851, the Drive outward took two weeks skirting to the west of the highest part of the Weald keeping to the easy ascent up over to Blackheath. O'corse we 'ad ter watch out for Rustlers our guide was a man from over Polegate way who came with us. "He only 'ad one eye, 'is ears an' nose picked up more 'n' we knew thereabouts because 'ed been thataway many times before. We were lucky to have him with us, we 'ad no losses on that journey.

That was the time I had my first sight of the great St. Paul's Cathedral. It stood out proud above the smoky haze across the valley with the river snaking through. You should've seen our beasts, they fair run down to the soft and wet grassland at Southwark. We stayed there south of the river for a span to fatten the animals after their long walk. Not too long mind otherwise they'd bloat.

When we crossed the river at Blackfriars, Maister Wren's Dome soared above us on our right. Too busy gettin' into the pens at

Smithfield at that time but I decided I 'ad to go back 'n see inside that wonderful building 'afore I left for 'ome again.

Cyril Watson an' I were the only ones that took a look inside the great Dome. After all the clatter in those streets the silence inside the walls was an over whelming peace like being in a huge box. I did try the porta at a tavern it was very thick and sweet with all the malt they put in it, not to my taste it weren't. We din't stay long. The pair of us never did see the other Drovers when we walked back down into Sussex. From the talk at Market a month on we heard tell we got 'ome 'afor 'em, t'was said one or two got way-laid in the hostelries 'n' lorst their money."

Grandfather told us, "Aw, I din't take to all that noise in London town, women shoutin' their wares from every direction. An' such jostling,' you couldn't get anywhere's. It t'were one step for'ard an' two steps back 'n sidewise. The streets were like dark tunnels full o' filthy bad smells. Gurt glad ter get back 'ome I were. Never went there again. No."

He said his animals sold well at Smithfield that year. The traders came to him ever after, not many times though,

"I didn't want my beasts to go to that smelly end. No room for middens to regenerate to earth."

One other thing Granfer told about that visit was how he was about to purchase a pottle from a ragged ol' gal squarkin' 'Hotboys hotboys,' when a large well set up woman with great bows on 'er shoes an carrying a huge basket of strawberries on a cushion set on her head that made her look damn near taller than himself, came bouncin' into the street and at once berated the untidy small strawberry seller. "Went at 'er 'ammer an' tongs she did." Then off the big woman pranced leavin' the little ol' gal quite winded. I bought a pottle poke right away an' they were clean an' lovely. Cyril, 'e ups 'n' says, 'Yer'll be lucky ter get those 'ome in good fettle, yer' lady'll get a mush.' Granfer said he hung that poke off his satchel to swing in the air. "You know your Gran planted those pokes in the bank and them's runners made their way across the back at the

top o' the orchard for years. A Grandmother who came with the old
Wagoner's family once told my Annie how they felt right at 'ome
in our yard when them's visited each year, 'cos of "the Harbeers"
growing on the bank in our orchard, said they reminded 'er of where
she were born. Annie didn't know what the old lady meant at first
until she pointed out the bright red 'Hotboys' in the grassy bank.'

* * * *

Grandfather enjoyed being solitary. He must have been blessed with
rare long sight. A great ruffly brow hooded grey green eyes, nothing
seemed to pass his notice. An eagle might swing and swoop low but
he would have seen it when the bird was way up high on a thermal.
He caught sight of hovering larks way above long before anyone else.
Rooks nesting in the crowns of trees in spring signalled the coming
weather pattern.

"Look," he'd point saying, "those are Herons flying." We would
want to know how he knew from so far off.

"Herons, they fly with that kink in their necks. Cranes fly
with their necks stretched out straight. Now see over there those
Herons are standin' on the water in their own reflections." And
he'd give a little humorous chuckle. I'm sure the presence of
all us grandchildren brought a deep richness to his days. It was
wonderful hearing all the experiences he passed on to us. My young
brothers and sisters stood wide eyed in wonderment at some little
creature held in the palm of his hand along with a story of where
it lived. We've certainly each got a piece of him now. He called it
reincarnation. Yes, that's what it is.

Grandfather loved people, especially in small groups swapping
stories. Evenings at the Inn would invariably end with songs and
the company revelling in plenty of laughter. When we got him to
ourselves there was always a shout for,

"Sing us a story Granfer," or "More, more tell us another." We
may be ten or more cousins gathered round his chair. He'd tell us
about Harold Hare, then lean down towards the littlest ones and in
a low conspiratorial voice say,

"I got right up as close as I am to you now. I parted the reeds and there was old Harry surprised as he could be laying long an' low 'is ears flat against 'is back."

"Couldn't 'e smell you Granpa?"

"Naw, wind was at me. I didn't smoke so I din't give him my scent. I chewed the herb of the field and hedge just as he do, I smelled same as 'ee. Off he'd be, up an' nip off quick before I could catch 'im; but I know'd which way ol' Harry would be goin' and' I'd be ready just near his path a little ways from a smoot. Ah, but not too near, then over his head with a sack an' I'd got 'im."

"What's a smoot?" The younger boys wanted to know.

"Ah now, that there's a hole left low in a stone wall to let Badgers an' Hares pass through."

Granfer only smoked his long cherry wood pipe in the evenings by the fire, his smoke floating away up the chimney. The children sitting round his chair, their little faces pink in the firelight. Gramps would sit back and suddenly wail,

"Whooer, pull my leg, pull my leg, got a bone in it." Up they would jump to help, little hands round his ankle. Then he'd let out a great fart.

"Ah baa, that's better, cracked the ol' bones back into place." My brothers and sisters fell in a tummy aching heap of laughing little bodies. He caught me out too when I was just a little girlie.

"Silly, Granfer."

"Yoo's awful, Granfer."

"Naughty, Granpa." Granny would agree hiding a smile behind her hand.

"C'mon now Clara," she'd say, "get these little ones to their beds. Day's been long and the candles won't last." Then they would come up with all their questions to take up time; the smallest ones holding onto his chair, grasping his sleeve and leaning against his knees trying to drag the time out before bed.

"Why do you call Mr Hare, Harold, Granpa?"

"Now why do we call you Tom, that's your name, that fella – he's Harold."

Our brother Jack was always the one with the patience, he'd lay in the long grass for hours watching the hares as they came out in the evenings. He called one Tip Top, you know, Hares have black tips at the tops of their ears.

"How do you know Harold's wife name's Rosemary Granfer?"

"Now I see 'is wife nibbling the Rosemary in the hedgerows, so as she likes the taste I thought she'd like the name. Harold and his brothers have boxing matches on the hillocks after harvest's gathered in. So you go to your beds an' when the harvest's 'ome I'll take you ter see Old Harry have 'is boxing matches." That satisfied them and up to bed with a candle they'd go.

We took a candle to each bedroom, Granny usually made the candles; there were paraffin oil lanterns in the bar and the kitchen but mostly Gran and Granfer were up by first light and to bed early especially in the dark months, they didn't need extra light. Some men would stay on into the evening in the light of the fire with an ale pot. It saved them a fire in their cottages and it was company for single men. When the days were longer everybody worked longer hours. Granfer was always out just before dawn whatever the time of year making sure the animals were safe counted and accounted for. Gran would be down in the kitchen to knock back the bread dough she'd set overnight. It was a busy life, not all beer and skittles, as they used to say. No, beer and skittles were fun – other parts of life were just the opposite. John and Ann's first son Robert died in his twenties of an Adder bite. That was so sad, he was a lovely lad. It somehow seemed ironic that Robert should be caught by startling an adder, 'cos of all the family he was so personally close akin to wild creatures on the Marsh. He used to watch for hours crouching deep in gulleys an' up o' top o' trees. Aah, that young man was such a sad loss.

But there were skittles. They had no skittle alley. Great Grandfather James, Grannies' father, had carved a sturdy big set of heavy wood skittles and the men played a game or two out in the front yard in fine weather. When the gathering was outside they kept us children running collecting up empty pots. Sometimes the dogs would find the odd mug kicked over, we tried to get to them before the animals lapped up the dregs but they always beat us to it. Then there'd be snoring dogs lazing about all the afternoon.

If we weren't about, Uncle Barney would collect up the pots for Granny."

John is standing just right of centre window
at the time of this photo he would have been in his fifties.

* * * *

"Uncle Barney. Ah now I haven't told you about him have I?"

A whole group of us children had been down to the shore gathering Samphire. We brought back basketfuls that morning and were so proud of our endeavours. Being unable to find Granny in the kitchen we trooped in the front door to the bar. In his usual place opposite Grandfather's chair, Uncle Barney sat against the wall his lurcher, Sam by his master's feet. Uncle Barney was Great Grandfather Robert Pilbeam's youngest brother, well Granfer's uncle really. We found Granny inside the inglenook unhooking a ham down from the chimney with Granfer's help. We children were full of our finds; the little ones squealing to Gran to 'Look, look Granny what we got for you.'

"Oh my, what a hullabaloo, you got gold in the bottom of yer basket?" Granfer dug into young Tommy's basket and chuckled making our little brother laugh with all the excitement. Uncle Barney smiled and supped his ale. A quiet man, he never did much more 'n' growled at any talk in the bar he didn't agree with, or nod at what he thought was right. We liked him but we didn't know him more than he being a familiar figure, who, most times, carried a little Harp on his back.

Now that day came a bit more 'n' different 'cos into our chattering throng a young man bounces, yes fair bounced in through the door, he were full o' eagerness of youth, and asks for a, small stout Beer. Granfer was just handing him his drink when the stranger says,

'Do you know where I can find a Mr Barnaby Pilbeam landlord?' Grandfather didn't answer straight away. Tommy, still full of his success in making us all laugh, wide eyed an' taps the man on the elbow,

"That's my uncle Barney." He says pointing across the room. The young man put his mug down and walked over to Uncle, holding his hand out saying,

"May I shake you by the hand sir? It is my honour to meet one of Mr Tennyson's survivors of the Light Brigade."

Well, us young ones stood staring. Uncle Barney didn't waste any time putting his ale mug down, he stood up sharp, saying,

"Gammon! (Humbug) Damned Americy practices." And marched briskly outside an' off up the lane, Sam at his heel. The man was horror struck. We were mesmerised. The young man started to shake before Granfer took him to a seat in the inglenook and sat him down. Granfer told us all in a low voice

"When a man has seen the carnage Barnaby saw around him that day no romantic poet can wipe away the memories." Dunkin' a hot poker into the young man's stout beer Granfer handed the mug back saying,

"He lost too many dear friends that day."

"Aye, true said Maister." A regular's voice agreed.

"An' weren't nothing ter do with Maister Tennyson nobut." Another added.

Other locals nodded murmuring their assent. That's when we knew what Uncle Barney had done in 1854. Granny herded us out back through into the kitchen. We'd forgotten our baskets of Samphire. She told us later she'd given the visitor a bite of bread, cheese and another stout to drink. "We put a poker in that stout to warm it through," she said, "that's good for shock."

When he was being helped onto his horse poor soul told us that he was a new reporter for the local newspaper. Granfer said to put his foot forward more carefully in future. Uncle Barney was back in his chair that evening when I was helping in the bar. Nobody spoke as he came through the door. But when I handed him his usual ale he gave me a gentle nod. Granfer smiled as I passed back into the kitchen. Dear Uncle Barney never married. He had no family. He had more affinity with dogs and horses than men and women. When horses were in the yard he'd stand by each one and speak low. Oh yes, Uncle Barney conversed in deep conversation. When bodies gathered at the Inn standing shoulder to shoulder with their ale pots, lively interchanges erupting into guffaws, or turning to quiet asides, folks were not aware of the seated figure silently placing his ale pot under his chair, stand tall then pass out through the crowd to the horses tethered in the yard for a sensible conversation!

That was Uncle Barney, respected by all the locals, misunderstood perhaps by some. Gramps said he'd had his fill of humanity in too few hours.

* * * *

Memory can be a blessed sense to possess as when –

Waking early on a summer's morning with the air smelling warm and dry in my tiny room up in the roof at the Lamb, I watched pale green light ebb and flow reflecting moving water in patterns across the sloping ceiling. Outside, House Martins with a second family feeding their twittering babies under the eaves flitted in through the open window scooping up a straying fly and on softly sweeping wings revolve out again on their busy food deliveries. I lay there thinking how our parallel lives exist in the same space.

The clunk of a bucket on the cobbles and click of a latch told me Granny was opening up her hen house across the yard. Cocky had already been calling the new day muffled inside the shed, while other Cocks across the hedges echoed their own messages in the distance.

"C'mon my dears," Granny croons softly not to startle the birds. She's answered by a few gentle clucks. Then her clogs click away up towards the gate to the orchard as she calls, louder rousing; "now there's my good Gorrals, it's a lovely new day." I can just hear the soft scrabbling sound chirrups and squeaks of the following hens, "You too Cockie c'mon then." I can visualise his Majestic flowing black tail shimmering with emerald glints as he emerges in all his proud eminence, strutting, always last following up the rear, the sun catching his neck feathers deep orange into gold and flame red comb. Old Cockie knows he's in charge. Granny's little family follow her into the orchard where the sun has warmed through the grass. I know she's filling their water troughs and scattering grain across the cobbled path before leaving her old terrier Jake to keep an eye out for foxes. Giving Jake a friendly pat she returns to the hen house to collect the eggs from the nesting boxes. Clogs tidily stowed inside the back door, the heavy stove door closes with a muffled, CLUT and the glorious smell of fresh bread rises into the air.

By half past seven Grandfather's feet come clumping to a standstill on the flagstones outside the back door. A pause and I know he's rolling his sleeves up before the rhythmic suck and thump of the pump drawing water from the well. I can feel the sharp cold of that clear water and its deep earthiness. The dogs are lapping noisily at their water trough. They and Grandad would have done a good few miles since dawn. Granfer's dogs were his workers. Usually 4 or 5 kept him company they each had their own job to do. The two Collies organised the sheep, a Terrier nipped any awkward rats, the Retriever brought home the catches and the two Lurchers would round up the cattle as they lope out faster than the other dogs, all working well together. 'Corse Granfer was the pack leader.

Granny calls from the kitchen,

"That you John?" an' 'e knows 'e better 'ave a wash afor' going in for his breakfast. Out back over the shallow sink he throws a bare cup full of water up from an enamel bowl sending water sparkling in all directions over his head and long sideburns, making a great shloshin' noise in his mouth, rubbing water into his hair and around his face.

Great Granfather Robert's beard bowl hung from a string loop over a hook on the wall above the sink when we were young. I haven't seen it for year or so now. Shame, it was a lovely Willow patterned one. No, Granfer never grew a beard like his father so he had no use for the bowl. He shaved himself with a bone handled cut throat razor about twice a week leaving just his thick sideburns. When he'd 'ad 'is wash he'd 'ave a good stretch before pulling off his great leather thigh boots. Granfer had two or three pairs of boots each carefully hung leg down over posts he'd set at an angle on the wall inside the back lobby after he'd dried and polished them ready for use. Those boots lasted him many a year. He looked after his footwear well, saying he needed them every day to work. Important part of life they were, he told us to remember that. "Always look after your feet younguns." He'd say,

These are the sounds that painted their pictures in my memory during the early mornings when I was blind.

It happened the summer of my eleventh year when I was thrown from a horse, my eyes suddenly couldn't see. It was like the lights had been taken away on a black night. When my brothers and sisters went home for school at the end of that summer I stayed back with Gran and Granfer. Our Mother couldn't have a blind child about not able to do anything. That's when I saw my memories so clearly. The sounds made the pictures and the smells made them more real.

I knew my way round so well that I almost didn't need my eyes, but it worried the family very much for my future. I was able to do cooking with Granny, even blind I could make bread 'n' cakes 'n' pies. Oh I did so love those weeks.

One morning Granfer was away out attending to his sluices and ditches and Granny had an errand up in the village, so I was alone at the Inn. There were no foster children about either that month so I just carried on with my cookin'. Rascal, Granfer's oldest bitch now milky eyed with age, laid dozing in the back porch but I noticed she was growling low. Then I overheard voices out front. Two men were talking, the latch on the bar door lifted and squeaked. A man's voice saying,

"Where do'yer s'pose they keep's the takin's Bill?"

"Round t' back, 'spect." Another voice replied.

Footsteps came through the bar and into the kitchen passage. Huh, I weren't gonna let them get any further so I started banging a heavy pot on the stone floor like there were a fight agoin' on, an ol' Rascal sets up a barkin' more'n she'd done for years. Between us we curried up a real cacophony. 'Corse I didn't shout co's that would give game away, I was only a youngster. Anyway I just managed to hear a sharp voice go,

"Lumme we're outta 'ere mate." And two sets of boots went 'ell for leather down the lane. Phew, I quite enjoyed myself, but I was frightened. I sat down in the porch with Rascal and fed her such extra bits o' meat.

Between us that good girl and I stopped those bad men. I was so thankful I gave her a cuddle for helping out.

There were a lot of talk in the bar amongst the men about my state of sightless eyes, and one man told Granfer about his mother who knew how to cure blindness. After some talk to persuade Granny, she wasn't very keen but relented, Granfer said he had to try something to help me. He took me in the trap over to Mrs Wallen and she pierced my ears. That's all she did. Made me jump even though she whispered in my ear, what she was a goin' to do. Said the ol' sailors taught her the cure, they wore gold rings in their ears so as to pay for their coffins, that's if they weren't buried at sea in their hammocks. Granfer wanted to pay for the little rings and a bit for the cure, but she wouldn't take anything, saying,

"Let you see it works an' I'll be satisfied with that news." I spent another two weeks with Granny. We had lovely fun cooking together, I learned so much from her.

Then one morning I woke up an' I could see those patterns on the ceiling again, an' being autumn the sun was lower across the room so I knew it was real and no longer pictures in my memory. It might have been the ear piercing. I will never know. What I can say is that Granfer sang it into a story that evenin' in the bar and all joined in with the chorus.

"An' now our sweet Clara can see again, an' now she can see again." I wished I'd written down all his verses. I think it went something like this:

"Gold rings they pierced through to the light
Pierced through to bring the light back to her eyes
An' now our Clara can see again
An' now she can see again.
It was a fall sent her into darkness
In that darkness she made tasty plum pies
An' now our Clara sees to cook again
An' now she sees to cook again
Our gal can see again."
That was such a jolly evenin,' hearing everybody so happy for me.

* * * *

Having no sight enhances the other senses to a sharper degree and that's when I learned something called, 'opinion,' during those days when I couldn't see.

I was mixing a cake for Granny at the kitchen table. Auntie Charlotte had come to fetch her Gracie, all my brothers and sisters had gone home on the carrier's cart that morning. Granny and Auntie were standing outside the back door talking and suddenly I could hear them having cross words. Auntie followed Granny back inside saying,

"Well it's not nice 'er havin' all those children it's not nice."

"Nothing to do with you Lottie, don't talk about your sister in that way."

"She's dirty and you shouldn't have to 'ave all her younguns here all summer long. Who pays for them? They must eat enough."

"Now you take your Gracie home my dear." Charlotte kept going on,

"She gives our family a bad name."

"Please stop it Lottie. If anybody gives our family a bad name it's you for gossiping behind people's backs."

"Mother, don't be nasty."

"Now then, what are you being if you call your sister dirty. Go home woman. I've got Katie to milk, I 'ear 'er a-callin. Alright my lovely, no use you bawlin' at me, I'm coming fast as I can." As Granny was washing her hands at the sink the door slammed and

40

Auntie Charlotte stalked off. I didn't like hearing my Mum spoken of in that way. Cousin Gracie kissed me goodbye before catching up with her Auntie. Now I come to think of it that must have been the last time I saw Gracie, I heard she ran away to America with her young man. Weeks later I learned more about the lives of women in my family. Although I was relieved to be sighted again it had been blissful having my Grandparents all to myself through that fragrant warm autumn. Sadly it was time to return to my parents in St Leonards and back to the last few days of my schooling.

Granny came with me over to St Leonards to see my Mum. They didn't see each other very often now the growing family took up so much of Mum's time. We arrived off the Carrier's cart in the middle of the morning. Mother had three young ones at home she was nursing one and two were playing in the hearth, the others were at morning school. Granny and I had enjoyed the journey. I wanted to tell Mum about my eyes and Granny said she could do with a lovely dish of tay. But when we saw Mum all red eyed and crying it was a shock for Gran and a big disappointment for me. At eleven you're too young and so full of your own life to be aware of anybody else's troubles. You've had no experience. I was soon to hear of and begin to understand what experience was all about.

"Ah, what is it Emmie my love?" Gran says, going across the room to take Mum in her arms.

"I didn't want you to see me like this Mother, so sorry." But Mum couldn't help herself, "It's 'appened again, this'll be the seventh, if it lives of course."

"Oh, my dear." Gran said with such sympathy in her voice.

The two women seem to have forgotten my presence; no homecoming greeting came my way. I just stood there looking and gradually becoming aware the fire was almost out and a muddle and mess around the room. I took up the kettle and went out to the yard to fill it at the tap we shared with ten other houses in the row. Coming back in through the scullery I heard Mother telling Gran.

"Mum, I've done everything to stop it 'appening again." She sounded so bleak, at the end of her tether. I carried on listening while rekindling the fire.

41

"Mrs Percy told me to fetch a pebble with a hole in it from the beach an' put it up inside me'self. She said don't wash it the salt will kill the germs. I didn't know what she means it ter do but I tried." And she cried even harder. Granny said the pebble would keep the womb entrance open that will stop the egg settling into place. "Well, that's what our layin' in woman told me years ago." Gran added.

"But Mother it hasn't worked."

"You know Emmie the only thing I can tell you is to sleep in another room. Sleep with the girls and get Tom to sleep in the boy's room."

"He won't Mum, 'e suffers so much with his damaged arm. We love each other I don't want to go sleeping in another bed, an' 'e says 'e needs me."

"I know but not like that, every night my dear." Granma advised.

I didn't fully understand what they were talking about but I did realise it was what Aunt Charlotte said gave the family a bad name. I always helped Mum with all her babies it made me feel guilty for staying away for those extra weeks when I was recovering, but now I was back I could help. The kettle boiled an' I made the tea.

"Never mind Mummy," I said, "I'm here now you'll be alright."

"Out of the mouths of little ones." That made her cry all over again, "It's not havin' the little ones Mum it's keeping them fed and clothed. Wouldn't you have thought Lottie and Lizzie would be thoughtful and pass on their children's old clothes to us? They're well off with their husbands both in business. Lizzie told me she might 'ave another one, she's only got Gracie and she's sixteen gone by."

"An' Lottie actually told me she didn't want her nice things turned into rags as soon as my ruffians got hold of them." My mother told Gran.

"Yes, dear, I'm surprised they let their children join yours at the Inn this summer at all."

"It must have suited them, didn't it Mother?" The back door rattled and a voice called out, "You ready Em?"

"Oh my gawd its Daw' and' I ain't got those sheets done." Taking her hat 'n' coat off and hanging them on the back of the door Granny got all brisk.

"C'mon now my love, let's get you straight. Put baby down. Clara will look after him and look she's made us tea. Well done. Now show me what's to be finished, we'll do it together. We'll sup a drop of warmth as we go. Clara knows where everything lives so we'll leave the tidying here to our good lassie." Faced with big sniffs and dried tears, Daw said she'd be back in a few minutes.

In no time at all, it seemed Granny and Mum were out back pulling the sheets into long sausage twists tightly round the wringing post while Daw and the other women were stretching and pegging them out on the long lines across the yard, everybody singing together while they worked.

Mum took in washing and ironing along with all the other women in the Row, they didn't have the lovely open air like Granny who could spread her sheets in the sunny orchard for the sun to bleach, but they made the very best they could of their long narrow cobbled yard. Between them, an' they all had children about their skirts, they gave a service to the local boarding houses. Knowing this I set the irons on the back of the fire. By the time Mum and Granny came inside for a spot to eat I had Granny's loaf and cheese on the table and a little cup of broth each from the basin of jelly broth in Gran's basket of good things. Later on the kitchen was full of hot steaming irons flattening the edges of the starched sheets, goffering lace frills ready to catch their delivery time, when Mum suddenly remembered, "Oh, and I haven't even said welcome home to my baby." Funny thing that. I was the oldest but Mum only ever referred to me as 'her baby'. I suppose I was the only one she had ever had to herself alone.

Granny stayed for a whole week. I heard more women's talk than I should have. By the time I went back to lessons I was grown up in some ways but behind a bit with my figures. I never understood long multiplication and division on paper but nobody ever bested me in what I owed and the change to give. And another thing, I could read long before I met a school teacher.

My brother Albert was born seven months later, so then Mother had four little ones at home, all under five.

* * * *

I told you Granfer had a very loud voice, well, so he had, when it was needed. In song his voice was resonant and his singing melodious rich, oft times soft and gentle. He could be sentimental too. He sang about ordinary people's lives, of fields and birds the things he knew and us children loved him to 'sing us a story'. He wasn't only a teller he was a good listener, roarin' with laughter appreciative of other folk's epic stories.

I suppose that's why so many gathered regular at the Inn. Our Granfer was a jovial man; in song and speech his voice was easy on the ear. People trusted him he was their intimate. Johnnie Pilbeam sang to the individual. He said he got his voice from his father, Robert. Robert who loved the Psalmody missed those church gatherings with the cello and violins and all the voices together singing the psalms. He joined in full and hearty from his place in the Inglenook, when in his last years he could struggle down the lane from his cottage.

"Never lose the ordinary man's stories," he would say, "that's the way we remember their lives down the years."

"There's often a song that carries a tale," another of his sayings, "so, sing us a song lad." Robert would call to his son John to begin,

> *Come all ye arouse the morning is clear*
> *The larks are singing up in the Marsh air*
> *Let's get running we'll seek for a hare*
> *Sing out follow through reed, give chase*
> *Sing out follow over still make haste*

> *Old Harry he led us a noble run*
> *Success to sportsmen everyone*
> *A chase he's led us into eventide*
> *Now drink me lads sit and bide*
> *Old Harry's to grace our board by 'n' by.*

All voices were raised along with ale pots as the company repeated the last two lines. There were many more verses and more additions when a poet came amongst the crowd.

Come all honest travelling men that work hard the long day
And join with us at the Lamb Inn to pass an hour away
Where we can sing and drink and be merry

And drive away all our cares and worry
Raise a jug of John's whipping old ale
Ye'll hear a rollicking good tale me lads.

Then they'd shout, 'tell us another, another we will have.' It wasn't always Granfather John who'd take up the call. Many others had their yarns to spin.

John (fourth from left) at Hailsham Market

John (second from left) with Pevensey Harriers

* * * *

I know it does seem only men frequented the Inn, but no, times when whole families called. Wagons carried quantities of goods on long journeys, sometimes across country between canals from port to port and across the Channel.

Grandfather always received word each time before the wagons of our regular summer family visitors arrived. A single rider called in a day or two ahead to give news of their approach. This one was a fair sized company and well organised.

On arrival the wagons were drawn up around the yard sheltering the women and children's sleeping quarters. Horses were tethered or let loose in our corner paddock. Oh dear, what with Grannie's hens nipping in and out around the horses hooves and the grandchildren playing with the new children and their family dogs and ours, together, there were often a rare old commotion. Our working dogs, having first rushed forward a few paces barking, loath to give way to the new hounds, easing off at Granfer's gentle order, lowered their heads to show irritation. The cats, well they scattered up in the barn to watch looking down from the beams where they had their own little bowl of water. A camp was set up in the yard and a circle of cobblestones was lifted to make a small fire pit into this the women put their own briquets of charcoal and dung, with a Diable hung above on its three legs. Smoke filled the air but the fire drew fast and settled to a glowering heat. Soon our nostrils were full of cooking smells. Granny made lots more bread that day to go with the jugs of ale and cider. Late into the evening we watched the men squatting smoking their short briar pipes and yarning round the extra handfuls of crackling wood sending its sparks swirling up into the darkening sky. After supper the musicians tuned up their violins and penny whistles, even the locals came out from the parlour to join the singing through the long summer evening. Later a fiddler accompanied by a squeeze box struck a quite different sounding tune. Even the wagon men got up and joined their women folk in the dance. Now that were a tad unusual for our regulars, anyway they watched, beginning to sway with the lilting tune.

The dancers threw their arms across each other's shoulders swinging their bodies in lines, stamping and sliding their feet in time to the rhythm of the music, the women whirling and dipping around and between the men who were moving in the opposite direction.

Aw, it were lovely to see the pretty skirts flying and twirling. As the dancing got faster and faster our locals were doing their own jigging around to the rhythm and even ducking and dancing under arched hand holds. Some of the children got over excited and we youngsters were just as bad. We had always been encouraged to dance to the squeeze box from when we were quite small. It was certain all would sleep well that night.

Come the morning the yard was full of the steamy breath of men and animals in the light misty air of dawn. Lazy whispers of smoke drifted up above the fire. Men were coughing and clearing their throats, the women clearing the breakfast and packing bundles for the wagons. With the final rope heaved and knotted across the wagons they were trundling away by time the sun rose over the hedges. They never stayed more than but a night.

One season a very quiet individual travelled with the Wagoners.

We had seen men with strings of plaited hair in their beards and at the sides of their faces but we hadn't seen a man with a single jet black plait hanging at the back of his head. We stood and stared.

"It's bad manners to stare children." Granfer told us.

"They do not stare sir, they are looking to remember." His speech in clear words of English was a surprise to us children. This man was dressed a little differently from the other Wagon men. He had on a heavily padded longish jacket and similarly padded knee boots. When he turned to face us we couldn't see his eyes. They appeared like long narrow slits and his hands were up inside his sleeves like his arms were folded.

"I thank you sir, for your hospitality." The man bowed as he spoke. Granfer never seemed surprised at anything or anybody.

"You are welcome here again, sir." That's all he replied. The man then turned and bowed to us too and walked away. We went on, staring.

"That gentleman comes from the faraway country called China."

"How do you know Granfer?" I had to ask. Granfer knew so much but I had to know HOW he knew all these things.

"Because, last night when you were all in your beds me dears, he told us about his country." Granfer told us the Chinaman was travelling with the Wagoners all over Europe. Wherever he stopped he made paintings in a small book recording the surroundings and what the people were doing." He asked all about the Inn and Granfer told him about his sheep and cattle and said that he was known as a 'Looker.' The Chinaman told Granfer his pigtail was known as his 'queue' and that he was Chinese like we are English. Apparently he nodded with approval on hearing Granny was a skilful Wheelwright.

"Ah," he said, "like Chinese women."

"Granfer," my brother asked hesitantly, "why did the man from China tap a little bottle on the back of his hand?' Grandfather laughed because Jack had given himself away.

"Ah, so you crept outa your bed late last night young man," but Gramps wasn't annoyed, "well I'll tell you. He was taking snuff tapping it out of a bottle." "Uncle Jube doesn't do it like that?"

"You're right there and I noticed that too, so the Chinaman told us that snuff was mostly used by wealthy Mandarin Chinese people who, because they had no need to use their hands their fingernails grew exceedingly long, and they even wore decorated metal covers over their nails; having such long nails prevented them from taking a pinch of snuff so it was kept in little carved ivory bottles and could be poured onto the back of the hand. Oh your Uncle Jube said he'd have to tell his fellow nozo's that strange tale. I've no doubt he'll have them all laughing." We gave granfer our quizzy looks.

"They call themselves nosologists." Granma explained with a sly wink.

On the previous day we had seen the Chinese man from a distance painting his pictures. He seemed very quick. We didn't go near to look, well, he scared us a bit 'cos he looked so unusual. I'm surprised at our reactions really 'cos you never knew who would fetch up at the Lamb. Granfer never turned anyone away. It was only if they caused a nuisance to the company or were dishonest, then they knew never to come back again.

The Chinaman was right. I've never forgotten him or the Wagoners who were always welcome, the times when they visited the Lamb Inn there were rarely a trace left of their presence. You would not have known cobbles had been lifted and a fire lit. Every cobblestone was re-laid with no sign of disturbance. Of course they did leave behind that feeling of elation their exuberant presence had created, not to mention the extra income for the Inn.

The Wagoners had Granfer fill their black jacks with ale and these were slung in the shade under the backs of the biggest wagons. My brothers found it very funny as they watched the wagons rumble off with the old leather black jacks swaying underneath. It looked as if the wagons had great heavy udders. Cheeky little boys my brothers!

We all stood with our grandparents, as we did every year, waving the wagons off as they trundled away down the lane towards the sea. Under the willow trees the men's deep voices were lost to the ear, dulled within the branches. When the wagons came into view again, swinging eastward up over the distant hill, the sounds of the creaking axels and cracking reins, mingling with the children's voices yipping with excitement to be on the road again, carried back on the air to our ears, until they were once again gone to a whispering.

Tranquillity reclaimed the yard. Granny was soon out there with her hens again serenading her 'gorrals' giving them a little extra corn, when she heard a rough throaty cough and juicy hawkin' 'n' spitting. Well! she thought, somebody must have overslept, one of the wagoners has been left behind. Until a second cough and spitting came to her ears only this time a small girl's voice squealed,

"Aah! Tommy you 'orrid thing you." The boys were copying the big gruff Wagon men and one of the girls had come in the line of her brother's aim. Granny had to move a bit sharpish to avoid a sister brother fight. The boys were advised by their Grandmother that young people shouldn't act out everything they see although she said those great muscled leather clothed men do look very dramatic, what with their long fancy combed beards and mustachios, and the women were sober and ladylike with their simple bonnets and shawls. I saw the looks that passed between my brothers and sisters, who were old enough, to be with me that summer, they blushed and looked away. I realised Granny must have gone back in to fetch out her last batch of bread and Grandfather had stood in the kitchen doorway masking her view while the dancer's skirts were being kicked high showing a little more than just their colourful petticoats. That may have been a high kick too far for our Gran in those days!

* * * *

As usual it didn't take long for the activities of the yard to return to normal. As noon approached Tradesmen passing along the Marsh lanes stopped for a sup and a yarn in the bar whilst their carter boys gathered in the yard to feed and water their charges. Chunks of crunchy bread, cheese with a fat juicy sweet onion to go with their small beer was sent out to the lads. They weren't allowed a pint pot of ale as some of those lads were too young, and anyway onion and the alcohol together, sent blood to the head twice as fast especially in middle o' day. Wooh yes, you must remember that. But it does go luvly together, a sweet onion with bread cheese and a pot of ale.

Granny Ann could turn a bowl of dough into loaves most times of day, course she preferred to keep to her regular routine allowing the dough to rise slowly overnight ready to bake in the early mornings. As Granfer always got up first he woke the fire up before he went out so it was ready for baking before breakfast. When Granny got up she knocked back the dough making it into loaves ready for its final proving before it went into a lovely hot oven and was out all golden crisp and cooled by the time we all sat down to eat. There were plenty of loaves left for the lunch times. Granny kept a store bottle of yeast on the go, made fresh every Monday morning with hops, salt, brown sugar and best flour. On Wednesday she added mashed boiled potatoes, then strained that into a clean scalded out bottle on Thursdays. That was ready to use through the rest of the week. There were a sack of dried hops to go through the winter, but at a pinch she could always buy some baker's yeast, but that was rare. She had prepared her own working yeast all her life.

Yes. Food was truly wholesome, mostly all produced at the Inn, 'cept for cheese that came from Connie's over on Squires Farm. What with Granfer's beef and mutton, Granny had a piggy or two in the sty end o' the orchard. Gran painted the Hocks with her mixtures of thick honey and ale before they were hung in the wide chimney to smoke. When Granfer unhooked them down the hams looked more like oak logs. To other cuts Granny gave a coating of black treacle and spice, they came down from the smoking looking like old tarred ships timbers. Ah, but a slice of Gran's ham with a helping of mustard and her soda bread went down a treat with a mug of ale. Granfer John called Gran's cooking, 'food for the Gods'.

Granfer didn't brew his own ales. No, that all came over from the Bexhill Brewery. Customers were served from jugs, like Big Pol, filled from the barrels in the cellar. He kept a lovely cool dry cellar. Granfer had a good reputation as an Innkeeper and he was able to keep that up right into his very last year with the help of his pot man Bill Tidy.

Nice man. Yes, Bill dropped in one day just after his ol' parents had died. Gramps was surprised ter see him.

"Well bless my soul Billy Tidy. Where yer bin keepin' yersel all these years?"

Bill, well 'e were a bit quiet, and it was hard to understand what he were sayin', but 'e 'ad a story ter tell. Seems he'd b'in kept out'a sight for years by his Ma an' Pa to protect him. Poor fella had a hare-lip too wide to allow hair growth for camouflage. Aw 'e did really look an ugly sight did Bill. Tried for Navy one time, he said, but the sailors thought 'e would bring bad luck ter ship so 'e wandered back to 'is parents 'ome and stayed in their shed making wooden tools and implements for the farmers thereabouts. Nobody knew 'e were there. Fact is people thought 'is Father had made the things Bill produced. Never gave it a thought 'ow the man who worked full time hedge layin' and labourin' 'ad the time ter go 'ome and make such well finished equipment. Both 'is parents had recently passed on. 'E didn't have a 'ome, an' no other family. They'd been in a tied cottage see. Granfer heard 'im out an' just replied,

51

"Well, yer 'ave a home now Bill. There's space in the Bothey at the end of the stables." So that's when Granfer had help lookin' after the cellar. As he got older having Bill's 'elp Granfer said, 'was a 'God send.' "It were meant ter be Billy, meant ter be."

Now Bill were encouraged to bring 'is tools down to the Inn, worked there in the little nook he could call 'is own 'till 'e died. Made Granfer a grand cider press one time, an' 'e did ox yokes, yokes for carrying pairs of buckets, all sorts made a' wood. Like the sturdy new stem Bill made that he and Granfer slotted in the cobbles at top o' the cellar entrance. They hitched a rope over the post to hoist and lower barrels down the incline. The days they buckled the barrels into the cellar were called Parbuckle days.

No, I never 'eard any remarks about the man's deformed face. T'would not h've been good manners and I doubt if Granfer or Granny would have taken kindly to such talk.

Expect I see Gran and Granfer through rose tinted glasses but I never recall them doing an unkindess to anyone. They certainly gave us happy times.

Parbuckle: a purchase made by looping the rope in the middle to aid in rolling casks up or down an incline

* * * *

Granma Annie had a lovely light coloured wood kitchen table where she did her chopping and baking. That table came from her parents who had little need for it since their family had grown and left home. Her father James, the Carpenter, had made the table, so when she and John came to the Inn and their family started Gran was pleased to have it in her own kitchen. By the time all us grandchildren gathered together in those long summer days we took up every inch even though it was a large table. Our mother had two sisters so our cousins Jack and Lilian, who were five and four were often with us; they were fun to play with, then there was Gracie, she was the oldest grandchild, she loved helping Granny. In the early years we were only three of us siblings. I was five, Rose three and that summer we had John with us, he was nearly two years old. Sometimes there'd be one or two fostered village children to fill the family too. The only way to seat all of us were on benches down either side at the table and that might even include any wayfarer who'd spent the night at the Inn, they joined the family meal as well. Granfer sat at one end and Granny perched on a stool the other end near the range because she had to get up so often doing the cooking. Granny still looked a young woman then with her glowing Chestnut ringlets on either side of her face escaping from her neat white cotton kitchen cap.

Granny liked us to have one meal altogether each day. Mostly it had to be breakfast at half past seven because there were no bar customers needing serving. Granfer came in for his breakfast by half past seven, by then he'd 'Looked' the beasts since four or five o'clock across the level Marshland, so he was really hungry by then. Meanwhile we'd be jostling around getting our hands washed and have to hurry into the kitchen.

"C'mon all you scamps 'n' scallywags," Gran would call, "your'n Granfer'll be 'ere any minute, quick up ter table."

We could hear him come clumping up to the path pulling off his great boots on the heel wedge beside the back door, while the dogs started lapping water from their trough. Then we'd hear a great splashing of water and hand drying, rubbing his face with a rough towel along with lots of grunts. I expect that was all for our benefit because Granny would be standing by the range waiting with a pan and a flat spattle, her eyebrows raised in mock surprise, mouth turned down at the corners suppressing her laughter. In he'd come water still dripping off his 'air and in the doorway he'd stop. Staring at us he'd bellow,

"What's all these people then Annie, who be all these scallywags at my table?"

"Them's our visitors John."

"I don't know ooh'd they be, they payin' their keep are they Mrs?" Then he'd come to the table and stare at each one, a big smile creeping onto his face. Little Johnnie cried the first time he was with us. Granfer made his face cry too. That shook us. We all stared, to see Granfer look as if he were about to cry for t'was a bit odd. Even baby John's expression stopped to see what the abrupt change was all about. Granfer took John up on his knee and kissed him tickling the baby's face with his whiskers and laughing all the while. We squealed at him, 'bad Granfer, mustn't frighten Johnnie.' But baby John was quick to catch on. The very next morning John sat waiting for this great giant to come through the back door into the kitchen straightaway he put up his baby arms saying,

"Granfer." and laughed. We joined in amazement our Johnnie was a bright boy.

Granny told us to, "settle down me luvlies pass round the bowls. Thank the Lord for our good food children."

"Yes Grannie." we all called in unison.

It was usually a good dollop of porridge with syrup or brown sugar and a cup of milk, finished off with apples, but not often in winter unless the apples kept unwrinkled well into February and March months. Apples were for cleaning our teeth Gran told us.

"No gobbling too fast Gracie, I know you want to help out some, but you eat gently for your tummy's sake first. Then you can help."

Meanwhile Gran had laid a steak or chops and kidneys in the pan on the range fire with maybe two eggs fried and served on top of the meat. Granfer ate this with a fat slice of hot bread fresh from the oven, usually washed down with Adams' Ale, as he called it. Sometimes we children had boiled eggs with bread and butter and whatever fruit there was ripe.

All said thank you before we got down from the table. As we had shared the meal we shared the clearing and cleaning. Boys and girls, everybody was expected to do their bit. Gran was a stickler for that. Rose and I were usually set to helping the younger ones and collecting all our clothes needing washing whilst the others did dishes and stowed them away in the big old dresser cupboards. Granny only expected to wash her own cooking pots and bowls.

For the rest of the day we each went our separate ways. Sometimes as a group we roamed meeting up with other village children, that's when the boys kicked a ball in the dry hard sandy lanes. A pocket of bread and cheese with some little apples went with me.

When we went fishing, Granfer would only take two at a time of us children, he said it gave us the understanding of peace and patience. Sometimes we went over to Wallers Haven or maybe Pevensey Haven or the Chilley. Granfer had long cane cones for catching salmon. He showed us how to weave eel traps from the flexible wiry withers turning them into cone shapes, showing us where to lay them down in the stream with the wide end facing the flow. When an eel went in after the bait it couldn't get back out against the angled willow twigs. Granfer called it snigging when he caught eels. With a three pronged eel fork, you can get eels all year round. We had to kill very quickly with a sharp blow, Granfer showed us how 'cos we must never let anything suffer and then holding the head he made a fine slit around the neck then pulled head away from body sliding the skin off to the tail, being very careful not to break the gall when you slit down the body to clear out the gut. Finally, wash it in the stream, Granny would spatchcock these or stuff eels with shrimps from the rock pools and walnuts from the orchard, and bake them in the oven.

I gathered withies at their best time of year and showed the little ones how to weave mats and baskets. I put some tapes for handles on one of those baskets, it made a useful shopping bag, lasted me years. I made one deep basket to carry a jar so I could fill it with eel lava. We used to pick 'em out of the water in handfuls. Lightly strewn with flour, Gran would fry them to a crisp, didn't need any salt.

* * * *

When we were very young Granny would be out on the sands along with us. A very proper lady even on the sands; she wore her skirts tied up neatly round her waist leaving just one innermost petticoat full length to her ankles. Often without her shoes, keeping those hanging on her belt, like she taught us to do, we'd wander along the sea shore she showing us what to gather and where to find the different shell fish; sea urchins; seaweeds in the rock pools and to give everything a good rinse to get rid of as much sand as possible. This was one of the only times we saw her take off her cotton cap to let her hair blow free. She kept her long golden chestnut ringlets hanging down either side of her face right up into her early sixties, long glossy and beautiful they were.

The pools among the rocks were alive with little brown shrimps to scoop up into our buckets. 'Corse you could get shrimps in the summer months, there were loads of them moving quickly through the water and across the watery sandy beds while winkles huddled together on the rocks. We found mussels and whelks and in the sand beds were cockles and deep razor shells popped straight up into our hands. Granny showed us how to rinse off the sand very carefully then bag them. When we got back to the kitchen she would throw all our finds into a pot, no washing because it would lose the natural salt. That fishy herby Hot-pot was very quick to make when we got back in the middle of the day. It seemed to be ready in no time at all. Then soaked up with chunks of bread, it made a lovely meal.

Up on the shingle banks alongside where golden yellow horned poppies grew we gathered samphire, they call sea asparagus. It grew up from the bottom layer of soil up through the pebbles on the edge of the salt marsh. Granma told us her Great Granny, Amy Hartshorn, said the French called samphire St Peter's herb.

I always carried a cotton bag folded in my pinafore pocket for collecting wild thyme and other herbs. I knew where medicine herbs were and I kept an eye for those, especially the Marsh Rhumwert 'cos that stops bleeding. Never knew when the little'uns might cut their selves. Come late August we got crab apples and September the blackberries, but not after the middle of September 'cos they got sour after that time. I loved collecting the wild garlic under cool damp hedges, but that of course was in the spring. Wild garlic made meat cooking just that little bit aromatic if it was shaken round a serving bowl before the onions and meat went in is just enough to keep it fresh and its lacy white flowers strewn through a salad looks pretty.

It was the year when I was eleven and had to stay on at the Inn after my brothers and sisters went home to St Leonards that I learned more about taste and smell. That must have been due to my blindness. Being the only child there I was able to ask lots of questions, learning about flavouring mixtures of meats by cooking whole unpeeled cloves of garlic amongst the meat. Only mashing them into the gravy when they are soft and creamy, and how pan fried Beef loves black pepper. Rich flavours the men liked. Herbs like Fennel and Dill partner best with fish and Rosemary brings out the delicacy in roasting potatoes, carrots and parsnips.

Granny and I made cakes, she teaching me to stir lightly with a spattle or she'd say,

"Now beat that mixture up a froth with your whisk, 'til it's pale cream and makes a trail in the batter." I learned how to make cakes rise well and how to prevent a pie crust caving in with an upturned china tea cup.

When we made jugged Hare all us children learned how to take his jumper off before being shown how to clean and truss the game. We were not allowed to kill an animal or bird without great care.

The preparation for eating was important. As we worked Granny would say, "Thank you Mr Hare."

We children would only have meat or fish for our dinner in the middle of the day. My favourite dinner was steak and kidney pudding steamed in a cloth. Steak and kidney was just as lovely in a pie covered with a crispy golden pastry. All the rich gravy with potatoes mashed into it and lovely cabbage. As sheep meat can be very greasy Granny would make small mutton pies for us children in little dishes so they would only have pastry tops and she would make the gravy with a puree of crab apples, so delicate and delicious for our young stomachs. It was a rare thing to eat lamb because it was thought to have no flavour.

In winter the puddings we made were hot from the oven. Soft sponge puddings with thick runny jam or syrup; fruit pies using the fruits Granny preserved or from the cooling racks kept high up in a shed carefully watched to keep the mice from nibbling. Sussex pond pudding with a sugared sweet 'n' sharp Raisins ball in its belly was gorgeous or 'Apple Charlotte' and 'Singing Hinny' full of honey and crunchy cobnuts we had collected around the field edges and lovely 'Spotted Dick' with loads of currants. Oh yes and a little bunch of Sweet Cecily in with her Cherry Rhubarb took away all the acid taste. After running and skipping all morning these dinners suited us growing children well. In the early evening we had tea with bread and dripping or buns we had made for ourselves. Our days had a regular routine looked forward to by all of us.

We loved our Mum and Dad but there were times when we stayed out of the house in St Leonards because they were arguing and rowing though they never came to blows like some of our neighbours. Life at the Inn on the Marsh with Gran and Granfer was calm and well ordered and really, well, very exciting. Everyday brought us different experiences.

There's no doubting our Mother knew we had a better chance to grow strong and healthy in the good fresh air. But I've often wondered how our Grandparents managed to feed us all. They weren't wealthy people. They certainly knew how to make everything go a long way using all of the free foods nature provided. Like Pigeons, Rooks and Rabbits. Some were strong flavours for

little ones but Granny knew how to cook poultry that made the
flesh soft and smooth with a gentler flavour for our young palates.

* * * *

I haven't told you about Granny's quilting and scrapbook?

Well, Gran never sat with her hands idle. We each had a quilt
on our bed, but one was special because she patterned into it family
memories – as the family grew so did Granma's quilt. There were
pieces of material from our dresses and the boys shirts all blended
into this great expanding picture. What she called a picture history of
our family. It wasn't meant to be used because the fabrics were all so
contrasting. Some were fine like wedding dress pieces and Christening
robe bits. She didn't sew them right next to pieces of Granfer's
working shirts but they were there too. The men's wedding shirts our
special summer dresses, some wedding veil trimmings and, much to
Uncle Barney's head shakin' disapproval, a piece from his old cavalry
uniform.

"You don't want that gel." he said.

"I do, it's all part of our family history so you be still there.
I couldn't leave you out." So she cut into his old jacket before
the moths took it all. "When your Uncle Barney first wore this
uniform," Granma told us, "we thought him a real dandy, upright
an' proud, 'all spit 'n' polish,' he called it. After the fiasco at Crimea
happened he had, 'no time for them damnable Lords who'd played
with us as if we were their toy soldiers.' But my mother Rosanne,
she said, when Barney was a young man he was very handsome."

I know where all the pieces came from because when we were
litt'uns Gran would tell us stories from each patch piece. I remember
one day, aw it was a really wet windy cold day, so we were sittin'
snuggled up on a rug round the lovely warm cooking range. Gran
had the fire door open. With the quilt lying across her legs she was
adding another piece and along with scatterings of her tinkly little
laugh she told us its tale. In the group were Rose and I; John, Harry
and our cousin Grace, who was five years older than me. I think
Gracie had brought some pieces of material, a lovely pale violet from
the makings of her Mother's going away outfit. As we listened to the

story Aunty Lizzie came in to fetch Gracie home. Aunty Elizabeth always interrupted, never saying a hallo to us children, hardly noticing we were there.

Soon after, while she was talking to Granny, Granfer stomped in the back door shaking off the heavy rain out of his hair.

"Oh, what lovely weather." he called. Going over to Gran he put his arm round her and gave her a big kiss on the forehead. "Smells good, what's cooking me luvly?"

"John get away with yer," laughed Gran, "you're soaking me in rain water." and she pushed him playfully with her elbow.

"Aw you are unkind to me woman," we children all giggled at his antics. Granny blew him a cheeky kiss. Although it was unusual for older people to openly be affectionate with one another in those days but then Gran and Granfer were still Georgians at heart, they loved each other and showed it. They always kissed each other Hallo and Goodbye it was natural to them. But I noted how embarrassed their eldest daughter looked.

"Take no notice Grace," she ordered her daughter, "I think we had better leave, c'mon." She got the girl swiftly into her coat and bonnet and they left.

Elizabeth was a cold unbending woman. Gracie enjoyed being with us cousins at the Inn. Sadly her mother disapproved of us children always being at the Inn during those long summers. But let's forget her. I did notice that when Gran included that pale violet material she sewed it in thin strips around an edge and that, sadly, told its own story.

Upstairs in her little hideaway sitting room Granny kept her scrapbook. Just like the quilt it was a magpie collection of family memories; cut out pictures, pressed flowers, bits of celebration cake decorations, babies' shoe bows, and ribbons, even a few tail feathers from old Cockie. Along with some of her own short rhymes and thumbnail sketches, it was another deep well of lovely stories.

Pity these personal treasures get lost or thrown out over the years. Maybe, they still exist in somebody's possession somewhere?

Oh no, Granny wasn't just a good needlewoman and green-fingered gardener, she made lovely sweeties for us from her jam and jelly making. It meant keeping the pulp of all the fruit skins and pips giving that another sieving to be rid of pips and coarse skins then grinding the last bits in her mortar with a pestle. Boil up the juice with sugar, dissolve some gelatine strain it into the boiling juice and sugar, just a little at a time. Moisten a tin and pour the mixture in and leave it 'til the next day. Cut into short strips with oiled scissors, they would keep very well in a jar if we didn't grab handfuls to fill our pockets. Mm, I can taste those jelly Jujubes even now. I don't know how she managed to keep such a fine flavour of the fruits in those sweeties. We did love making toffee apples before we all left to go home in September. In the late autumn, if the weather allowed clear passage across from St Leonards, some of us joined in making marzipan fruits and cinnamon biscuits before Christmas.

I liked to go up to the village shop when Granny got her sheets of gelatine and I bought liquorice sticks. It was all hot an' dry in the shop and smelled of bacon and groceries. When he was much older Granfer walked up to the shop to buy his Baccy. Sometimes we would walk up there with him but mostly life gathered around the Inn.

* * * *

The village Constable rarely came down to the Inn so when he was summoned to intervene in a dispute he knew he must, 'attend soon as.' A local, and friend of Granfer's, had promised to collect an item from Pevensey village for Granny and to drop it in as he was passing on his way home. Jim duly delivered the item into the kitchen for Annie. More than half an hour later Granfer saw Jim was still out in the yard and standing, not by his own wagon but beside the wagon of a man from over Bexhill way. He wasn't a regular.

"Yer'll right then Jim?" Not a man to waste words Jim just nodded to Granfer. A few moments later the owner of the wagon came out of the bar ready to leave. Before he reached for his horse's reins Jim up an' says.

"You've got my rope."

"Nar yer wrong, that's mine mate."

"If yer feel like that," returns Jim, "I'll send for't Constable."

"Do as yer like mate, y'er wrong."

The two men faced each other, neither prepared to move. Granfer quick-beckons young John onto his horse.

"Fetch the Constable John. Make haste tell him I need his services, soon as."

In very little time Arthur, our village Constable, arrived on horseback into the yard. Granfer nods to the two silent men across the yard.

"Good-day gents," says the Constable, "What's ter do 'ere then?"

"He's got my rope," says Jim tilting his chin towards the owner and wagon that has a new rope tied across the canvas covered load.

"Nar he's wrong, 'tis my rope."

Jim replies sayin,' "Unwhip the end Constable and see what you find inside."

The Constable goes over to the wagon, pulls out an end of the rope and proceeds to carefully unravel the whipping, teasing open the twists to a few inches in where he sees a narrow strip of oiled cloth. Withdrawing and smoothing out the strip he reads the name, "Jim Penfold. Well, we couldn't have better evidence than that." says the Constable, "Get it off your wagon man and return the rope to its rightful owner."

The man did so with bad grace whilst all stood watching. Of course
by the time the Constable arrived the customers were standing outside
in the yard watching events unfold. Jim nodded his thanks to the Constable, laid the coil of rope on the back of his wagon and slowly replaced the strip and re-whipped the end. Retying his load with odd bits of twine, the man flung himself angrily up onto the board seat, slapped his horse's rump hard with the rein and moved out of the yard. The Constable remounted his horse and followed the wagon stopping the man further down the lane. It wasn't Arthur's way to put a man to rights in front of his adversary, he'd never frighten an offender he said, "No, that's no good. A frightened man's a dangerous man. Want ta keep danger out a' my patch, best thing."

The Constable motioned him on his way then turned, gave Granfer a wave. Grandfather raised his hand in thanks. I don't think the man ever called again.

"Take a small ale Jim?" asked Granfer.

"Thank' ee John but no, I've more to do today." and he drove off towards his home.

"Solid chap ol' Jim." a local remarked as he walked back inside.

The last man to follow the crowd back into the bar was one of the draymen, a young man, who, having just delivered barrels of ale into our cellar had stopped for his lunch. I overheard him comment.

"Yea, but don't 'e walk strange."

"Who, Jim yer' mean?" one of the regulars asked.

"That's right, the owner of that rope."

"If you'd spent best part of your life ploughin' wi' 'orses rather than a sittin' up 'igh there on yer box you'd walk like Jim."

"How's that then?"

"Jim's deformed 'is ankles from all that strainin' against plough 'n th' earth, that's 'ow, an' it can't be 'elped."

* * * *

The summer afternoon was drifting into evening, as the sun's lowering rays sent lengthening shadows across the shining sands. We could just hear the trickling edge of the sea away as far as we could see. It was the longest tide of the year.

My bag of finds trailing in the puddles was near to full with many small edible creatures from the little pools among the rocks. This time of the tide seaweeds and mosses that cover the rocks had gone crisp dry. We were five together in a scattered group, subdued now, the joyful squeals heralding our discoveries earlier in the day had ceased, for we were tiring. Nearby John was pulling a clump of heavy flat seaweed, the type you hang by the back door to tell you the state of the day's weather, up from a rock, but it wasn't a rock and he was indicating to me with a rapid arm wave to come nearer.

"Take a look." he said. I bent to help him. Something was just visible under weed but lodged between rock and one of the huge tree stumps we knew was part of the ancient submerged woodland. With a suck and blop the unexpected turned visible.

"Phew," John breathed at first unable to make a real word, "Gor! It's like an old dagger the tip's broken off straight, look."

Our sister and two young brothers were slowly making their way across to see John's find. The atmosphere seemed to be, quite suddenly, utterly still around us two. John and I, both together, looked up and out towards the sea. Three great helmeted men were riding, towards us, their horse's hooves kicking up a great splash of water, that wasn't there, but, maybe nor were they; because they appeared like liquid smoke even though the sun glinted off their armoured shoulders giving them a solid look. The three horsemen rode between us, around us, I couldn't be sure but as we turned our heads in unison to follow their progress they were gone. John looked at me, and I at him. No words exchanged. Rose, whose wander made her nearest to us asked,

"What are you two looking at?" Then her hair blew over her face and she shivered violently. "Gracious what a cold wind." She said. But there was no wind. "C'mon boys," she called to Tommy and Harry, "better wend our way back."

"Cor' John, where'd you get that dagger?" Little Harry startled us with his fast chatter asking how John came to find it? We thought it had been stuck there in the rock but the dark blue red showed it had come from deep in a soggy oak stump.

"Is it heavy, let's feel?" wanted Tommy, then he dropped it, "Aw it is." he complained and we all laughed. He had broken the tense atmosphere. John hefted the dagger, its hilt against his shoulder like a rifle and started to walk.

Looking homewards I saw Grandfather standing on top of a dune sending us a lazy wave.

"There's Granfer." We all waved back, his arm dropped to his side satisfied. By the time we reached shore the sea was lapping up over our ankles. Gazing back out to sea from high on the dunes the rocks had already disappeared. A long outward tide comes back in fast.

That evening, when we had finished our tea, Granny let us bring in our heavy find and lay it for all to see on the table under the oil lantern.

"Do you think it is old Grandfather?" John asked rather formally.

"I do." he replied. "It's eroded but it certainly looks like a dagger." They discussed its probable original length and how long it could have been lying in the sea bed.

"Didn't you think to look for the broken tip?" asked Rose. John and I looked over the table to each other. Our brother just shook his head. "I would've." she commented.

"You weren't in it." returned John's sharp reply, unusual for him. Granfer noticed but said nothing.

The sun, sea and hot air had done for Rose, Tom and Harry were already trailing up to bed. John and I were still in the kitchen helping Gran. Granfer came through the back door with two buckets of water for Granny's morning washing and put them beside the range to take the chill off overnight. Water pumped from the well in the yard was very cold. Left inside overnight meant it came up to the boil faster when needed for the wash next day. Then, instead of going through to the bar Granfer sat back down at the table. He knew we were itchin' to tell something more. Even Granny picked up her quilting and sat nearby. John simply told exactly what we two had experienced.

"I've seen them too." Granfer revealed, in a low voice.

Gosh John and I were relieved and excited all at the same time. However, we showed our emotions quietly. It didn't seem right to whoop and skip!

"It was just about the place where I saw you two standing. I were a young lad pokin' about among those rocks when I caught sight of what looked like white marble showing just clear of the sand. Well I recognised it was the top of a horse's skull almost fallen into fine little pieces. A little ways off I see's the lower jaw bone that's when I thought ... it must have been one of them little war horses an' there they were, three of 'em, ridin' very fast all glistening an' splashin' right at me they came, in a great wafting breeze and they were gone. Thought I were seein' things. I've never spoken of it to this day."

Eyes concentrating on her quilting, in her chair by the range, Granny made no comment. Granfer went on to tell us he had a friend whose family had been Armourers for generations; even supplied the locals who fought for King Harold.

"I still see 'im every now an' then," he said, "Let me 'ave your find, we'll wrap it well in a sack, tell no-one. I'll take it with me ter market an' when I see 'im, maybe 'e'll know more about it."

Turns out Granfer first met this young chap across the western side of the Marsh along the back of the Downs.

In those days, well before he became a married man, Granfer had the wanderlust, lookin' around to see life. He told how he used ter walk miles across Sussex North and East and West. Never forgot a face. Even now sometimes folks from way back who he'd met on his travels would drop in at the Inn and stay yarning. They may not have seen Johnnie Pilbeam for 20 or 30 years. Granfer told how he'd fetched up on one of those wandering times at the Armourer's place at the foot of the Downs. Their son, who was his own age joined him and they walked on together way over to Horsham and down to Portsmouth. "Saw Admiral Nelson's ol' Victory lying in the harbour, we did. Ah now, that year we must a' both been seventeen years old." he remembered.

Grandfather kept our find closely wrapped and hidden on his wagon. He didn't see his friend from the Armourer's family, for some months but finally they met and the man confirmed it was a dagger, middle-Eastern in origin and from the time of William's successful invasion. However, Grandfather had been told how men came across the Channel to reconnoitre the possible landing areas all along the coast. Some did not return. It could be a man and his horse fell overboard and in them days those floundering in the sea were usually left un-helped. It was thought to be against the will of God, 'The Sea having already claimed the life for the Lord.'

Our lives were overflowing with new happenings every day. Loss and death were all part of it. Best of all, Granfer was there to explain.

* * * *

As I awoke I could tell this day would bring a new experience.

It was a feeling of apprehension that sits in the pit of your stomach. We were nearing the end of our holidays. Young John and I had wandered far out to where submerged ancient forest and foundations of flint huts became just visible at low tide. Those places were now inhabited by an array of small sea creatures in surprising glowing bright colours. John always wanted to venture to watch such exciting visions. I was ever a careful big sister cautioning him not to go out too far. I knew the sands so often shifted their spread, especially after heavy weather. You could see the signs of the deep black tree stumps and roots by the shining water topping the sump holes where quick sands could unexpectedly suck you in.

From a crouch John was up and running fast across the sand. Only my eyes followed at first. But then I noticed he was dashing towards a child caught in the quicksand. The next instant her body was sliding down. Fortunately the little girl had long thick hair. Johnny grabbed a great handful and laying his body flat along the sand he held on tight. I daren't go too near, even to cup the child's chin in my hand. With a heart-squeezing chance I caught the attention of two groups of fishermen, at first one group just waved back to me, for after all I was just a small girl. Then the realisation dawned and one man picked up a landing plank and started to race across the sands. Thankfully a cry went up and all five men came to our aid. I will never forget the little child's horrific screaming and Johnnie's efforts to reassure her. The fishermen threw boards around her but it took a long time to ease her body up. At one point a silence descended and peace flooded her face like a mask as if she had accepted her fate, her tears spent. Just as suddenly as it all began her little body slipped out of the clutches of that hole. Like a newborn foal she staggered a few steps a smile spreading back into her eyes, then she ran, ran, ran to where a woman stood, hands on hips. I could just hear her voice shouting,

"Where've you bi'n?"

The men stood gazing in blank exhaustion. All sound was again restored; sea birds circled crying, their eerie calls penetrating the air. A wind wafted up. Winter equinox was on its way. The men were lifting John gently, for he'd become solid, unmoving unable to open his hand, still clamped full of long hair. One of the men patted him on the back. "Well done lad. She won't forget." Although I could see John had suffered more. Those fishermen knew it too but their own extreme experiences had taught them to bluff on. It was their way.

I'm sure that in the bar that evening Granfer heard the story because he took John aside before bed that night. He and my brother were sitting talking together on the stairs as I came up with my candle. In its light I saw John's face had cleared and a smile had begun to resurface. Granfer thanked me for my support.

"You have both witnessed another's struggle. Fighting for life is our strongest sense, that little lass ran back into her life. We all know who helped her keep her most treasured possession, John."

That day brought us another lesson strengthening our own understanding of existence.

You know, the human being who can interpret life for us when we are young makes a deep lasting impression. I will never forget Grandfather Johnnie Pilbeam.

Photo from a newspaper obituary 1910 showing John Pilbean's portrait that used to hang beside the Inglenook at the Lamb Inn.

* * * *

Looking inland across the Pevensey Levels the land lays low and marshy for as far as you can see. Over to the west, past the stony hill topped by George Deeplove's tower mill, the steep sloping ridges of the chalk Downs rise bright green against the sky gradually fading blue into the distance. North on low grey hills another mill, a fan tail, can be seen through the haze along the horizon that slides ever lower down to the east and the seashore just beyond Hastings.

The Marsh of my childhood was a network of drainage ditches and sandy lanes inhabited by trotting horses pulling carts of provisions and heavier horse drawn wagons carrying dry goods and collected fresh produce. Farm wagons met flocks of sheep. Men and their dogs herded cattle across lanes from gate to gate and the postman did his rounds on horseback at his own gentle pace. At the farms, postie Bob Turner, would shout until someone came to take their post. Same when he approached the Inn. He would never use the horn to announce his coming like other posties I knew of in Sussex. Bob said it sounded too much like the noise of the battle field so he carried on his shout, 'Postie,' until John or Annie came out with a half of ale. Exchanging his drink for their letters he remained sitting in the saddle. Handing down the empty pot he'd say, "Thank 'ee Maister, or Mrs. Chirrup." and off his horse would amble. As a small child I could never understand why he should tell my smiling Grandparents, to "Cheer up."

* * * *

As I became more aware of the world outside Gran's snug bedroom; my requests for, 'one more story,' now included keepsakes that were part of her stories. Patting a shining powder blue patch, Gran said it came from the family honeymoon bed cover. "And this lovely pink rose print was the dress I wore when I first walked out with your Grandfather, Thomas Cowley."

Prompting me to ask,

"Where is he Granny? I've never seen him. Did Mummy see him?"

"Yes – she used to sit beside him on a Sunday morning and dip her toasty soldier into his boiled egg when he wasn't looking. She was a little Tinker, just like you. She was eleven years old when he died."

"What's died Granny?" And so she told me about death with her fingers resting on a deep rich purple plain coloured patch. It was such a dark hue I almost could not tell its colour,

"That piece came from the cover used by my Grandmother Anne's family. She said it was the final counterpane over what she called, 'the dear departed."

Her face filled with a most lovely smile but Granma Clara didn't dwell on those thoughts she was a positive lady. She told me that it was after her husband Tom, passed away that she started her own patchwork quilt, like she had seen her Grandmother make. "Useless feeling sorry for yourself," she said, "fill your time, don't waste time moping. Work to earn your living then enjoy the time that's yours." As the quilt grew it gathered something of each generation, "So, how could I ever feel alone." She said, "Remember all the joy, revisit the sad times they have their space but mostly cherish the memories, let everybody live in their stories."

I may have been an only child but I wasn't lonely. Kept safe from the war that raged around, I was rarely aware of any fright; like all small children I took each event as a norm, having no understanding to question events, for I had no understanding of the shortages the adults were coping with; the displacements and sleep deprivation caused by constant watchfulness, or the bombs that damaged buildings and lives.

Part Two
My Turn Now

Lily aged four

1

To me, life is a series of stories

While Granma had kept me wrapped in her world, food rationing was changing family traditions. Since her retirement a year before the war started, Granma's contribution to family life was to make the Saturday lunchtime steak and kidney pudding. I learned that everybody she ever cooked for loved her rich savoury pudding. The recipe had always been one of her specialities. But when meat went on ration the family could not manage to have both stewing steak on Saturday and a roast joint on Sunday. So it was decided to have steak and kidney or a roast meat dinner on alternate weekends. It was now that Artie decided to give up the long held tradition of the father, or 'man of the house,' standing at the head of the Sunday dinner table carving the joint. He said that job was best left to Dolly because she knew how far the weekly meat ration had to stretch. Allowing a woman to be in charge of the Sunday meat joint was initially frowned upon as a break in family tradition, but changes had to be made. Saturdays became fish and chip day and on the alternate week Gran made steak pudding, my mum took the time off. With me in the pram, she would walk down to the Shakespeare Arms, at the bottom corner of Chatham Place, to meet dad on his walk home from work; there they would have a drink together, just like the days when they were a newly married couple living opposite the pub in their first flat. The Publican's family and the 'Regulars,' had sent a lovely congratulations card for my birth. It was one of those pretty things Clara thought too nice to be put away; she wanted it placed on the mantelpiece to be seen.

"It was," Granma repeated, "far too nice to be kept put away in a drawer."

Dolly had other ideas; she decided to put it in a scrap book to stop it fading. Seventy one years later I have it in my own scrap book. Made in the shape of a baby's bonnet with real lace around its curving edge, it still has a pearly satin sheen.

In stark contrast to the card that joined it in January 1942. Printed with a, 'One' on cheap rough light austerity card it tells its own message about the year it was made.

Some months later, a story from one of those Saturday lunchtimes at the Shakespeare Arms, started another family legend. It seems my baby pram was parked outside the pub door when the Baker came by to make a delivery. Apparently he chucked me, the baby, under the chin and must have said something like, 'Coochy coochy coo,' because, a few moments later, he fell into the pub doorway laughing, saying, "Yer know what that baby out there told me? '*That's not funny.*' I suppose it's the two year old working class version of, 'I am not amused.'

The postal service never failed the population. Consequently Clara kept in close contact with family as far as she could. Her third sister Nancy wrote to say they were retiring from the Restaurant in Soho, but that she had to go on her own to live with son Bill and his wife Ruth in Hailsham because, ' and you won't believe this Clara, of all things the authorities have interned Valentino saying he's a foreign alien.' A month later Valentino was back with his family so the couple could finally buy the place they had always planned for their retirement in Eastbourne. 'But I ask you,' wrote Nancy, still in disbelief, 'dear Valentino is more English than the English, and to think Cabinet Ministers had been our customers at the Soho restaurant for years and years! We were so well known. Oh well that's what silly wars do for us ordinary folks'.

2

The Willows

Granma called her small blue and white nightstick, Tubby. Her cup and tea dish were known as Laura and Bea. It never occurred to me that it was unusual to give names to pieces of china, just something that came so naturally in Granma's speech. She often linked the places and people from her childhood with pieces of Willow pattern china. Like the story about the afternoon in the 1880's, when on a visit to the Inn; she found her Grandmother Anne sad, because one of her favourite jugs had lost its handle. 'Rosie water jug came from my Great Great Granma Amy's collection,' Anne said, 'Amy was an Herbalist making salves; soothing and healing lotions for women, that she and her sisters sold at market. And, oh dear me, Amy was herself sold to a dreadful man!" Granma Clara said she, herself, was too young to ask more at the time adding – 'Your mum will tell you Amy's story when you are older.' I held my mother, Dolly, to that."

'It was Amy,' Clara said, 'who had the first Willow pattern china in our family. Her son James, youngest son from her happy second marriage, who brought home the box full of china he found on the beach after a stormy night out in the Channel. When Amy's granddaughter Annie married John Pilbeam most of that first collection of Willow china went to them as a wedding present.

Grandma Clara said the part of her life she spent her happiest years were at the Inn with her own grandparents, especially the story of how Annie and John met and their love began. As the story unfolded the room seemed to fill with the perfume from the Lavender and Rosemary hedge in Grandmother Annie's garden. However many times Granma Clara told me her family stories, she made life with her Grandparents sound magical, telling about the sights and sounds of the Marsh; the visitors at the Inn and all their 'goings on,' Grandfather John's story songs and the people that lived and worked there; the garden, the orchard with the bee skeps and the animals the fish and the birds.

She used to ruffle my curly hair calling it, 'frogswool!' I never knew why, then kissing my head she'd murmur, 'mm lovely, – little ones smell so lovely'.

Granma wouldn't allow anything to make her sad for very long. Even so, however much Clara snuck herself away in gentle storytelling, Dolly noticed her mother's physical being showed current events were taking their toll, as they were for everyone of course.

3

Small Talk

Dolly changed the subject aiming at taking Clara's attention away with a bit of local gossip.

"Saw that Mrs Stebbings along the street, you know the one whose family came from Glasgow;" her mother didn't seem to be listening, "the Grandparents worked in the factory that made the Willow pattern pottery?" Clara looked up, "You met them in Queenie's little shop?" Clara smiled in recognition. "Well, Mrs Stebbings doesn't speak anymore but it does look like she's got a job though." Dolly was cutting potatoes for chips and Clara was making a batter with seasoned flour, water and a little bicarb, "Goes off every morning real early, seen her through the window when I get up for the early morning feed."

Clara got the frying pan out and removed the lid that covered the fat left from its last use. Every last drop of dripping was saved. No use turning out into a basin, washing out the pan only to tip it back in the pan and wash out the basin again.

"Never seem to see her come home though." Clara lit the gas while Dolly added a bit more lard to the chip pan. "Artie says he sees her about the town. But when he spoke to her she just looked back at him as if her eyes were all glazed."

In their separate pans Clara's batter was crisping and Dolly's chips sizzling. Mouth watering aromas filled the kitchen. Finally Clara spoke,

"I haven't seen her family about anymore?"

"Sad she keeps herself to herself. She could come and join us girls at the 'sale of work' round at the church hall but I haven't been able to catch her to suggest it."

"Put a note through her door love." Clara suggested.

"Ah, here he is." Dolly poured hot water into the enamel bowl in the sink. And, for the moment Mrs Stebbings was forgotten.

"Mm, smells good." Artie said, taking off his jacket, rolling his sleeves up and lathering his hands and arms vigorously with a large block of red carbolic soap. As he dried himself on the roller towel that hung on the back door Clara laid the hot plates on the table and Dolly served the fish and chips from the pans.

The two women had worked together whenever they were both in the kitchen, usually on a Saturday; although this was Dolly's kitchen she carried on the old ways because it gave her mother the feeling she was part of things and there were times when Clara cooked the Sunday meal that allowed Dolly time to herself with her baby, or an hour or two with Artie to work on their allotment.

After a little afternoon snooze for Granma there was always something practical to set her mind to, like the time she and Mum decided to reuse old woollen garments; Gran unpicked and folded the wool onto a Skeiner, ready for Dolly to wash and hang to dry, out on the line across the back garden. Later, between them, they would roll the wool into balls ready for knitting new jumpers. Dolly had given Clara the unravelling because she thought it would give her mother a sitting down job. Besides it provided free yarn to knit up new jumpers to sell at the Mother and Baby sale of work at the church hall in Exeter Street. The best, 'Second time around' jumper pattern she found in a 'Make do and Mend' magazine was for a Mother and Daughter set. Dolly was so proud of her efforts making those two blue grey and white stripy tops, they lasted until I grew out of mine and they were passed on to my cousins.

4

Time off, when's that when it's at home?

Artie went to tend his allotment in Dyke Road Park on Sunday mornings. As the evenings grew longer he sometimes managed to put in an hour or so but his working day was long followed by night time fire watching hours (patrolling on the roof of Bostal House in West Street,) that still had to be shared with others in reserved occupations, including a few of the older retired men and women. The family finances were helped out considerably by having the vegetables he grew. Some people only sowed potatoes to swap for green vegetables which were often ready in gluts, so their system of swapping and exchange worked out very well. Dad started off by having a bit of a problem with some of the elderly men who organised the allotments. They thought the gardening tools should be locked in the community shed and shared by all. They were also rather against working on the allotments on Sundays. Unlike the retired men and women who could spend their whole days digging and weeding, Artie could not he had his own household repair jobs to do. Some weeks Sunday morning was the only time he had and that's when the shed door was locked, so he decided to keep his own spade and fork at home and that was seen as unfriendly. But for his practical purposes it was how it had to be.

It was during the busy early years of wartime that Artie started spending two hours on Saturday and Sunday afternoons, not just resting in an armchair but in his pyjamas sleeping in bed. Clara said,

'Don't worry Dolly dear, he obviously needs it. After all he's burning the candle at both ends.' She was right because however much he looked after himself especially as the winter months drew in, the heavy coal smoke laden air took its toll on everybody's health. For some years Artie had the Chemist on the corner of

Lancaster Road make up a special chest rub; a mixture of Amber and Camphor oils. Each autumn a fresh supply stood corked and ready labelled, 'For Mr Arthur Smith.' Rubbed onto the chest it certainly was effective in keeping the head clear alongside having a warm body.

My father was always on the move. He was one of those people who took any fight of stairs two at a time. I loved joining him for a Sunday morning digging on the allotment. An incident occurred on one of those gardening sessions that Granma handed me back for my own repertoire of stories. She told me I was hardly more than a toddler. As her retelling unfolded I too recalled the morning clearly, going along Coventry Street hand in hand with my Dad. I was skipping to keep up with him and as usual he started skipping alongside me and we were laughing as his spade and fork, wrapped in a sack, jangled under his other arm. It must have been when he first started calling me 'Skipper.'

On the allotment I watched for a while as he kept dropping peas and that seemed all wrong to me because I had often heard the words, "waste not want not." So I trailed behind as he walked along beside a string stretched across the ground dropping peas. When he got to the end of the line I held out my handful of peas saying,

"You dropped them Daddy." To my great surprise he sat down heavily on the grassy pathway and roared with laughter.

Granma said they were having Sunday dinner when Dad told how I handed him back all the peas he thought he had so carefully sown. She and Mum couldn't stop laughing.

"Children do such innocent funny things."

Dad's friend, Mr Stevens, kept rabbits and pigeons in his Exeter Street back yard. When there was a glut of lettuces Dad would often swap them for the odd pigeon's egg for me. Little fried Pigeon's eggs are delicious. For a long time I thought my dad had grown these eggs himself until one Sunday morning when he took me to see Mr Stevens' rabbits and pigeons.

After working on some essential plumbing repairs at an old farmhouse near Twineham in mid Sussex, my father came home with a bunch of grapes and a jar of honey, sent by the farmer's wife, 'for his little girl'. I thought they were little green eggs and I learned that bees had made the honey. I later asked dad if he would be going to Mrs Bees' house again because I liked her honey. Saying that children's growing minds have their own ways of thinking logically, Granma suggested.

"Now's a good time to tell you about what bees do for a living. My own Grandmother kept her bees at the end of the orchard behind the Inn - - -." Her daily flow of stories usually came out of a current incident giving her a way of explaining what was happening. If Mum or Gran were not telling me how something worked they would be making something or cooking and letting me join in. 'Ah! Now, I need some baking powder to lift a cake up to the sky. Come on Missy, let's go and see what the world outside the house is doing, shall we?'

5

Let's go foraging

Off would come her wrap around pinafore and on would go her tidy button up shoes and neat coat. My coat and shoes were similarly buttoned and given a brush down.

"Are we ready? Then off we go." Across to the Chemist to buy a small bottle of Olive oil then back along in the opposite direction to Queenie's shop in the middle of the street. On the way she told me how to make a tasty herby salad dressing with the oil and a touch of vinegar; even better lemon juice when you can get a lemon. As we went in the shop door, I overheard a voice say, "Here's our neat little lady," referring to my Gran. The voice was right; Granma would never slip along the shop in her slippers and pinafore. She said the way you look reflects your home; she would smile at the young Mums gossiping in the shop, fags hanging from their mouths, stockings rolled down round their ankles and their feet in run down dirty old slippers, frequently exclaiming, "Aw my giddy Aunt, look at the time, the kids'll be comin' outa school for their dinners any minute."

"Oh dear bit late aren't yer Phil. What they gonna giv'em fer dinner terday?"

"Bread 'n' scrape." A Phil or a Daphne would call back over her shoulder, into the emptying shop.

"Spent too much time gossipin' on the doorsteps." my Mum said when told what was going on in, 'the world outside,' Gran was laughing saying,

"What do those women think they look like?" then she'd follow up her semi criticism with, "They've got to have a bit of company for themselves, poor girls, what with their husband's away in the forces."

There were more retired folks in Coventry Street when Granma Clara lived with us. Like Clara they were quietly industrious each in their own fashion. Whilst Clara was a cook there were the knitters and the sewers, among the older ladies who crocheted children's cotton socks for summer and knitted wool ones for winter; mostly from unravelling old jumpers. There wasn't a child in the street without a good pair of socks in the winter. Our next door neighbour, Aunty P was bedridden for many years, but still one of the most industrious of the older generation. She made a complete layette set including embroidered sheets and pillowcases for each newborn baby in the Street, all by hand in the tiniest stitches, even making a complete outfit of clothes, dresses, petticoats, knickers and dolls pram covers for my dolly. When she wasn't sewing she did enormous puzzles with 1000 or more pieces on a board across her bed. I often sat up beside her on the bed searching for the unusual parts, then sliding down to pick up the strays that fell on the floor.

Mum made dresses for me and used up the tiny off cuts of material sewing them into little rosettes attaching these to hair slides to match the dress. Few had idle hands or time to spare!

Many of the retired men with special skills like my Grandfather Sam Smith and Uncle P. went back to full time work during the war years because the younger men had been called up. At the weekends Uncle P. became the street's champion wine maker. His wine and preserves often changed hands with the products from the hands of the knitters and sewers.

To Uncle P's great advantage, my Granma Clara was a canny finder of wild fruits; Elderberries, Blackberries and crab-Apples. She had a nack of seeing edible plants where others never noticed. Early in the season a basket of gently gathered Elderflower heads for Champagne; golden Dandelions and nettles all went into the big stone bottles in Uncle P's cellar. He paid Granma for her foraging in eggs from his chicken, not to mention feathers for patchwork cushions.

Tucked behind a roll of elderly lino in a second hand shop Gran caught sight of a small basket on wheels,

"I gave a thruppenny Joey for it." she said. That little old basket trundled along behind Gran through the war years and as soon as I could walk I went with her. Round her waist she wore a narrow leather belt to which she buttoned a short leather pouch, "My sister Rose made this for me years ago," she told me, patting the soft pouch, "of course it was bigger then, to hold all my kitchen knives and it hung inside the back kitchen door." She noticed that puzzled me, so smiling she said, "When your Mummy was your age we used to live in St Georges Mews down in the centre of town. We'll walk that way one day when you're older." There were two slots in the pouch to carry a very slender paring knife and a little piece of wet stone. She could pare the zest off a lemon finer than any knife specially designed for the job. She kept her knife sharp on the wet stone, spitting on it before setting the blade to its surface. By the 1940s that knife was as spare as a skewer, ideal for snipping tiny aromatic tips of green tussocks from what some knew only as weeds.

On dry sunny days Gran would say, "Let's go foraging." When the school bell told us the children had gone inside to their lessons we started out.

I could only have been about three that first time so it seemed to me we walked miles but really it wasn't that far because she could spy out tiny new growth in between corners to pathways that went along the edges of Twittens behind the houses. Passing forgotten gardens she'd spy a tuft of Oregano or a woody old Rosemary bush with a tip or two of new growth. Our wheelie basket would soon be full of tiny nosegays; lemon thyme, to go in the batter for fish and a few bright new stinging nettle tips pinched off for a savoury tart with the fat from bacon rinds, "rich in iron those nettles." Gran taught me that Dandelion leaves tossed with torn Cos lettuce and a leaf or two of wild garlic softened with a little olive oil makes all the difference to your digestion. Just take a leaf and rub it between your hands then hold your palms up to your face; that's the way to get the full aroma. You'll soon learn thyme from oregano, bay and rosemary. "Only take what you can use today. Leave some for others to take, there will be new growth tomorrow just keep your eyes open."

At the height of the fruiting season Mum and Gran would sit together out in the back garden topping and tailing fruit; running Elderberry heads through a fork, nipping out Dandelion petals or peeling and grating Parsnips for Uncle Ps expert wine making. The old neighbours swore, 'His mixtures were superior to any good single malt.'

As the extra long double summertime daylight dwindled into the autumn months the final vegetables and fruits from the allotment were cleaned and chopped in the kitchen, runner beans were layered with salt in an earthenware crock, onions in sweet vinegar. The fire in the room where we ate our evening meal and listened to the Wireless was never lit before half past five, Mum used to sit at the end of the kitchen table doing her sewing while Granma snipped the Gooseberries. When Mackerel came our way a Gooseberry sauce sat next to them on our plates. Bone hard Quinces fell to Gran's paring knife the pieced fruit simmered to softening in water, its juice finally dripping overnight from a muslin cone into a clear liquid to make jelly. At the back of a very old house she caught sight of a tree hanging low with strange dead looking fruits she said were called Medlers, even those were made into a thick 'cheese.' Filling only one small jar it was served on Boxing Day with her cold Confit of Rabbit, along with a small glass of Dandelion or Elderberry wine. Just a little went a long way. There was never enough sugar to make more than a small jar or two.

Being taught to look for the unusual I made an unexpected discovery. At first I could only point because I had no idea what to call what I saw but what I showed her brought a smile to Gran's face.

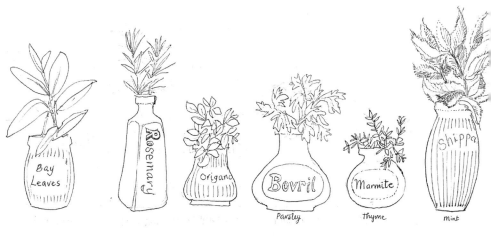

86

At the end of the street the wall behind a shop was painted plain grey and at my eye level, which must then have been 36" (92cm), I noticed some words written with a pencil. At first Gran didn't say anything so I asked what they were,

"The top line says, 'Russell of Spring' and the one beneath, 'White Streak' and the one below that says, 'Baby Joe.' I didn't understand so as she walked on she said, "I think I might know what that's all about but I'm not sure. We'll take another look when we pass this way tomorrow."

The next time we passed that way the words were different, but although Gran stooped slightly to see she walked on by. Back in our house I was eager to know what the words were and she said, "Mrs M and Rudie Boy." It wouldn't have been any good her explaining at the time because I was too young to understand what any of it meant. Years later, mum told me that a neighbour coming off nightshift would stop briefly by that wall, as if to do up his shoe lace, but he actually wrote that day's horse racing tips. Apparently he was our local racing buff who spent his nights studying the form and noting his tips on the wall from which he earned a percentage of the local's winnings. His activity eventually caused a bust up between a Bookies' runner and his clients who lived in Coventry Street and who always seemed to be backing the winners. A real fracas took place on the street corner one morning between, the runner and some of the young mum's who often placed small bets with him on their way home from seeing the kids off to school. As he gave them their winnings from the previous day he confronted them on their unusually winning ways. "Oh dear," Granny reported to my parents, "The poor ol' Bookies' runner came away with both eyes blacked." But of course the young women lost their source for a little flutter. No other runner would go near them.

There was always a lot going on even though not all in full view. People were determined Hitler wouldn't win an inch and it wasn't only my Mum and Gran who toiled with a will to survive. Many of the gardens behind the roads like the ones around Coventry and Exeter Streets, Porthall, Lancaster, Buxton, Stafford, Chatsworth and further afield – all Brighton in fact, contained chicken runs, pigeon cages, rabbit hutches; there were well tended apple trees, plums, pears and hazelnuts, gooseberry and currant bushes even though the earth in the small back gardens on our hillside was liberally speckled with chalk and flints. The houses in Coventry and the surrounding streets were built in the 1880's on the chalk cliff that had been cut out to accommodate the Railway line from London earlier in the 19th century. Their garden walls still leached out chalk in heavy rains that being the reason the water is so hard. But the growth within those walls was returned each year in abundance due to the watchfulness of their gardeners.

Each morning the milkman with his horse and cart trailed slowly along the middle of our street. Alfie Eaves with his churns and measuring jugs on his bike cart came earliest from the Porthall end while the Co-op's big heavy horse pulling their green and cream Dray came from the Prestonville end. Neighbours took from the local Dairyman because he was an old friend, others took from the Co-op to keep up their divi. The milk horses rumbled the cart's fat rubber tyres slowly along to allow the milkman time to run back and forth across the road with his deliveries of cardboard topped pints and half pints and empties. The milkman's horse didn't' stop near our house but Gran – often waited in readiness early in the morning behind the front door, just in case. Wearing a sacking garden apron and her outside shoes, her bucket and shovel at the ready, she told me to sit at the front room window and to yell if I saw the horse leave us a present. This was the only time she went out in the street dressed in her grubbies.

The horse that gave us the best haul pulled a high bright red Bakery van that delivered Co-op bread. It came three days a week and the Baker man stopped for his morning tea break at the house opposite. On would go the horse's nosebag and off went the Baker into our neighbour's house where he was surrounded by women, all family members, who had been bombed out of their London homes. They sounded a rowdy lot for quiet old Coventry Street, but they were heaps of fun and obviously good company for the Baker on his tea break. Anyway, he always came out laughing, towing a crowd of little eager hands each hoping for one of yesterday's stale sticky buns. Or, maybe that last comment was planted in my mind by my father's jovial observation!

Meanwhile the horse had performed well. Gran had scooped up its great gift. She didn't go out to collect every time the horse performed though because others had to have their turn.

Back into the house; just inside the front door, off came her shoes, then along the hallway to the back garden, slipping her feet into her garden shoes by the back door,

"Never put manure straight onto the earth around the plants, you'll give them indigestion." She would say. Her haul was left in the bucket covered with water to break down the solids, the water she swilled the shovel in went into the watering can ready for the evening watering. Mustn't waste anything Gran would say. With her hands thoroughly cleaned in soapy water she would tie her hair into a pretty chiffon scarf and go dusting her room. My Granma Clara was a woman of thoughtful routines careful with time, resources and money.

Nobody was well off but with swapping and lending, people managed. My parents swapped our bacon ration for our neighbour's cheese ration so that my Father, Artie, could take cheese sandwiches with him each day for lunch, which he carried in a brown paper bag in his knapsack. If he ever came home with any leftover cheese sandwich, he hadn't had time to eat, I grabbed them. Although it was stale and dry I loved that old cheese. It was a treat.

BOOK THREE: 1941 – 1952

6

Gossip

Mr and Mrs Divall round the corner in Stanford Road had a grapevine in their greenhouse. The grapes grew plump and sweet. Every morning Mr.Divall emptied the contents of their gusunder on the ground round the vine root. Clara said how sensible and resourceful they were. Not many people swapped with them who heard about Mr Divall's morning ritual.

"The dirty old devil," one woman said, "I heard he seduced his own daughter-in-law." Seduced! The word came out so strongly, I didn't know what she meant.

"How do you know that, Madge?"

"Well, she told me, didn't she?"

"Who did?"

"'is wife of course."

"What d'yer mean, Dot?"

"Yes Dotty, she told me 'ow when Josie came over with the telegram 'e persuaded 'er to stay the rest of the weekend with them for company. Well then?"

"Well what?"

"Go on then," taunted Peggy, "get on and tell us before the kids start comin' out." Gran and I were waiting at the school gate for my cousins when I heard this conversation. I suppose I was considered too young to listen. Little did they know, I had a good teacher and in time, so many of these stories were explained.

"Dotty said he took Josie up a cup of Ovaltine and was in the room with 'er for ages."

"Well, so what 'e could've b'in listening to her, poor girl."

"What! Jack Divall, I wouldn't trust 'im, an' 'is rovin' 'ands." Bunty Streeter cackled.

"You're right there gal. Dotty says when she woke up about half past two in the mornin' Jack hadn't come to bed an' the light was off in the spare bedroom."

"'e's still a virile man with an eye for a skirt," added Bunty, "Not surprising when you think how overweight and slow poor old Dotty's got."

"She's had a real bad time with the change, so she says."

"Yes, but 'es got ta' be in 'is seventies."

"So what!" another Mother screeched, "age don't stop 'em does it?"

"No, you're right there gal, as soon as my two young lads discovered it weren't for stirin' their tea there's 'bin no stoppin' em."

But for all that, what the group of Mothers waiting at the school gate didn't know was that although Jack Divall was too old to be called up, he wasn't too old to be leader of a rescue team that pulled people out of bomb damaged buildings. He'd saved many from very unsafe wreckages where others wouldn't attempt to go.

Mr. Divall was a great character. He wore his snap brim trilby at a slightly rakish angle. I'd seen him take a last look at himself in his hallstand mirror on his way out; snap the edge of his trilby, give himself the saucy look and wink of approval, which he often treated any woman to, that he passed in the street. I liked him – he struck me as being kind and thoughtful. It was Jack Divall who had spent 36 hours digging into the wreckage of a building down in the town opposite St Peter's Church. He refused to give up, especially when he'd heard a faint voice beneath the great slabs of broken masonry. Nobody on his watch was left to die alone. He gave them his super human effort. His rescue unit had no heavy lifting gear, just their bare hands, crowbars and brute force. After five hours the team had found a way inside and typically Jack went further than any other man. He'd say, 'No, you stay out there you got a young family'. Jack and Dotty's boy had been drowned in the Atlantic by a U-boat strike only a few months before, so Jack made it his business to save somebody else's family from the heartache he, Dotty and Josie had gone through. A strained voice had answered his call, the route was becoming more tortuous and when Jack finally managed to catch hold of the trapped old man's hand he realised the water main had been breached and swirling water was rising fast. He shouted to the workers above giving, the coded message to his crew to bring in more help, and bloody quick. He had to grab the man's shock of white hair to hold his head up out of the gurgling water, through the gloom he recognised the face, or thought he did. 'Nar, can't be,' he thought. Jim Russell's got brown hair only saw him yesterday with his kids up the park'. But it was Jim. Some people say it's a myth that hair goes white with shock. Jim's definitely had and it was loose, coming out in handfuls. Still Jack was determined not to lose Jim, he also knew Carol, Jim's wife wasn't in that building and she'd need her husband. One of the rescuers found a way to divert the water but it took another 24 hours that Jack laid alongside Jim in the narrow crevice. Jim suffered both his legs broken. From his Hospital bed he said he never wanted to hear another Music Hall song ever again. 'Blimey, Jack knows more dirty songs than I knew could exist. If it weren't for that man I wouldn't be here'.

Jack was honoured by the King and wore a small emblem under his lapel with humility and a little pride.

'Keep your eye on the good in the man.' Gran remarked to the Mother's congregated outside the school gate.

'Yeah, we need all of them that's like Jack.' replied Jack and Dotty's next door neighbour. She had come to meet her Grandchildren and stood by quietly when the conversation about the grape vine started, but she couldn't let it end there. So it was she who told Jack's story.

As for yours truly, I did remember the first words of that conversation. They stuck in my mind prompting the full story being told to me when I was old enough to understand its full meaning.

Paper patter for stylish summer sandals

7

The family heave a sigh of relief

Mum had joined the Women's Voluntary Service
(WVS) and was getting ready to go round to the
school to help serve orange juice and cod liver oil
to the children at morning playtime.

"That looks nice dear." Clara commented as
Dolly, using Artie's shaving mirror, was rolling
her hair into a Snood and tying the ribbon into
a small knot at the top of her head. Gran had
crocheted the Snood from a pattern, *'Ideas for
the Practical Working Women,'* and was already plaiting raffia to sew
into soles for making a pair of sandals using a paper pattern given
with a woman's magazine under the title, *'Keeping the Girl's up to
Date.'*

"Right then, come on tupp'ney let's get going." As she stooped
to pick me up there was a sound of somebody coming in the front
door, Clara heard it too. Easing open the kitchen door to look along
the passage they saw an old man, quite small. Scrawny you'd say.
He was standing with his back against the front door staring down
the passage at them. At that very moment the air raid sirens started
wailing.

"Jimmie?" Clara said softly but the man didn't reply he just sank
down trembling hard against the door.

"It's Jim." cried out Clara, who, for a woman gone seventy fairly
sprinted up the short flight of stairs from the kitchen and along the
passage. Dolly followed, carrying me. The look on the man's face
showed total abject terror as the sudden blaring of a wailing siren
split the air, its urgency spreading like liquid fire into every orifice;
ears, head, heart, limbs, and bowels. Feet could be heard running
along the street. Clara knelt in front of her son. His body was
trembling so violently the whole door shook with him. This man,
her son, looked twice her age.

"Jimmie dear, you're safe now." she spoke quietly as she smoothed his thin hair. The sirens stopped, everything seemed to hang in a silent vacuum.

"She wasn't there," croaked a small distant voice, "She wasn't there," he repeated in disbelief, "and the door was locked." he struggled to say again but his breath ran out.

"Who dear; who wasn't where?" Clara asked, as they sat on the floor facing each other.

"Hilda, do you mean Hilda love? Dolly asked. "She's got a job. She's alright Jim."

I can't have been very old but I remember this scene, its sounds, its feelings so clearly as I crouched down with Mum and Granma facing my Uncle on the mat inside the front door.

Jim breathed a sigh – deep, deep sigh of relief.

The two women helped him to his feet walking either side along the passage and down into the kitchen. Dolly filled the kettle while Clara wiped her son's sweating, tearful face with a flannel and towel. The all clear siren sounded.

"Must have been a false alarm." Dolly said, relieved. After a while a twinkle came into Jim's eyes,

"You bloody luverly women. Come on give us a kiss."

"Oh my I'll be late, an' my first day too. I must trot. See you later." As Dolly ran out of the door, Clara called after her, "I'll nip round the 'phone box and call, 'The Dudley,' see if I can catch Hilda before she comes off duty."

"Cor blimey I don't want 'er ter see me like this Ma."

"Best she does luv, no harm in that." His mother said, trotting out through the front door. Returning a few minutes later saying, "Just caught her finishing her shift," as she came in from the telephone, "soon be on her way here."

Clara didn't start asking her son questions about where he'd been. That would come later when he was ready. All he said was,

"France is a lovely country, just wish I'd seen it when I wasn't running."

"It's been nearly two years luv."

"Is that all? Feels more like a lifetime." he answered blankly.

An hour later the front door opened and a tentative head

peered in. Through in the kitchen Hilda saw a small grey haired man sitting holding a Willow pattern tea cup cradled in both his hands. She had to pause and just look because when she last saw her husband he was a sturdy, richly dark haired man. This man, wearing a khaki battle jacket of the British Army looked too old and weathered to be a soldier.

He looked up and smiled. A smile she recognised taking all the strength from her knees. Hilda sank to the floor. Clara was with her in an instant to hold her daughter in law as she cried hot tears, draining deep relief. Hilda couldn't sit on Jim's lap his legs were too bony, muscles like taut rubber bands. They'd carried him almost nine hundred miles in twenty months; running, hiding working in the fields and climbing through mountainous terrain – his story would all come out over the years. Not yet though. So they sat beside each other holding hands just being together. Clara left them alone while she dusted and hummed happily upstairs in her room.

Artie was almost bowled back out through the front door when he came home that evening.

"He's home, Jim's home." Came shouts from the kitchen, "Just walked in, just like that." Artie could hardly believe his ears, but of course he did.

"Hilda called for a taxi. They went home in style the pair of 'em." enthralled Dolly, "What a relief. Hilda wrote a quick card to young Don, while they waited for the taxi," What Dolly didn't know was Clara's taking Hilda aside when she returned from telephoning the station taxis.

"Listen Hilda love, tomorrow you may find yourself angry with Jim. If it does well up inside you it's only natural dear. Hide it if you can. It'll do more harm than good. Bang the pots 'n' pans about but keep the words to yourself." Hilda got on well with Clara. She knew Clara's wisdom.

"I'll remember. Thanks." The two women embraced in thankful relief.

"Bye Doll."

"Bye Hilda. My god I'm so relieved for you both."

"Bye bye sweetheart." Hilda said giving me a big kiss. "Wish I had my Don and Kathy at home with us now." (Young Kathy had been evacuated to a family in Yorkshire near her brother.) Jim made a brave attempt to smooth his hair back and pull himself up straight to walk out to the taxi.

"At least he'll sleep in his own bed tonight." Clara said, "That's if he can sleep."

If the arrival of a taxi in the middle of the day caused a bit of a stir in our street, apparently it caused quite a commotion when Jim and Hilda emerged in style from its prestigious passenger compartment in their street. A cheering crowd gathered to see one of their own come home.

"No charge." said the Taxi Driver.

"Gercher," said Jim, "you're a workin' man."

"Here give this to the Mrs," Hilda said and she plumped a bar of Chocolate into the driver's hand. Then she laughed saying, "Don't worry I haven't pinched it, a hotel guest gave it to me this morning." That interchange was to last with each jovial meeting between them and the Driver for years to come.

8

Life on the Home Front goes on

When the cricket season came round a group of family and friends boarded a green Southdown bus in Poole Valley for the ride out to Newick for a Sunday afternoon match on the green. Uncle Fred's second wife Hannah's parents, Mr and Mrs Hodges lived opposite the Cricket Field. Old Mr Hodges was the verger at the church and the cricket green keeper. So all was well organised.

Clara was up early making sandwiches with soft boiled pigeon eggs, jam sandwiches and apples. When Art and Dolly came into the kitchen the picnic basket was set ready for their jolly day out, and Clara, well she went back to bed with her memories. The long walk down town to catch the bus followed by a day out and the long walk back in the evening had become too much for her. A day pottering in the little back garden did her just fine.

Friends and family meeting in Poole Valley laughed and joshed at the women who didn't like going up the stairs on the green Southdown bus, but with all their happy bantering and the odd 'heave ho', they all got to the top deck. The children racing to the front seats; Fred's twin girls, now a pair of 'Tom boys' with their dog Tinker, being held apart by Roy's girlfriend, Mildred, whose own twin brothers were always ready for a scramble to beat the girls. Much earlier that morning the boys were out having taken over Roy's place helping Arthur and Hetty get the Sunday papers delivered before Arthur could shut the newsagent's shop and get down to the Lewes Road side of St Peter's Church to meet the bus.

Out came the sandwiches, the bottles of homemade ginger beer and lemonade because the boys were ravenous after their early morning work and of course the girls and the dog joined in. On the journey along the Lewes Road more players for the team joined the bus stopping in Falmer Village, then down along the tree lined avenue to the New Market Inn picking up Mildred's newly married brother, who luckily, was home on leave.

Up the long hill to Lewes the bus turned left at the prison and over to Cooksbridge, across country to the Kings Head at Chailey crossroads where all the men joined the Driver and Conductor who took their break at that stop. The women stayed on the bus or sat on the grassy bank with the children.

It was a long day out on the cricket field in the heat. The children played quietly around the pavilion only letting out their shouts and squeals when tea was served. On the bus journey home the children soon fell asleep the adults were subdued in blissful relaxation, glad to be away from news of the war for a few hours. An early black and white snapshot shows sisters-in-laws Dolly, Hannah and Hetty standing in the long grass laughing, their hair tied in scarves (the fashion of the day). I'm being held, the babe, above the turmoil of my cousins and Tinker the black and white nosed shaggy sheep dog, an image better than any diary entry. Many more bus journeys and cricket matches including the men who could still come followed throughout the 1940's.

When I was old enough to roam alone I sat in the long grass watching tiny coloured insects that seemed to congregate chattering in a group like the women in Coventry streets' little shop. I loved listening to the wind gently hissing high in the trees; the patterns of the branches fascinated me since the patch of garden we had was too small to have anything as big as a tree.

9

Creating calm and enduring aggravation

In our town garden Granma's pottering produced a splash of healthy Sweet Peas, their powerful perfume gloriously overcoming sight and smell of the dust bin beside the slate roofed coal sheds causing those two domestic service areas to be hidden through the summer months. When Artie commented on the colourful sight, Dolly told him Clara said her own Grandmother Annie grew Sweet Peas against the wall beside the kitchen door at the Lamb Inn. Artie, recognising Clara's green fingers created a bright little oasis in the flint walled box handkerchief sized garden, gave it over entirely to her as he had so little time to do anything there himself.

It was hard to see how more greenery and flowers could find a place amongst the scarlet American Pillar Roses that rambled along the top of the flint wall boundary with the school playground. Gooseberry bushes filled the boarder and Lettuces and Spring Onions grew in season tucked along the edges while pots of herbs stood on the window ledges. Pale apricot Roses mingled with Dorothy Perkins, growing up the corner of the house wall along towards the back door and over each of the kitchen windows.

Bushes of gooseberries heavy with red and gold fruits in August destined for jam and wine. Tall clumps of golden rod appeared in their time, finally eclipsed by Michaelmas Daisies before autumn turned to winter.

Clara went for perfumes adding Stocks, tobacco plants – shush, don't tell – and night scented stocks all in a space measuring 10' x 12', including a central square of rough hand sheared grass. We hardly ever saw the neighbours to one side because the Honeysuckle grew in screening masses along the adjoining wall. Although we could hear them particularly on summer evenings as they sang their duets from the operas while doing the washing up by the open back door.

On Monday mornings we woke to another orchestra of sounds; women sloshing elbow deep in sudsy washing, mingled with the delighted squeals of their under fives, scrambling after bubbles as they floated away on the bowlfuls of water their mothers threw along the open channels, followed by deep throaty gurgles sucking air down drains into silence. Silence while Mums pegged cloth to lines for the wind to blow snap and plop into the sheets. If rain started, high pitched calls of, 'Raining,' came brisk on the air along the back gardens. It was the turn of our noses telling us what was happening in our neighbour's houses. Mondays told us what a family had had for Sunday dinner by the smell of their leftovers; Shepherd's pie or bubble n' squeak. The scent of hot honey rising off irons smoothed with beeswax blocks when the ironing was done on Tuesdays. Yes the sights, sounds and smells remain evocative of times and places all through our lives. If there were the ingredients to hand, cakes and crisp pastry came out onto cooling racks on a Friday ready for Saturday and Sunday teas. That was when Granma told me about her days at the Blue Tea rooms, near the Clock Tower, baking cakes all day long.

Although routine seemed regular and well ordered something always had to interrupt life when there was a bit of a lull; upset the apple cart so to speak – well, there was a war on wasn't there!

A low heavy thrump followed by the sound of splintering glass, made Dolly scoop me up from the bed and, run all in one swift move, taking the stairs two at a time. The gloomy first flight up appeared darker than usual. At the turn of the landing a shaft of sunlight lit the air showing soot falling in fine glittering particles, from the usually closed roof hatch in the ceiling, enveloping us in black sticky dust.

"That Hitler's ruined my dinner!" Clara was staring down at her dinner plate on the table in front of the window. A large upper pane of glass had a jagged split right across, sending shining shards smothering the food. Dolly asked in a shaky voice. "Are you alright Mum?"

"It's my dinner he wasted that's not alright."

There had been no air raid warning. If there had been Clara would have gone downstairs into the Morrison shelter in the front room instead of staying to set out her meal on the little table under the widow; it being a weekday, she had cooked on the fire up in her own room.

A bomb had dropped on the Railway line sending part of a railway carriage over the roofs to land as far away as Stafford Road, the blast so intense that for all the sticky brown paper strips crisscrossing the window glass one pane had so completely shattered falling on her table. It was sheer luck that the very moment the glass fell Clara had been at the other side of the room fetching her salt and pepper stand.

On the other hand, the window in the room below, where Dolly had been, standing doing the ironing, had not shattered, probably because it was sheltered, from the shock, by the high red brick school building.

It wasn't until later when Clara and Dolly were sitting down in the kitchen with a scratch meal and a cup of tea that both women started shaking violently and Clara had abruptly dropped her old Willow pattern tea dish. Thank goodness it didn't break, Clara thought. Granma Annie's cup and tea dish had been through some troubled times. But she wouldn't pack it away out of her life, not now of all times. Her philosophy was that it's just the time when we want old friends near us for comfort.

During their trembling tea drinking, they hardly connected the rumbling sound above as anything to do with the earlier commotion, but it did. Most of the plaster from the ceilings in the top floor rooms fell on the floors.

It was a few weeks later that a Plasterer and his mate came to repair the damaged ceilings. The elderly Plasterer was a craftsman and one of those men called back to work out of retirement. His mate was a 14 year old school leaver who was too young to go into the Army or even the Home Guard, but he obviously didn't want to be a Plasterer.

A watchful listening only child, I soon caught on to the atmosphere. As the days went by the Plasterer was at the end of his tether trying to find his reluctant helper who was constantly hiding in corners having a secret smoke. One morning while Dolly was talking to the Plasterer by the front door my legs couldn't get me down that long flight of stairs fast enough so I tumbled and rolled down. – Bumpety-bumpety thump – standing up with just a hint of a wobble at the foot of the stairs I called out the words the Plasterer had been growling under his breath all week, "get up them bloody stairs lad". The Plasterer looked decidedly embarrassed before he and Dolly split her sides laughing.

"That's the kind of education you get during a war," the Plasterer said. "I'm sorry Mrs Smith."

It made another story to give the family something to giggle about. The adults needed all the laughs they could get. The next happening wasn't anything to giggle about. Artie went down with a bad attack of Quinsy. His Mum-in-law almost held her breath during those hard winters in the 1940's. Artie might be in a reserved occupation, living at home with his own family but, like her own husband during the Great War, she had seen how hard the men at home worked during wartime. The extra load these men shouldered was never clearly recognised. Her optimism was pinned on Artie being younger by thirty years and stronger too, than her Tom had been during the war he worked through. The Doctor, my Father had been registered with for twenty-five years, did come to the house but stood well back away from the bed. It was the first time doctor and patient had set eyes on each other. The patient had a beard and couldn't speak. Dolly said her husband was 39. The Doctor looked dubious. Hmm, there wasn't a grey hair in this bearded man's chestnut brown head, so he had to believe her. Although by the look of him this man in the bed before him could have been getting on for … eighty?

It took Artie six weeks to rid himself of the Quinsy and finally shave off the beard. Whatever happened you all soldiered on regardless, giving up wasn't possible.

I clearly remember the Doctor's cold looks. He acted in such contrast to our own Doctors, John and Grace. I know I wasn't very old but I do remember that scene as I sat on the bed beside Dad. Faces have always meant a lot to me.

At last spring seemed to be emerging out of the gloom. It was only two weeks into March but, as Gran said, the rising sun in a clear sky gave hope to the heart.

10

"Something's happened to Rose."

Clara came into the kitchen earlier than was usual for her. Still in her dressing gown, she sat down heavily in the chair at the end of the table and repeated, "Something's happened to Rose."

"I didn't hear the Postman." Dolly said filling the kettle, "Has Les sent news?"

"No, no letter. I felt it." Clara laid her hand against her chest. "I've felt it all night, it woke me up. Hit me in the heart like a blow."

Dolly stooped down beside the chair and put her arms round Clara. My goodness, Dolly hadn't realised how much weight her Mother had lost. Worry, mostly, she thought.

"I'll write to Putney. If she's there, she'll soon let me know or Les might be on leave. She said in her last letter he's somewhere in Surrey. Not far away."

No reply came from Rose. "Surely she couldn't still be feeling angry with us for that disagreement over Leslie?" Clara said.

"No surely not, that was years ago Mum. No. She'll write soon as she's got time." But Dolly knew perfectly well Rose would have sent immediately to tell her sister not to get so jittery.

No word came at all. Then more than three weeks later a letter from Leslie told how he'd come home on a surprise visit to find the house empty. The neighbours hadn't seen his Mother for three weeks. They thought she'd gone to stay with relatives to get away from London. Somebody suggested Leslie got in touch with the Police. It was then he heard she was in a Mortuary with other unclaimed bodies. In fact they knew who she was by the contents of her coat pocket and a Warden had called at the house in Putney but it seems he didn't leave any notification.

Rose died in a crush on the underground during a day time raid. They said it seemed like she was on her way up the stairs trying to come out. Leslie never knew what his Mother was doing anywhere near Bethnal Green.

Rose was gone. Poor Rose, she and her sisters had not met for a few years. Now Leslie was really alone. Clara wondered what he would do. She need not have worried. Leslie was far more resilient. He promptly gave up the cottage he had rented for his Mother in Putney, taking all his belongings well away from London to join a friend who was in a similar position. They rented a flat together to keep all their possessions and have somewhere they could call home when they were on leave. A new life began for Leslie. He and his pal went walking and climbing in their time off. When he visited his Aunt Clara and cousins, as he did from time to time, they said he was like a new man. Funny the ways life takes you, they said.

11

The Forshaws

"Here, look at this gal." Alex's voice had an air of triumph as he came in the back door of their house in Seaford. "Found it left on top o' one o' the bins. Canadian soldier poked his head out the cookhouse door, and said hope we'd enjoy it; heard our rations were tight over here." Pulling back the sheets on the newspaper bundle Joyce found a whole ham joint.

"Oh my goodness Alec what shall we do with it?"

"Eat it of course."

"But it's stolen!" she said.

"No it's not, it's a gift."

"You sure dear?"

"'Course I'm sure, an' you should see what's been thrown out in those bins. The ole' pigs are gonna do alright on this lot."

Alexander Forshaw had managed to secure a licence to collect the bins from the local Army Camp because he was a food producer and he had a truck. He'd bartered something he had no use for to acquire an old Austin 12, from which he cut the body off behind the two front seats; made up a wooden platform and added slatted sides so he could carry water drums and bins to go collecting pigswill for his animals.

The following Sunday, when the Gran and Granddad from the semi next door joined the family for tea, they found the neighbours and their two children from the other side, all sitting at the table to ready to share an extra special ham tea.

Joyce was like that, she couldn't enjoy a windfall without including the neighbours.

BOOK THREE: 1941 – 1952

12

Dolly

Mum went round to the school at playtime at half past ten each morning, with two other ladies from the street; they served the children orange juice and cod liver oil, down in the basement in a white tiled space next to the boiler room. I was quite small when she started taking me regularly with her. I sat on a bench behind the ladies. The children filed along the front of the serving table and were each given a large china beaker of National Orange Juice. Most of us children had never seen an orange if we were born after 1939. I will never forget the taste of that juice; its strong clean flavour was both sharp and sweet making your mouth water, it was lovely and a perfect foil to the spoonful of cod liver oil that was also given, either as a mouthful before the juice or stirred into the orange juice. The oil wasn't very appealing being golden green and much thicker to swallow. Even less palatable was the cod liver oil and malt mixture the District Nurse had given to my mother for me; that was very thick and fishy, it made me feel so sick that Mum finally relented and gave the brown greasy cardboard covered tins to Raymond, the boy across the road. Who, I was told, simply loved it.

Dolly made it her daily afternoon routine to walk out with me in the pram, all the time talking about the places we were passing and what had happened there including the names of where we were going and who lived and worked in those places. I don't think there was a street, road or twitten in Brighton and Hove; from the seafront up into the viewing high points, Tongdean and Roedean, the Race Course or Blatchington in the west, where she didn't walk. Of course she couldn't get near the promenade in those years but it mattered little. Everywhere she walked she pointed out the places where family and friends were born and died. Like her mother Clara, she was always full of anecdotes and stories of their lives.

On shopping days she would start at Uncle Arthur's Newsagents' in the Prestonville Road for a quick chat followed by a regular, 'Haloo' through to the room at the back where Mr Ovenden had his Barbers' saloon. Then off round to the Co-op in the Dyke Road with the ration books to join a queue for each counter; cheese and fats, groceries, bread. To me it was fascinating watching the counter assistants screw little wooden cups onto a wire and pull a chain sending our money flying above our heads across the shop to the cash desk; I longed to see the cups bash into each other but there was no hope of that; bells would ring and the change flew back to the counters, including little pink strips of paper giving a record of what you spent so you could keep a check on your 'divi'. Our Co-op 5-digit number was the first number I learned and have never forgotten. We only visited the Butcher's department on a Saturday for the family weekly meat ration. Granma used to tell Mum to 'get as much offal as you can, it's good for the blood.' On the days we didn't buy food we bought paraffin at Cardwells Hardware in the Prestonville Road. I liked the pungent smell of polishes and wax. Men moved briskly along the squeaking old floorboards, counting out screws and washers or cutting big chunks off blocks of soap. A visit to the private lending library, further along Prestonville, was saved for the afternoons – no food and definitely no fish or paraffin was allowed inside Mr and Mrs Goldsmith's library. The owner and her husband took turns in standing at their desk raised high on a rostrum where they could observe clients as they chose books. They thought no one noticed them watching to see their books weren't being secreted under coats and in big pockets. I overheard a neighbour telling Mum that, Mrs G would make a fuss clearing her throat if she saw somebody inserting markers to indicate the naughty pages for friends to dip into when they came in later. The lending library shop smelled of stale air and definitely no children's books.

Walking back towards home we would pick up shoes from the shoe repair shop for neighbours – never our own because Dad had a Last on which he'd repair all the family boots and shoes. Mum bought his supply of rubber soles and heels or pieces of leather from the shoe counter in Woolworths in the London Road.

"Ah now this is where Dad did his first plumbing job at Mr and Mrs Farrant's." We were passing a pub in Liverpool Street. I learned later the job wasn't a very pleasant one. Cleaning out and relining the lead trays running along beneath the foot rail in front of the bar was a task given to young Plumber apprentices. In North Street she pointed to a tall red brick building saying, "Here's where Uncle Fred worked before he moved to Whitehall." Dad told me his brother worked organising taxes so I visualized him walking up and down lines of taxi cabs wearing a peaked cap and carrying a clip board. For years I thought that was his job, until, (and it was some years later) I joined the conversation at the Sunday tea table; I said I did not see Uncle Fred looking after his Taxis, when our school outing bus went along Whitehall towards the Houses of Parliament. A short silence was followed by every adult convulsed in guffawing laughter. It took time for somebody to get their breath long enough to say how shocked Uncle Fred would be – him and his pinstripe trousers, black jacket and tie – more choking laugher, "waistcoat and bowler hat!"

"Peak cap 'n' clipboard!" Uncle Arthur gasped holding his sides, "Ah! stop making me laugh. The sight of Fred walking the street wearing a peak cap 'n' carrying a clip board is killin' me! Oh dear my gal you've got the wrong end of the stick there."

"My brother Fred," said Aunt Hetty, "is a big chief in the Inland Revenue. Taxi cab inspector indeed! Oh dear I shall never forget that one." And they started laughing all over again.

Passing by the Royal Pavilion Mum pointed out the offices of the newspaper where Grandfather worked for many years. On the cliff hillside towards Rottingdean stood Ocean Breeze where she was a lady's maid, "The stories I can tell you about 'Madam.' I did like her though." On our way back along Eastern Road we passed Sussex Mews where Clara and Tom had their first little married home in 1902. Down in the town centre, where Mum spent her first eleven years, we walked through an archway to St George's Mews, where, sheltered inside the passage, faded remnants of the posters the printer pasted up, still clung to the walls. Along the cobbled yard the sounds of a piano came from behind two large double doors. "That's Mr Moffat tuning a piano." Mum told me, "We won't interrupt him now. I'll take you in to meet him another day."

Along the Western Road we looked in on Peter running his mother, Fanny's hat shop, while she remained in Paris. Down towards the sea Adelaide Crescent looked dull and dirty trying to camouflage its bright curved façade. Off the seafront passing the Dudley Hotel, where Uncle Jim and Aunty Hilda sometimes worked, we went through St Ann's Wells, passing the elegant house nearby where Algernon performed delicate dentistry for the rich, and where Clara got her job because her beautiful smile showed off her naturally white teeth. That story set another puzzle for me, as did the goings on in the house where the Hunters', Helen and her Mother lived. It looked dowdy and unloved through the war years. But one great piece of news Dolly took home to Clara from Peter. A rare letter from Fanny told how she had met Helen Hunter in Paris, saying she was living with her new husband, Roland. What a refreshing burst of joyful whoop's 'n' squeals 'n' clapping that piece of news filled our kitchen, prompting Clara to say, 'Why shouldn't people live happily together? I'm so glad for them both.'

13

Nothing on the Wireless

Some nights it was safer to go to bed in the Morrison shelter, downstairs front room. Although it was my bedtime, Granma Clara would often join me whispering her stories until, I, or she, fell asleep. Her tales gave me the feeling I was watching stories; pictures painted with words describing family members in the landscape and shoreline across the Pevensey Levels.

The windswept laid back scrub grasses on the low dunes; small stands of trees leaning away from the prevailing wind, parted by glittering water channels wandering deep between hanging willows and tall reeds, fringing the ditches in their season. Granma said how her own Grandmother, Annie would stoop to peer down into the dense undergrowth, 'There,' she'd say, 'look, a little Warbler's nest.' "But, 'til we were used to the sighting," Gran said, "our young eyes had difficulty catching the subtlety of greenish grey before hearing the tiny bird's trilling little song."

Gran passed on to me tales of yet another generation; her own great, great, Grandmother Amy conveyed to her children, the joy she and her sisters had on their monthly trips to market. Amy told how they looked forward to a little bit of freedom whilst their Father did business in the beer house. He sounded as if he was an insensitive man with a cruel streak. For, selling his youngest daughter, as he did, went deep within the family tales, retold right down the years, even to me.

Later in that story, Granma described young Amy looking out from the house, where she was kept a prisoner and seeing the treeless wilderness of Romney Marsh; the view faded into the haze away to a sea, shining like a line of silk thread. The eastern marshland appeared a much greater barren mystery than Granma's own Pevensey Levels. The wild open space; the tension of a terrified young woman who had no idea where she was, until, through the haze, sight of the familiar shape, Rye town on the far mauve blue horizon sent her a spark of hope. Colours made their mark in my mind's eye as Clara used the colours, shapes and weather temperatures so freely in her descriptions. Joy and sadness were all described to me. "Never you mind little luvver." Granma Clara would say, "Amy's life all turned out well, come the years. Give it time. You'll see, each generation of women have passed on Amy's story."

The only times Gran left things out was when I would not have understood; she'd stop and say, "Your Mother will explain that." I'd get no sense that I had to wait because the next exciting part of a story quickly followed on. Maybe she'd be describing the sharp sound of a Marsh Harrier's cry high on the wind or the soft happy snuffles of a baby lamb suckling its mother for the first time.

Story telling was Granma's sanctuary, her world within a world, her safe haven.

14

Artie thought he had lost her

"Dolly!" Artie tried to shout, but it came out hoarse, half choked. He didn't try again, he just ran. My Father ran up the street. The woman who appeared round the end of the street had made my Dad's face light up. I saw it as I stood on a chair alongside my Granma at the window where I had been looking anxiously for what seemed like hours. Mum usually returned from her trip to the pictures on Saturday well by teatime but this was so late that I was crying. Granma's dark cotton flower sprigged dress front was wet with my hot tears and one of the little red rosebud buttons on her sleeve had almost been chewed off in my anguish. Gran picked me up and was out on the front step in time to see my Father lift Mum in his arms and swing her round.

"Put me down silly devil." we heard her shriek with laughter. Arm in arm they marched on down the pavement to our house; the grin on Dad's face as wide as the road.

"Don't be daft Artie I'm perfectly alright. We saw next week's picture and we even had the best seats. The Manager from the Academy led us all down the road and the Manager at the Odean went straight up onto the stage and told the people already there in the audience what had happened and they all clapped and cheered him, then turned and clapped all us newcomers. 'Aw! It was wonderful!"

So high with the excitement of it all, she couldn't stop talking the experience. Dad, all the while making the tea seemed delighted and obviously relieved. I felt Granma reacted differently.

Dolly took me out of her Mother's arms and without speaking to me, kissed my cheek and went on talking.

It was obvious to see how much my Father loved Mum. On the other hand Mum reacted with cool irritation towards him. Instead of knocking off at half past twelve that Saturday Artie had stayed to finish his job, working on through the afternoon so the customers would have their water turned back on for the weekend. Therefore he didn't arrive home until half past five/six o'clock. On his way home from the Seven Dials he saw the local evening paper headlines saying something about a bomb dropping on a cinema. He didn't take much notice until he got home and found Dolly hadn't come back from her regular outing to the pictures. Granma was already getting a bit concerned but really did get worried when she heard about the newspaper headline Artie said he'd seen. Our next door neighbour had the late edition of the paper delivered and read out, 'Bomb in Cinema in West Street'.

Without another word Artie threw his knapsack inside the front door and immediately turned back along the street. An hour or so later he walked back into the house saying he had phoned the hospital from the call box at the top of Stanford Road and they hadn't any news of casualties. He had practically run all the way down to West Street and found nobody at the Academy Cinema. He'd asked the policeman on sentry duty who said there was an unexploded bomb out the back and no film had been shown there that afternoon.

Mum and Dad in their courting days
This pose is typical of my Mum, she was always full of fun.
Dad's hat sat on the shelf in his wardrobe for 20 years.
I never saw him wear that hat

While Dolly still hadn't returned, Dad, Gran and a gathering group of neighbours stood out on the pavement wondering what had really happened. Other neighbour's returning home along the street suggested the facts were more like an unexploded bomb went off in the yard at the back of the cinema.

It wasn't until half past seven, nearly a quarter to eight before Dolly appeared in all her innocence walking towards them from the end of the street, most surprised at her reception and to see her little child still wide awake instead of being tucked up in bed.

Not long after this event I had a session of my own little childhood dramas.

I can still see the pink painted high chair I was sitting in at the dining room table, when a high pitched noise seemed to come from behind, causing me to turn to see what it was. Then it came again and this time it came from my throat. It certainly put a stop to the conversation. When I coughed a second time a long whooping sound followed by another elongated strangled whooping sound.

"Oh dear me," said Clara, "Lily's got whooping cough."

Following that, I had a red running eye. Mum had made a cotton cushion and tied it round my head to soak up the tears. Doctor John came to see me in my bed saying, "Hallo long Jane Silver let's have a look at that lovely eye. Ah yes. Have you got a box of matches Mrs Smith?" My Mother showed surprise but handed him a box from beside the candlestick. He selected a match, broke off the little black end and using the opposite end pulled my eyelid gently back and slid the matchstick around inside the upper and lower lids. "There we are, all done. No more tears now." he chuckled, "Get plenty of fresh air my dears. Goodbye." It seems my eyelashes had got caught inside the eyelid, very painful.

Out and about again in the Dyke Road Park brought me face to face with another story that this time it was my turn to tell my Gran,

"Jacky Dill got hung on a spike Granma." I reported. Granma Clara looked across my head at Mum's face and immediately put the rolling pin down beside her pastry, wiped her hands on the cloth hanging from her apron tie and sat down on a kitchen chair drawing me towards her.

"Slow down sweetheart." Giving my Mother another glance she looked back at me without a word. The question was in her eyes.

"Jacky climbed over the fence to get the ball and fell on a spike."

"Oh, did he?" she was nonchalant. It didn't really work because I had seen his screaming Mother being restrained and the ambulance men running through the Park towards him.

"Is he alright?" Gran was very concerned. My mum answered,

"Well, we'll have to wait and see. It went right into his throat." That bit of information just slipped out, but then I'd heard the boys in the Park say it all.

We didn't go up the Park for a week Mum couldn't face it but then that was where she met the other Mothers for a gossip and a cigarette while we little ones could play out in the fresh air, so we soon back enjoying each others' company.

Nobody changed the spiky railings. The sea still shone across the tall houses out Hove. But it was never the same again. A shadow of that shocking sight was always hovering in that area of my memory.

15

Life along Cov

"Murder, murder!" a woman's voice called. I'm already awake standing up in my cot, beside the window in the big front bedroom, peeping between the curtains onto Coventry Street. A brisk rising wind had started flipping the lids off the pig bins that stood in pairs at intervals along the street. The clattering lids bowling along the pavement must have woken me up. Now I'm the story teller absorbing what 's happening all around and filing it away in my memory – no matter if I didn't understand it at the time, I am descended from a story teller so this new happening will all come clear in the end

Clouds are scudding across the sky; at intervals a bright moon floodlighting my view of a woman standing at the end of the street, she's the one shouting, "Murder, murder." I had no idea what that meant but the sound sent a feeling of urgency across the road to me and to my parents as well, because I can hear my father, on the other side of the room in their big double bed, say in a low voice,

"There she goes again." Who goes I wondered, as I pulled myself up a bit further, better to see through the corner of the blackout curtains. In the spaces of moonlight I see a policeman come running round the end of the street heading towards the lady who is standing leaning back against the wall. When she sees the police constable arrive she lifts her skirt. I'm riveted but I have no idea what's going on. When the policeman reaches the dishevelled figure I see him lunge towards her – well it's not quite like that she grabbed hold of him. Something's flashing in the moonlight, swinging at the end of a chain. It's the Constable's whistle rhythmically swinging on its chain plinking against the wall. I wonder if I should tell my parents that there's dancing in the street but I didn't because it looks odd. I've seen the family dancing at Christmas but not against the wall like these two people. All of a sudden the woman lets out a piercing screech and the policeman

seems to topple over backwards into the shadows. From my parents'
bed I hear my Mother's chuckling,

"Sounds like Mr V's come home early." I see the woman is
scuttling along the pavement, hopping in one high heeled shoe
while crouching to pick up the loose shoe, scooping up her handbag
and trying to pull her clothes straight as she runs along just in
front of a heavyweight man. He is letting out a roar as his shoulder
catches the policeman in the chest making him topple backwards
into the gutter. Two cats scatter from under the big man's thudding
boots, his arm stretching out grabbing at the woman, who is
scrabbling frantically to get up the steps to the front door. But she
doesn't quite make it because I see him give her a hefty kick up the
bottom. The door slams behind muffled words. Something must
be very wrong because the policeman was standing in the middle
of the road staring down the street as if he were half awake. I fell
asleep. Sometime during the next morning, a Sunday, I overheard
my parents' conversation,

"That's the first time he's caught her at it." said my Mum.

"Yes," laughed Father, "she got a double surprise last night."

"How's that then?" Mum asked.

"Well. Old Eddie Short's gone off sick and that was a new
young constable taking over his beat."

"Oh gawd, then he must have had a surprise himself."

"I bet," chuckled Dad, "don't suppose Eddie had time to tell
the new chap anything about his, USUAL." Usual what? I
wondered.

So many, 'goings on' occurred in the times of the blackout. It
seems one of the local Bobby's took his 'usual' at the end of the
street. Trouble was, that particular night 'the husband' came home
extra early from his night shift just when the new young constable
was being treated to something he didn't expect.

When I described to Granny what I had seen, there was a
moment I thought I saw a smile cross her face as she stuttered out
how the lady probably had the cramp in her toes just like she had
herself when she got into a cold bed last night. Of course at the time
I didn't know what the adults meant by, 'goings on' or the 'usual,'
it was all part of the conversation. But I've kept that scene in my

mind. Now the years have brought understanding to the images I saved from those early days. I have come to realise the adults always found there was something to laugh about. Now I know how much laughter was such a source of relief to them.

I overheard a lot of talk at the meal table about the old ways and attitudes changing fast during the war years. There were many women alone while their husbands were away in the Forces. Some had young families, others were totally alone and some were newly widowed. It meant if you didn't have a man to take you into a pub for a drink you were not welcome in a public house. Unless you were with a group of women friends and there was a saloon bar, a publican would refuse a lone woman entry.

Life could be very lonely and some women didn't have a wireless unless their man had built one in the 1930s, or hired a set. A woman couldn't sign a rental agreement.

Like many old fashioned pubs, the Marquis of Exeter on the corner of Exeter Street and Upper Hamilton Road still had the foot rail that ran along against the front of the bar in the main Public area. Placed on the floor at the end of the bar was a squat blue and white china spittoon and believe it or not it was a Willow pattern spittoon. I know that because my Father told me it was Willow pattern. Nearby stood an old upright piano where Mrs V from Coventry Street played the old tunes. She hated the mucky old Spittoon so pushed it, little by little, unobtrusively with her toe, further along under the foot rail.

Mrs V was determined to make a difference in her circumstances. The only way she could go into the pub on her own was to be the pianist, and to avoid any hint of shenanigans the publican paid her in drinks. She felt she was doing herself alright until a 'regular' let fly a gob in his usual direction, but due to the Spitoon's slight change of position, landed his contribution nicely on Mrs V's peep toe high heeled shoe. Should she shriek or hold her peace, because one way or another she'd lose her nice little job amidst lively company; on the other hand she'd be a woman making a fuss in a man's world. It seems the 'regular' had had enough of a woman's presence curtailing men's 'language,' and what with the Spittoon's new position after half a life time where he expected it to be, he decided to throw in the towel and change his drinking venue. He wasn't the only one,

My 1940s sketch of the Porthall Tavern
– an unusually decorative old building

16

The Porthall Tavern

Artie was another who changed to a place where he could have a
quiet drink after work. He said the constant jangling piano made
it difficult to hear what people said and anyway, you couldn't get
to the bar at the Marquis anymore for the crush of soldiers coming
from the camp up on the Dyke Road. Of course Mrs V was in her
element surrounded by lively well set up younger men. At least she
was a married woman and that gave her some status. It was a fact
that men could be amicable with women who had been married, or
were widows, but would snub an unmarried woman who the older
men would often seek to talk down in conversation.

The Porthall Tavern occupied a curved corner at the junction of
Stanford Road and Highcroft Villas opposite the bridge at Porthall
Avenue and Dyke Road Drive. Originally frequented by the
Railwaymen using the gate by the main signal box; its' decoratively
curved mottled windows and etched pattern glass panelled doors
made an imposing rather select stopping off venue for a quiet
drink. Although it was more than just a pub it was a workingman's
club, having a large room to the side with a full size billiard table,
chairs and tables for cribbage and shove-ha'penny including its
own fireplace for a cozy coal fire. Most of those who recently used
the games room had gone into the Forces in 1940 and without a
reasonable supply of coal to keep such a sizeable room comfortable
it had fallen into disuse. The Tavern was run by two sisters, Miss
Cole and Mrs Wood, who had lived all their lives on the premises
and taken over the license from their parents. There were three
small bars, two had bare floorboards and wooden chairs, no room
for tables; they were a corner 'Public' and a middle 'Public', where
the customers could call in to get their own jug filled to take away.
The third was a 'Private' bar with a linoleum covered floor, wood
chairs and one small table. Everywhere had a soft beer coloured
atmosphere reflected off the etched mirrors and old fashioned

curvaceous glass stoppered counter jars that used to hold Sarsparella and pickled eggs.

Accessed through the Publicans' own entrance hall and served through a discreet hatch window at the end of the big bar, was a room known as the Saloon Parlour. It had its own begrudging air of comfort for which the patrons paid a penny extra on all drinks.

Newly refurbished by the Mr and Mrs Cole, when they took on the License in the late nineteen twenties, their grand brick fireplace topped by the latest innovation in electric clocks backed by a tall mirror, both in a watered down Art style circa1930. Box pelmet curtains surrounded the lead paned ripple effect discreet window glass. After all it was not nice to be seen in a Public House by passersby. A selection of ill matched wood armchairs defied complete comfort, all bar one which had an extra soft seat and back pad that a certain elderly gent considered his own. The central oak dining table gave customers a feeling they were guests of the Publican; their feet under the table rested on a carpet in an unassuming design of beige and brown. The whole atmosphere was biscuit brown and burnt orange, as the colours were known in the furnishing trade's 1930 catalogue!

The main drinking bars were originally spit and sawdust, beer only and open early for the men coming off shifts from the Railway Signal box; at midday and evenings for the men from the Shunting yard. By the late 1930's the Clubroom had become a friendly venue for the locals, even offering one night a week when Ladies were allowed to enter, although never into the partitioned public bars. They were walled off, but had small slots of coloured glass swinging windows. Through these windows the men could look to see who was in the other bars, and close them to avoid notice when they came up to the bar to be served. All three bars were fronted by a half circle of highly polished red mahogany counter topped by a central collection of shiny brass and ebony pump handles behind which the Misses Cole and Wood ran a sedate premises serving their male customers like old friends known by Miss Cole as 'her boys.' The regular 'boys' frequented the Private bar and were greeted by nicknames after characters from the Daily Express story strip, 'Rupert the Bear'.

Artie was 'Rupe' short for Rupert. Jack Divall was Bill Badger; Edward Elephant, that was Alfie White the Milkman; Ron Hamilton the Solicitor was known as the Prof. and Fred Henderson the Park keeper/allotment secretary he was Algy pug. Miss Cole herself was Tiger Lily; in real life a little lady with black hair pulled back tight and plaited in flat circles either side of her head known as 'earphones'. She always wore a three quarter length flowered overall, just like the one our first teacher, Miss Timpson, wore at Stanford Road Infants. If one of 'the boys' said something amusing she laughed with a high pitched trill of three 'ho, ho hos,' causing any newcomers to jump out of their skins the first time their ears were subjected to this slightly good mannered squawk.

Mrs Wood was her sister's opposite, a tall erect woman in her fifties, her husband no longer in the land of the living. Lillian Wood kept her grey hair cut in a neat short bob; she generally wore a navy blue v neck man's pullover, white shirt and slacks. It was unusual for men to take to a no nonsense woman who wore trousers, but Mrs Wood was liked and respected by all. It seemed she was one of them, but she didn't go in for soppy nicknames, that she left to her endearing little sister. Although little in terms of height, in years you could never really tell which was the elder or which the younger.

* * * *

My Father always took a turn out on the front doorstep, of our terraced house, to smoke his last cigarette before locking up and turning in. The night being particularly black he first became aware of a truck slowly trundling along the curb toward him by the low growl of its engine, followed by the ghostly lowered beam of one headlight. As he took his final draw, the driver braked hard bringing the vehicle to shuddering halt. Immediately two soldier boys tumbled out from under the canvas back; accompanied by smothered cheers and voices calling, 'make it quick Chuck' and 'get going pal'. Father was almost tossed into the front garden by the two lithe young Canadian servicemen who ran straight past him taking the stairs two at a time towards the top front bedroom where my Mother was getting ready for bed.

"'ere 'old on, where d'yer think you're goin?" shouted Father, spitting out the cigarette end he'd almost swallowed. The truck driver, realising he'd got the wrong house yelled to his mates, "Chucky baby, HOLD iiiiiT."

"I can't." squeaked back a voice. By then Dad was leaping at the stairs collaring both lads by their scruffs. Artie, not a tall man but strong, had them out of the house faster than their feet could go.

"Wrong house lads." he told them laughing.

"Sorry Sir," whispered the driver. "I saw the red glow and thought it was Patti's place." As he spoke a torch flashed outside his venue further along the road.

Patti Loveday and her three daughters were said to wash socks for soldiers! Before the soldiers came they had a few local discreet regulars who, on the quiet, had dropped in undercover of the blackout. When the Canadians arrived business became very brisk and Patti needed help. It so happened Patti didn't have far to look, for as soon as Walter Wise left all dressed up in his new uniform destined for who knows what war zone Chickie Lea offered to help Patti and the girls. Chickie said she wasn't going to languish her lonely nights away on bread 'n' scrape.

No, Chickie would have it all. She had her kids in bed by six o'clock, telling them that's what everyone did behind the blackout curtains to let their Mum's go out to work. She was always ready in good time when one of Patti's girls called round to, 'Auntie Chick's' place, whispering through the letter box so the old couple in the flat upstairs couldn't hear her say, "Ma needs yer now."

When poor old Walter was demobed he found more little Chicks living in his house than he remembered before he left. Years later Dad said Walter had told the lads in the pub he couldn't complain because he'd had his own 'moments' in Italy.

The Americans brought, 'In the Mood,' across the airwaves through the BBC. Clara said she felt like she was walking amongst herds of frisky young bullocks, "All those huge men everywhere. They're very polite but make you feel surrounded." Patti and the girls gave the local kids their old eyebrow pencils they used to use to draw seams up the backs of their legs because they now had the 'real thing' – nylon stockings. While the soldiers kept the kids happy with strips of gum.

17

Seeds, Love and Memories

Clara was determined to remain outwardly positive. But the first three years of the war was an ordeal of constant tension and distress; as it was for all the old neighbours, who like her, were fighting to preserve some essence of routine in everyday life that was so often disrupted by Air Raid Sirens, followed by a bowel clenching race to shelters. Whatever had kept us all awake the night before the sun always seemed to shine the next day, especially in the comfortable refuge Clara had made in the upstairs back bedroom of our house she called her bedsitter. Her feather mattress, covered by the family quilt, slumbered against the wall opposite the fireplace where the small black iron kettle waited on the trivet in the fender, ready to boil for a cup of tea. It was the same kettle she had bought to have in her sitting room at Adelaide Crescent, where she was the Whiteside's family cook, in the 1890s.

Even as the war news raged all around Clara kept the top sash of her window open all year round, she said it allowed a constant change of air to waft in the natural rhythms of the year. I soon grew to know she meant it kept her in contact with the inevitable sequences of nature and her country upbringing. Although her window faced onto Stanford Road's school playground, between the pot plants on the windowsill, she could see the long view up across the Downs to the Chattri; the white stone dome built to remember the Indian soldiers who played their part in the Great War. It had been left to go dull during the nineteen forties but you could always see its shape, especially on sunny summer days, reminding her, she said, not to forget the young Indians who came to convalesce in Brighton during those horrible years and what their mother's must have felt.

Wafting the perfume from pots on the windowsill gay with flowers, Clara told me, "These cost nothing but a few seeds and a bit of love."

"And green fingers Mother. You know you've always been able to dab a stick with one leaf in the soil and it would grow in no time." Mum added with a wry laugh.

"And you always forget to give your plants a drink," retorted Granny, smiling at her daughter. "You wouldn't forget to feed the cat."

So they chatted and laughed while sitting on the quilt, high up on her feather bed with Granma painting yet another word picture for me. She said her first long stay at the Inn on the Marsh was in 1870 while her Mother Emily, John and Ann's third daughter, was giving birth to her brother Tom, Emily's third child. Rose, Granma Clara's sister was then only a year old and still at the breast.

Clara was a little more than two, for that long hot summer she said she had her Granma Annie all to herself. Of course she didn't remember detail, all that came later while she watched as Granma Annie took in each of her siblings; when they joined the growing band of grandchildren, coming into John and Annie's summer care. Granma Annie always declared that first summer alone with Clara had been one of the happiest of her life. She loved all her grandchildren but as they each arrived the years took a little more of her own energy.

In 1870 Gracie, daughter of Elizabeth, John and Annie's eldest, was five years old. Gracie was allowed to visit the Inn to help her Grandparents occasionally when her parents were away on business. The little girl proved to be a bright practical child. Strong, not hefty; happy although repressing her exuberance as her Mother had taught her, 'that a lady does not run or shout and she keeps her wrists, ankles and shoulders covered.' Something Grace recited from her memory almost ninety years later. Many were the cuddles Gracie and Clara shared with each other and their beloved Grandmother through Clara's babe and toddler years.

Clara gave me the feeling of her love for family and a happy home life. Her room in my parent's house in Coventry Street held all that warmth mingled with the sounds and smells of the Marsh all the year round, picturing the Inn and the farmyard, and the children playing in the long hot grass. Grandfather telling stories of the wild life; showing the grandchildren the pathways each animal took, revealed by their footprints; pointing out the birds, where they flew across the waterways. During the quiet hours fishing, he'd look up and breathe in the taste of the wind, watching the cloud patterns disperse across the huge sky, or maybe he'd note the warning signs of wind and cloud gradually whipping up the squalling beating downpours toward the autumn equinox. In the very dead of winter when heavy frost patterns opaque the window panes and bitter cold cracked the air, nobody passed the Inn for weeks. As Granma spoke her Grandfather's words, her face took on a glow as she added how they would wake up one morning to see a fine haze of green shoots after a soft spring rain.

At other times I sat at the end of the kitchen table with a biscuit, hot from the pan, while Gran moved smoothly around, bowl under her arm beating the contents with a spoon or whisk; the other hand now and then raising pot covers to peek or stir; she'd tell of her days at her first job at the Anderson's, with her mentor and teacher Mrs Charlish.

"The Anderson's Manor House was at the edge of the Marsh."

"Is that where the man who still writes to you, used to live Granma?" I asked.

"Yes dear it is." She answered going swiftly back to what she had been describing. "They had a big kitchen and a wide open fire with a great iron fire-back. Two cauldrons, on brackets either side to pull across the fire and a long spit in front with drip trays beneath. Oh yes, old Mr Franklin Anderson used to order whole beasts roasted on that spit. Sometimes, when I was quite young, Grandfather John took me with him when he delivered a whole sheep or side of beef. One time the old cook gave me a funny bent Horse Radish she called a Banana. I didn't like it, it was tough and bitter. The kitchen maid laughed at me and showed me how to peel it. I'd not bitten into anything like that before."

"Grandfather had a roasting spit at the Inn, set up in the front of the Inglenook. It swung away to the side when it wasn't in use because all the sleepy eyed old regulars sat round the fire on winter evenings."

"Yes, a lot of people came to the Inn," she'd say, almost to herself, "there were many a lone farm worker in a Bothy or tied cottage without a family; maybe his wife had passed on in child birth and overwork. The men were alone, so to eke out their farthings they came to the Inn after work where they got a bit o' company, a gill of ale, and warmth from the firelight. None of this new wireless we have here, no, they had Grandfather's story songs and a Concertina. It didn't have to be a special occasion to dance. One of our Uncles, Robert, he played the violin and Gem Baker had a whistle pipe. Tinny sound they made together. 'course it was only us oldest three grandchildren who were at the Inn on winter nights but usually we'd be in bed though Tommy, naughty Tommy; he'd creep to the top of the stairs and dance halfway down 'til he tripped and Granma caught him. I saw her smiling as she went back downstairs telling him if he got out of bed again she'd give him a hot bottom."

Granma Clara's stories came out in short bright memories tripping from one subject to another; from soup stock beneath a savoury pudding in a cloth, or maybe a sweet pudding in a basin with vegetables in the top steamer, all on one gas ring. Oh yes she knew how to be economical with the fuel when the gas oven was turned on in Coventry Street. For Pancake Day she'd make small paper thin pancakes; you couldn't get greaseproof paper so each pancake was laid on a saucer making a pile of saucers and pancakes that she put in the bottom of a cooling oven to keep warm after the bread and cakes had baked. Rolled like big cigars and sprinkled with lemon and sugar or syrup, was a lovely treat. There were savoury pancakes too, folded in little pocket shapes and filled with smoked haddock in a creamy sauce made with fish bone stock, a little paste of flour in top of the milk; seasoned with finely chopped Dill or Fennel, if we had been lucky on one of our foraging trips, then served with a dab of Parsley from a pot on the windowsill, and a generous spoonful of Gran's lovely gooseberry sauce to help it all down.

One of my favourites was her roasted vegetables made with any root vegetables available at the time and a handful of snipped herbs like Rosemary, Sweet Thyme, Oregano leaves, pepper and salt, all in the roasting pan with the meat. We ate the finished pan of veg with our meat and roast potatoes, or the mixture would be added to clear stock making a lovely rich soup. Mum said Granma had been famous for her soups.

Ready to lay the table, she would transport me out of our terraced house back kitchen, acting out another far away drama – "Always the very best tableware at the Anderson's dining room." Granny said, as she opened the drawer at the end of our kitchen table to fetch out knives and forks for our meal, "Every guest's name was set at their place and at least three glasses; one for water; one for wine to go with the main course and one for the Dessert wine. Then there'd be finger bowls." Finding a small bowl she'd place it near my right hand, "Their bowls were of delicate fine china, usually plain white for water, often rose water or orange flower water; the kitchen maid had to make the flower water fresh each morning. Each finger bowl, at a lady guest's place would have a flower head floating in its scented water." With the tips of her fingers she'd flick a petal off a flower from one of the pots on the windowsill, flourish it in the air and float the colourful item in the small bowl in front of me. "For Madam." she'd say, accompanied by my childish giggles.

"One big plate for meat, but those would be kept back in the kitchen to warm. The soup plate rested on its saucer with a side plate for bread and a huge spoon for soup." A serving spoon went down beside my plate. "Not one of those new round spoons they call soup spoons nowadays. Meat knife and fork, fish knife like a little palette knife, a dessert knife and fork and spoon; cheese and fruit knife and fork – ah no, got that wrong, Mrs Anderson used to like the cheese before the pudding, all the savouries together, sweets to finish. They had different sets of china for each course. Mr Anderson brought home a set of fine bone china dessert dishes with fruits and flowers painted on them. They were exquisite." Gran saw me looking puzzled.

"Ex-quizit?" I asked. Granny laughed.

"It was china as light as a feather with edges like exquisite fine lace. Mrs Anderson wasn't pleased with it though because we couldn't clip the silver pip trays on the delicate edges and she hated guests scattering grape pips or seeds on her beautiful tablecloths."

"Have we got any pip trays Granny?"

"No dear, we usually cut the pips out for you in case you swallow them. We don't need pip trays." A boy along the street had

said if I swallowed apple pips a tree would grow in my stomach.
I thought he had a silly look on his face at the time so I kept it to
myself because Gran's stories were far more interesting.

"We are not so untidy as those people are we Granny? You must
have had a big huge kitchen for all those things?"

"Yes, and each had its place in drawers and cupboards. Some,
like the china for serving and eating from was kept in the dining
room sideboards, the cutlery and those pip trays were locked up in
their own special cabinet in the silver pantry. We never touched the
silver; a man called a Butler looked after the silver. All the heavy
china bowls for mixing and copper pans for cooking were cleaned
with sand by a scullery maid in her room, off the kitchen, where she
had a deep stone sink."

"Like the old sink Daddy took out to the garden?"

"Yes, but much bigger."

"Daddy said our china sink came from Belfast. Where's that
Gran?"

"It's called a Belfast sink darling." Gran always answered my
questions before telling me more of her story. "But I didn't have to
clean pots and crocks."

"Pots 'n' crocks," I echoed, "that sounds funny."

"I would often lay out Mrs Charlish's preparation table because
she was teaching me the art of cooking. We had an ice box from
her friend Mrs Marshall. The ice-creams and sorbets we made
were a dream. Cook sometimes allowed me to plate and garnish
the desserts. One evening I arranged a fruit ice cream and sorbet
on the lacy edged dessert plates and decorated each with a fan cut
strawberry and some Maidenhair fern. You should have seen Mrs
Anderson's face."

"Whoo, why?" I asked, eager for the verdict.

"Well," Granma said looking up to the ceiling and putting on
an exaggerated face. "First she looked at me daggers, but when a
lady guest squealed with delight at the sight of her dish of ices Mrs
A's face changed and she just simpered."

"Simpered?"

"Yes dear, simpered – put on a silly smile as if she was being
modest, then replied, 'Oh it was just a little idea of mine. I'm glad

you like it my dear.' No our employer never thanked anybody for doing a good job for her table – she just expected it and if it was extra special she would treat it as, ' one of her, own, little specialties.' Not like at the Whitesides." Gran's memory had travelled back to the kitchen at Adelaide Cresent, where she had often said, 'every member of the family said thank you from the Grandmothers to the children. It was such a joy to cook for them.'

"That's the way, give it a good squeeze and push it around." Gran was saying to me as I was kneading a small ball of yeast dough, when Mum walked into the kitchen. "Oh don't let Lily waste food Mum." She said,

"Not waste at all Dolly, the sooner the child learns the feel of yeast dough the sooner she'll know how to work it without waste. That's the way I taught you."

"But there's a war on now."

"So was there then, if you remember."

"Whoops, you're right. So there was." Her daughter agreed

BOOK THREE: 1941 – 1952

18

Something's brewing?

Winter was hanging on into early spring 1944. A rhythmic jingling of the chains on the ice covered road was almost hypnotic, musical. The sound filled the air from over a mile away down the long sloping hill known as High and Over, inland from the town of Seaford, trucks and Bren-Gun carriers slewed and braked, snaking in one long unbroken line down the Alfriston Road passing the tall flint wall of the cemetery to the sharp left hand bend before climbing up a short icy slope. At the turn in the road, outside the Forshaw's house, a truck slid under a gun carrier, metal ground hard against metal, another truck slid into its rear; the sound changed, but the jingling chains carried on coming.

Paul ran to the gate; already, at four years old fascinated by anything on four wheels with an engine. On the road trucks leant at odd angles; a young soldier lay in the road being treated by a medic, other men stood around lighting up cigarettes. In the gathering dusk the tiny red pin points moved about like fire flies.

Watching the contentment flood across the soldiers faces reminded Paul of his father, went he stopped for a quiet smoke after mending the truck.

19

It must have been the last time

The night our family gathered together must have been in the summer of 1944. It was to celebrate Uncle Arthur and Aunty Hetty's Silver Wedding. Looking back on that event I think it was the last time the whole family were able to come together. Although I was very young, I remember standing among them outside the Porthall Tavern, Grandparents, Parents, Aunts, Uncles and cousins, all watching in silence as a black pointy thing, with fire spitting out of its back, flew across the darkening blue sky, making an ugly roar. It was coming in from the sea, north up the Steine Valley towards the Downs. I could feel the distress in the hands tightening as they held mine. The relief that followed brought an outburst of words,

"Bloody Hitler, what havoc is that blasted thing on its way to cause?"

"London no doubt, it's following the railway lines by the look of it."

Hitler had started sending his V1 bombs grinding across the sky, delivering more deaths and damage. The sound of their coming was distressing but the relief of seeing them pass left bitterness for the destruction they were about to cause. For some people it was a signature tune to hell. When the family went back into the pub my younger cousins and I had a companion on the doorstep that evening. Aunt Amelia, who had married Grandfather Sam Smith in 1937, would never enter a public house. She had signed the Pledge just after the First World War and was quietly adamant she would not go in with them, even when Grandad joined the family to celebrate his daughter and son in law's Silver Wedding. She sat on a chair outside the door with an orange squash, disappearing into the crowd alongside me and all my cousins, too young to go into the bar.

But it was that ugly deep grinding noise in the sky which has fixed itself in my memory.

20

A kind of, gathering in –

Blackout curtains were being drawn earlier in the evenings.

Autumn 1944 and another Christmas was on the horizon. Good cheer? What good cheer? Sometimes it was hard to laugh when those flying bombs brought such sudden disasters, but then thankfully funny instances broke the gathering tensions; like the silly situation caused by the blackout when Ernie Allen, with his jug of beer walked round the same unlit streets three times, because he couldn't find his house on a moonless night. One of the 'boys' from the 'Private bar' at the Porthall Tavern had gone out to the gents and noticed Ernie passing the pub with his jug. On going back into the bar he said, "Didn't I see Ernie over in the Public getting his beer ten minutes ago?"

"You did." Mrs Wood answered.

"Well, when I went outside I saw him walk past clutching his Mrs's old washstand jug in his arms."

Laughter rippled round the bar, but all the men got on with their drinking until another habitué from the 'Private' bar came back from the gents asking if Old Ernie had come by for another jug o' beer; but he hadn't. He was apparently, just passing the pub for a second time. So, although it was a bit chilly my Father opened the door a crack to watch out in case their pal passed by again. Someone pointed out,

"His Mrs is gonna be none too pleased if she's waiting for 'er regular sup." Just then, there he was again, a figure hunched in the gloom, trudging past the pub door.

"Hallo Ern." called my Father.

"Blimey Artie, is that you? I thought I'd been past 'ere before."

"More like three times Ernie." shouted a wag from inside the bar.

"Trouble is chaps," Artie observed, "he's got no landmarks."

"No, course, there aren't any trees up Stanford, Upper Hamilton and Coventry Street." Wide white bands had been painted round every tree in the town to avoid people bumping into them in the blackout. Another cheeky quip called from behind the door,

"At least there ain't any trees to bump into an' smash his beer jug!"

"Time gentlemen please." called Mrs Wood.

"Come on lads, let's walk 'im home." said my Dad. So arm in arm either side, front and behind four of Miss Cole's 'boys' walked their neighbour back up Stanford Road, round the corner into Upper Hamilton, turning right into Coventry Street.

"Now look Ernie," said Artie, "next time watch out for the first two trees at the top of Lancaster. Can you make out the white bands?"

"Yeah, only just, didn't think o' that." Ernie replied.

"Well then you'll know you're at the end of Cov."

"Might not see 'em if there's no moon." wailed Ernie.

They all crossed to the opposite side of the street and along to his door, rattled the knocker and opened the door calling out, "'Ere 'e is luv. Sorry we've kept 'im out late. Cheerio Ernie. You'll 'ave ter get yer Mrs to give yer a ball o' 'er knittin' wool next time yer come for a jug on a moonless night! Tie it on yer door knocker 'n' follow it back 'ome."

"Gercha, get on with yer" Ernie called back over his shoulder. Humour kept them going along with the tale of Mrs Allen; when the air raid siren wailed the warning she shook so much, her tin hat clattered against the brick wall she was sheltering beside. Her hat made such noise that she didn't hear the All Clear siren. Her hat kept on clattering against the wall long after the wailing had stopped, she was still shaking with fear. When somebody grabbed hold of her shoulders and pulled her away from the wall, the silence surprised her. "That is," Dad told mum, "until a bloody bomb went off only 'alf a mile away."

21

The Forshaws

What was bad news and disasters for some could be seen as an opportunity for others. In 1944 there wasn't anywhere safe in the South East of England, from a V1 going off course and falling out of the sky before it reached its target over London.

One particular farmer and his wife had stuck it out for 5 months but couldn't live under the constant nightly threat of a V1 dropping, so decided to leave.

Alex Forshaw was at Hailsham cattle market when he heard on the grapevine about the farm sale. Quick off the mark he found out the asking price and straight away went to the Bank; borrowed from relatives and found items to sell, all to fill an envelope of white fivers as near the figure he could muster. The farmer took it. Only two nights previously a bomb had killed three people half a mile down the road from his farm. Alex got his longed for acres. The afternoon Alex, Joyce and their twin boys drove in one gate, the farmer and his wife drove out and up the lane with all he could get in his old truck. With no time to waste, Alex and Joyce immediately set to milking the cows; feeding the pigs; chickens and ducks. Peter, an elderly Airdale left in an outhouse, took Joyce into the big barn to meet the Bull, tethered in a stall under the hayloft, then out to the yard to fetch the chickens into their coop. Joyce reported to Alex that the dog seemed to be quite confident it was his usual job. The house, built in 1604, the year after Queen Elizabeth I died, was damp and bent over. Situated against the Railway embankment, just behind the house, stood a venerable old barn, but by its extensive scorch marks, it had regularly caught fire from the sparks flying out of the chimney stacks of passing steam engines climbing the steady gradient up through the property to Heathfield. But it was theirs. If it hadn't been for the constant nightly threat of being blown to bits finally rattling the previous owners out of the area, Alex and Joyce could never have afforded to own their own farm and Alex was not going to let a few bloody sparks and bombs ruin his life's dream.

At the end of their first day, the two new young Farmers, exhausted, but full of visions for the future, were sitting by the stove having a well earned hot drink amongst the jumble of boxes and assorted furniture, when the back door opened and a man walked halfway across the kitchen before he stopped abruptly in his tracks. Alex and the man asked in unison,

"Who are you?" The answers came as a surprise to both men. Alex found the farm had a resident Labourer, who slept in one of the ancient cubicles for farm workers in the roof, and Harold, the Labourer, who had been on his regular day off, arrived back from the local Picture House to find he had a new employer.

The Farmhouse built in 1603.
Nobody wanted to live there as it was in doodlebug alley!

22

A Little Taste of Luxury

Just before Christmas 1944 Granma was rummaging around the cupboards and came across an old bottle of ruby port forgotten from Christmases years back. It prompted her to take a short journey down town to a small confectioner's factory, whose owner she knew from years ago, where she was able to wangle a block of cooking chocolate in exchange for a pound of sugar she'd been saving up.

One evening when Mum had to go to a WVS meeting and Dad was out fire watching, Granny made me my first taste of hot drinking chocolate.

"Shoosh," she whispered, although there was nobody there but ourselves,

"I've found some lovely chocolate. Try this. Little touch of sugar for you because it might be bitter."

"Yuk." It was too bitter for my young palate. But nevertheless I got the taste and enjoyed the comforting bedtime drink.

Before tucking me up in bed Granny brushed my hair. I never knew why but she always called my hair, 'Frogs Wool.' "Now don't forget, when you wake up just say, "thank you for bringing me safely through the night." I never asked who I was thanking. She never said.

On Christmas Eve when all the family gathered round the fire in Arthur and Hetty's in Upper Hamilton Road front room, somebody said,

"Now where's Clara got to?" Granma came marching in proudly holding up a tray with a set of heavy old wine glasses, another back of the cupboard discovery.

"Chocolate wine." she announced.

"Weee." shouted an excited voice; my Auntie Hetty's.

"We used to make this at the Anderson's back in the 1880s. Mrs Charlish showed me how you melt the chocolate and mix it

143

carefully with ruby port wine. We served it in the evenings from a copper pot poured into small porcelain dishes." Aunty Hetty wanted to know where she got the chocolate and the port.

"Don't ask," my Dad told her, tapping the side of his nose, "my Ma-in-law has got a 'way' with her."

"That's right." Uncle Arthur said. "She can get away with anything, Happy Christmas all."

"Yes, let's hope when we celebrate the next Christmas there'll be no war."

Our gas stove in the kitchen
at Coventry Street

23

Making do

Early in the New Year 1945, Granma found we had just one
apple left on the shelf in the cold store Dad had set up in our cool
cellar.

"Now what shall we do with that? I know, we'll make you
a birthday cake young Lily." I had to ask, "With only one apple
Granny?"

"Yes," she said, "It's called an upside down cake, one small egg,
½ oz of sugar beaten up to a white froth. ½ oz of flour folded in and
finally a dessert spoon of precious butter – but it's special so we'll
let ourselves be generous. We'll pop this little basin on the steamer
alongside this week's Saturday pudding and Bob's yer Uncle, there'll
be dinner and tea all on one gas ring."

"I haven't got an Uncle Bob."

"I have and he can do just about anything." she said chuckling
to herself.

Whilst we were washing up the mixing bowl Granma started
on another story. I could see she was concerned my Mum was still
being sad about the news that Glen Miller had gone missing.

"Who's Glen Miller?" Gran asked when she'd found Mum in
tears.

"He's the band leader Mum. You know, Moonlight Serenade
that you like."

"Oh yes, oh dear I'm sorry to hear that."

Since Christmas Mum had really been down in the dumps,
Gran was acting out more distracting stories.

"For afternoon tea I had to put on a lace cap." With a twirl and
a finger flourish she popped one of Mum's lacy crocheted dressing
table doilies on her head, "I had long ribbons from the cap hanging
down my back."

"Your Gran had lovely long golden hair in those days," my
mother told me, "and she had to put all her hair up on top of her

head with the lace edged cap pinned on the top sloped forward towards her brow."

"Yes I did, Mrs Anderson told me I had to look fashionable but, oh dear, the stable boys said I looked real cheeky!" Granma said. "Often young Joyce, our scullery maid, would call me back, 'Don't go yet Clara you've got a stray lock of hair loose.' So I always came to her as my mirror to make sure Mrs didn't shout at me. We didn't have a mirror in the kitchen. Aw no, Mrs wouldn't hear of a mirror for servants. Ar', but when we had to polish the dining table, she told us, 'to make it shine like a mirror. It had to reflect our faces,' she said. The candelabra was set on its' centre when dinner was served in the evenings."

"Did the Anderson's have dinner like my Daddy does?"

"Your Daddy has his dinner when he comes home from work."

"And he listens to the 6 o'clock news doesn't he?"

"That's right dear. The Anderson's led a different life, they didn't go to work."

"Did they have a wireless?"

"No there wasn't any such thing in those days." Granma replied.

"Who told them the War news?"

"There was no a war then either," she said. "The Anderson's in their Manor House had all the time in the world and no food rationing," went on Gran, "They ate with elaborate decorated silver cutlery and cut glass. Fruit on gold edged china dishes and little nosegays of flowers along the table. Starched white napkins had to be folded in swan shapes or crowns. When the ladies withdrew after the Cheese course to Mrs Anderson's drawing room to have their dessert, all the parlour maids went with them. Mrs wouldn't allow female servants to stay in the dining room to serve the men, no, that was left to the butler and men servants.

'Men's talk can become coarse,' she told Mrs Charlish, 'I do not want my servants hearing coarse men's talk.' Anybody would have thought we had never heard men's risqué talk. Although I must admit Granma Annie would never hear of coarse talk when she was in the bar at the Lamb." Gran put her finger to her mouth and winked.

"My job was to make sure the silver tea tray, with a spirit stove and kettle, were all ready in her drawing room where she entertained the ladies after dinner. Mrs A would make a great drama out of unlocking her tea caddy and blending her teas; pouring in the boiling water on the tea leaves in the French porcelain teapot her Mother Isabella left her. I handed round the fine china cups and saucers with their hand painted butterflies and insects. Very proud of her French porcelain she was. If she had guests she wanted to especially impress, our tiny new housemaid followed behind me with a silver tray offering little lemon wedges, a jug of cream and a bowl of sugar. None of your ugly tongs though, oh no, we had to cut the cane sugar then grind it fine so guests could spoon it into their tea. And tiny Mabel was dressed in a floral dress with long sleeves and a matching cap. It all had to be carried out daintily, followed along with a three tiered silver cake stand with sweet cakes – only just mouthfuls. The men had their coffee in Mr Anderson's Library. His wife told her lady guests that coffee was filthy and only fit for men."

"Is that why there are pictures of men on the Camp Coffee bottle Granny?" I asked. Granma Clara laughed at that.

"No sweetheart. Camp coffee in bottles is only essence of coffee. The gentleman drank their coffee from the beans we roasted and ground in the kitchen. We can't afford that kind of coffee."

During one brother and sister conversation I overheard Aunty Hetty say, "I wonder that child doesn't get bored with those antique stories Clara's always telling her." My father replied,

"It gives the old lady something to live for Hetty. I wish our Mum could be here to tell Lily about her life. She and Pup, (that is what Dad called his father) had plenty of adventures in their time, it's good to hear about our Grandparent's lives, and Lily's a good listener.'

"Oh yes, you're right there Artie,' she agreed, "Lily is definitely a good listener!" There had been another Sunday morning; I was four years old, my eyes just level with the top of the kitchen table, as I watched Uncle Arthur counting out his week's takings from his newsagent's shop, when I asked,

"Do people give you that money for humbugs, Uncle?" He gave me a quizzical look and went on counting – copper pennies, halfpennies and silver coins, separating them into tobacco tins; brown ten shilling notes and blue pound notes into one old shallow cigar box. Slapping its lid closed he finally turned his attention to me, smiling, and asked, "What humbugs?"

"In your newspapers," I insisted, hardly able to see how an adult could be so dense. Before he had time to answer, Aunt Hetty flicked her drying up cloth at him saying, "I told you but none of you will believe me. Gran's been telling this child stories ever since the day she was born." He laughed at that.

"There you go again, but it is true – her mother will bear me out."

"What's this about humbugs then?" he asked with a twinkle in his eye.

"Granny says it's all humbugs in your newspapers."

"There you are what did I say?" chortled Aunty.

As usual, while my Dad worked on a plumbing job in his sister's house in Upper Hamilton Road, I often climbed the stairs to Aunt Hetty's top front bedroom. I loved playing what I called, 'tidying Aunty's drawer,' in the low, bow front dressing table standing in the bay window. The top drawer was full of colourful scarves; long and short gloves, twinkling brooches, pots of rouge and lots of bottles; a tall one, always half empty of Lavender water with a bright lady on the label, small deep blue smooth ones that slipped round in my hand like soap, full of Evening in Paris and the latest Californian Poppy in a faceted gold bottle printed in gold with red and yellow poppies.

Wrapping myself with the scarves, I spread rouge on my cheeks and winked one eye the way I had seen Patti do when she walked passed men in the street, making myself go all coy at such grown up antics. I waved my massive gloved hands at my reflection to waft away the thoughts. Aunty came up to find me saying Daddy was ready to go home for Sunday dinner. He had been doing, a 'little job' in the house for her, because 'Uncle Arthur was all thumbs and no fingers,' is how she described her unhandy husband.

"Aunty, do you like the taste of lavender water?" I asked.

"Good heavens no dear, no I wouldn't know what it tastes like. You do have some strange ideas."

"But Daddy says you drink it." Her fluffy eyebrows rose as she roared with laughter, "Ho! My brother's a cheeky young blighter, don't you take any notice of him." I had overheard my Mother suggest getting a nice little bottle of Lavender water for Aunty's birthday and my Father answering,

"Better make it a big bottle, Hetty never buys small ones. I think she must drink the stuff." he remarked. He was right. I *was* a good listener and sometimes it was to get him into trouble.

Well, not real *trouble* his was just typical brother's sarcasm about his sister.

BOOK THREE: 1941 – 1952

24

The Forshaws

In the spring of 1945 you couldn't get a tractor for love or money.

But Alex Forshaw was a very practical man, he didn't see not having a tractor as a problem, but a challenge, which he had solved by cutting the body off a 1930s Austin 12, behind the driver's seat and adding a flat platform from scrap wood.

He came into the kitchen one lunch time with a big smile on his face.

"I've just collected the pair of spadelugs I got the blacksmith to make. He's made a damn fine job."

"What are spadelugs?" Joyce asked.

"You remember that piece of old angle iron I found in the barn? Well, I took it down to the blacksmith last week and he's cut and welded it into a pair of spoked wheels." The quizzical look on his wife's face prompted further explanation.

"I'm going to bolt them onto the back hubs of the tractor." Ah, then she understood.

Alex on his tractor

Being on the Weald in Sussex; famous or infamous for its clay tracks, it sometimes took 2 hours to get the tractor, with its load of 40 gallon drums filled with water for the animals, through a gateway off the lane and into a field. The spadelugs would dig into the clay and prevent all those delays. Unfortunately it worked only too well. Over the winter the lane turned into a quagmire of yellow clay as Alex's 'idea' cut its way through the surface leaving an impassable ridge in the centre, causing the tractor to ground on the sticky middle of the track.

Something else had to be done. The lane ran steeply down from the farmhouse, under a railway bridge; always wet; down past a large pond on the right and an old brick kiln on the left, also always wet; then on towards the lower fields with a left turn into the Rick yard where Alex was building a fatting shed for the pigs; urged by the man from the ministry of Ag and Fish, saying, "Get those pigs ready for market; the sooner to feed people." But transporting the materials down the lane had been a nightmare, so a new approach was needed. There was plenty of hard core from damaged buildings, but labour to do the work was still scarce. The war was coming to an end in Europe, so a request by farmers was made to the local POW camp for some labour.

Alex went to the camp and found he could have ten Italian prisoners for a shilling a day to work breaking up and spreading hardcore in the deep ruts. Joyce wouldn't have to feed them because each prisoner would bring a packed lunch.

At the end of the first day Alex came in for his evening meal more frustrated than if he had been trying to get the work done on his own.

"I told the warden not to bring any more Ities. I've spent the entire day getting them up off their backsides. All they wanted to do was sit lazing in the sun."

At the end of the second day Alex came in to the kitchen and sat down with a satisfied sigh, "That young German lad they brought me this morning, for a shilling a day, has broken up all the hardcore. He hasn't even taken a break; if he goes on working like that we'll have the lane finished and be taking the bricks down to get on with building the fatting shed by the end of the week.

On the third morning, five year old Peter and Paul thought they would go and see what a real German looked like. Paul recalls he was surprised to see the young man looked just like himself; lightly bronzed by the sun and almost white blond hair. What was more surprising was the young POW's back was heavily pock marked up the middle with shiny white scars.

BOOK THREE: 1941 – 1952

Part Three

BOOK THREE: 1941 – 1952

1

Then it was all over

A stunned silence seemed to pervade the air, before all along both sides of the street upstairs windows sprouted Union jacks, some as big as our dinner table cloth. We had a party in the street. Jelly and custard, blancmange and paste sandwiches, cakes in little paper cups. Orange and lemon squash. We played hunt the thimble and didn't get shouted at for jumping into front gardens and breaking flowers. Musical chairs round a line of old kitchen chairs set out along the middle of the road opposite Queenie's shop. Children shouted and ran round laughing and screaming. At first I was an onlooker because I had no brothers and sisters – most of my early years I'd been alone or listening to Granma's stories; making pastry dolls or putting together constructions with my father's old chromium plated Meccano set. But when the younger ones started dancing I was in the thick of it with the other children, avoiding our parent's hands trying to settle us at the table. The tea, the music and the singing, I had never known people being so noisy, it was almost breathtaking. By the time the Canadian soldiers from the camp, bringing their sacks of gifts for the children, got down to Coventry Street, it was beginning to get dusky; people stood around in small neighbourly groups; I was sat up on the gate post on a one of our neighbours' soft cushions. A soldier handed me a box. It contained a set of cardboard bricks printed with nursery rhyme pictures. I couldn't speak. My father looked at me, "Say thank you." he said. But I was speechless. How could he give me bricks, they were for babies.

"Say, thank you." he whispered urgently in my ear. The soldier smiled. I couldn't speak and I couldn't understand why my parents didn't tell the soldier I was four. BRICKS! They were beneath me I thought. I was shocked that my parents had let me down. It seemed like a betrayal. The bricks sat in the bottom of my toy box, I don't know for how long, surrounded in an aura of quiet and disgust.

Dusk surrounded all – no street lights but somebody had decided to bring out some old pieces of furniture to get a bonfire started in the road. Who cares – it's a celebration, they said. A group of young men hefted a piano out from a house on the lower side of the street where there were no steep front steps and Mrs V immediately started playing; 'Roll out the Barrel' and 'Knees up Mother Brown.' Youngsters pranced round the fire. Mums and Dads danced; watchers sang at the tops of their lungs and everybody joined in with the 'Okey-Cokey.' Sitting on their kitchen chairs out on the front doorsteps watching all the excitement, some of the older neighbours, my Granma among them, shed a few tears, half hidden by the dark shadows spreading away from the bonfire. Hands reached out, and voices called to, 'wipe away those tears,' as the old folks were hauled up into the line with laughter and hands on the hips of the person in front, they soon went swaying up and down the street around the flaming bonfire singing along to the 'Conga.'

Five months later we celebrated all over again, although the atmosphere had changed. VJ night was different to VE night. On VJ night, music came from a gramophone with younger folks jitterbugging in the road. Joined by a few returned soldiers who were dads and brothers, the pavement was filled with a gathering crowd of onlookers. This time they had dustbin lids full of steaming hot potatoes on the flaring heaped bonfires. Collections of horded candles were dug out of cupboards and set along the garden walls that had been denuded of their cast iron railings early on in the war. What the hell. Bring out the candles it's all over now, all of it.

All over for some, but not for Muriel Stebbings, she hadn't heard from her husband. Last anybody knew he was in the Desert. But then nobody really knew because Muriel hadn't been seen in the street herself, she certainly hadn't answered her door when the neighbours called to get her to join the celebrations. For many residents of our street the war had only brought loss, nothing to celebrate.

2

While the young were filled with excitement –

The feeling of euphoria stayed high for a long time after the party, scorched patches in the tarmac left their visual evidence of the street bonfires.

On the first school Monday following VE day, people within earshot of the Stanford Road school playgrounds experienced a new sound in the air.

At the start of the morning playtime a number of small boys' voices began to fill the infants' playground space; softly at first,

"We won the war. We won the war. We won the war."

As more voices joined the chanting grew in volume. I ran upstairs to our back room window where I could see the sweep of the infants' playground and hear the same words chorusing from the juniors' playground partially hidden from my sight by the school shed roof.

"We won the war. We won the war." The chant went on without a break. Little boys in gangs went stomping round the playground, beginning by two or three boys at a time, throwing their arms across each other's shoulders, chests out, feeling the importance of their inclusion, whilst their chanting got louder and ever-more shrill – "WE won the war – We won the war – We won the war – We won the war – We WON THE WAR"

In no time boys of all ages ran to join the ends of the lines, until they formed an unbroken ever-growing long line snaking in waves back and forth up and down chanting to the rhythm of their marching steps. This great wave pushed the tiny children and the girls out of the way with the little children pressing themselves against the school walls, squealing with contagious excitement; as some banged on the door in fright, calling to be let in. A crescendo of sound seemed to beat back and forth between the high red brick school buildings and the cement faced back walls of Coventry Street's houses. Back 'n' forth, back 'n' forth rising into the air as if pushed up and up. I could see women and old men coming out into their back gardens. Even one or two people who were walking down Stanford Road stopped by the railings; looking towards the playgrounds, cocking their ears to hear the children's piping voices; children that were mostly out of sight, listening to the musical sounding chorus. They were all listening. Stomping, chanting, stomping. Eventually a bell rang out loud dashing the chanting to an unwilling murmur, reluctant rather than hopeful this time. Far over in the Senior Boys' yard there was no sign of them joining the young children's excitement, they, it seems, were old enough to have their own way to celebrate.

Apparently, so the story goes, the senior boys were taking advantage of the absence of teachers, distracted by the unusual noises in other places they were having a quick drag on their rollups down in the boiler room. We knew this story because, later in the day, the Caretaker's wife complained to the canteen women, "Those lads left all their squashed out butts on my husband's boiler house floor!"

— the older generation were full of expectation

"Now we'll be seeing some changes." I heard my Dad say.

One evening, the previous week, he and Mum had got dressed in their best coats as soon as Dad got back from work at half past five. Dad came rushing in the door for a quick wash, calling to me to get into my coat. Then we walked very sedately round to the infants' school where I was told I had to wait outside.

"We won't be long." said Dad.

On the wall beside the door a large sign in black letters on a white board said, 'POLLING STATION,' with a notice saying doors closed at 6pm. I had no idea what that was but I did know there was huge expectancy in the air as if everybody was holding their collective breath. The BBC Home Service was at the ready, that's when my Dad jumped up from his chair shouting, "Now we'll see some changes." I was used to seeing him take the stairs two at a time, he was always full of 'go'; but this had real punch behind it. This was all about what the people called, 'the new government.'

Grandad Smith said he heard Mr Atlee say he wanted to see, *'peace abroad and social justice at home'.*

"Amen to that." our next door neighbours commented.

In all the talk it was agreed that Mr Churchill made a good leader during the war but nobody wanted a return to the 1930's because it had been a tough time for working people, made harder by lack of access to health care. They didn't want to go back to that kind of fare.

Coventry Street in the 1940s

3

Changes

Our street was a long street. Two terraces of just on 100 grey stucco
fronted houses, facing each other across a tarmac road. The footfalls
I had known passing along the pavement mornings and evenings,
all my life, were now taking on more regularity and vitality than
previously. Less of the dodging in and out, driven by the often
urgent need to get where you were going, powered by alarm and
worry that one might get caught out with no shelter near at hand.

New the regular stomping progress of the arm in arm Mr
and Mrs from Durham's solid pace, slowed a measure; while their
neighbour, the Police Sergeant, remained determined and brisk.
Little Miss B's quickstep in her down at heel button ups stayed the
same; but her husband Charlie had come home with a slight hop
after falling off the roof of a barn when he was a prisoner of war.
Rose clip clopped her way to work at the Council offices; ahead of
slurping slippered Mrs Harris who, although you couldn't see her,
you knew the fag would be drooping from her mouth.

So far the only vehicles I had seen along the street were horse
drawn delivery carts and the rag 'n' bone man calling, 'Rag-a-bone,'
and once a hearse as I peeped through the closed curtains. I'd been
too young to see the elderly taxi that Aunty Hilda had called to take
Uncle Jim home the day he returned from his prolonged Dunkirk
retreat. The only other tradesman pushed a brown box cart in
front of him calling, 'Piper-pieper,' in a similar rhythmic chant like
the rag 'n' bone man. The paper man only called on Sundays and
he knew what papers everybody took. His high pitched call was
supposed to warn of his approach so you had your money ready as
he came near your door.

As soon as the men started coming home in their de-mob suits
the first car appeared in the street. Mr Pyecroft in his neat uniform
and peaked cap drove a taxi and when he was off duty the vehicle
stood at the kerb outside his house; gradually, as the years went

by, being updated and replaced in their ever growing splendid new livery. We were very proud when he brought home one of the 'Streamline' black taxis sporting a smart cream bonnet top. In the years to come black and white gave way to turquoise and cream.

Nevertheless, even with the odd vehicle passing through many more children now played out in the street. Long skipping ropes draped across the centre of the road. High jump ropes stretched tight from lamp posts. Hopscotch layouts were chalked out along the middle of the road. Even when a vehicle was heard to approach children moved only slowly to allow its passage, standing still to stare after its passing, before returning to their games. It wasn't until the Council replaced the small cross hatched black blocks with large pink paving slabs that Hopscotch pitches abandoned the tarmac road to chalk their numbers on the conveniently placed square paving slabs.

The neighbours didn't like that at all, especially if the chalking was outside their houses. Everybody had been so pleased to have the uneven old black bricks replaced with the neat large smooth slabs. Many didn't want to lose their lovely newness with disfiguring chalked hopscotch games. Some of the older women talking in Queenie's shop complained to our Mothers that we were making the street look scruffy. One remarked,

"The residents of Buxton and Stafford Roads will think we're slummy."

"Yer mean our kiddies are makin' the street look low class?" chipped in a younger Mum.

"No," was the reply, "I said scruffy."

"We're definitely NOT scruffy." snorted an elderly lady.

"Scruffy! Leave that to Exeter." laughed somebody else going out through the bell jingling door.

A few evenings later after calling me in for tea Mum settled a few ruffled tempers by throwing a bucket of water over the chalk lined pavement and brushed away the evidence of our afternoon's game. Before that there had been a dust up with a young lad who, having been left behind by his classmates going off to do their National service, had taken to standing in the middle of the road shouting at the children playing nearby, and ordering them off the road. He really frightened the youngest, who were only recently venturing into the street, now free of bombing. Trouble was, his contemporaries, returning to civilian life, were no longer boys and he couldn't understand their off-hand manner, so he turned to taking it out on us small children; he was becoming a bully. The latest bit of local turbulence with the chalking on the new pavements gave him the opportunity to police the street, aggressively targeting the girls who were the hopscotch players. Curtains twitched, it wasn't long before word got round that his mounting physical antics were all too visible and all agreed that bullying was unacceptable. Just too young for his National Service, the Town Council stepped in and an occupation was found for him. My mum said he reminded her of their elder brother Freddy; when he couldn't join in with his class mates, he would get frustrated, throwing hurtful punches at her brother Jimmie and then he'd pinch Dolly.

Calm was restored for all in the street, especially for those playing outside their houses in the sun, before the changing season led to cosy corner pursuits. Bead swapping, marbles, tab cards and five stones became all the rage during the winter months.

BOOK THREE: 1941 – 1952

4

Even shocking changes

Clara had witnessed huge changes over the years spanning two
World Wars. Women were wearing floor length skirts in 1913 and
high necklines boned up under the ears; arms were covered to the
wrist and long hair piled up under huge hats. In barely seven years,
1921-22 skirts were shortening to above the knees and corsetless
women danced with free abandon in skimpy dresses, that seemed
more like a chemise you wore to have a bath. By the 1930s a little
more modesty had returned.

Hats in the 1940s were like tiny tea-plates perched on the
forehead and due to the shortage of fabric, fashion changed taking
skirts above the knees again.

"You'll never believe what I've just seen," Granma said, as she
placed her shopping basket on the floor beside the chair she had
settled herself on with an appalled thump. "A woman smoking in the
street, well, I was shocked, I couldn't believe my eyes." Dolly made
little comment. Since the first few months of 1941 Dolly had herself
taken up smoking. It was no wonder Clara hadn't noticed for Artie
always had a roll up in his mouth from morning til night, the general
atmosphere must have masked her daughter's growing habit. Dolly
would buy a packet of five Players Weights to smoke when cooking
alone in the kitchen. The wireless on, she would sachay round from
sink to gas stove, along with Tommy Dorsey's, 'Sunny side of the
Street' or be swinging to, 'In the Mood,' and gliding to the melody
of, 'Moonlight Serenade'. Glen Miller's band was her favourite.

When I was old enough to go to the shop on my own Mum sent
me for her cigarettes. Although Queenie shouldn't have served a
child she used to put five cigarettes in a sweetie bag telling me to put
it in my pocket. All the children knew the drill as we all came out
running home to our mums, sucking a sweetie and all were happy.

Clara would have been shocked at that behaviour too, if she had
known.

5

Independence regained

Granma Clara had never lost touch with all her brothers and sisters, even if it had been only the irregular letter during the years from '39 to '45.

Before Grandmother Annie died in the 1890s, Clara and her siblings went to the family's Inn on the Marsh for the long summer holidays. After their Grandparents died Clara and Rose hosted the younger brothers and sisters in Brighton. Since then most of Clara's siblings had moved away for work, their families had grown and they all had their own children whose husband's were returning from the Forces. Letters had become more frequent and suggestions were buzzing back and forth that they might like to take their holidays by the seaside, in Brighton as their parents had done in the old days? These requests for holiday visits had come to us in Coventry Street because we had a whole house and that was where their Aunty Clara was living. With that in mind Gran, it seems, took her opportunity to regain her independence; find a room of her own to rent and return to the days when her retirement in 1938 had brought that lovely first freedom.

"I shall be moving back to my little place at Porthall." Granma announced in the early summer of 1945. "Won't be the same two rooms but there's another one on the ground floor that will save me going up all those stairs."

"Why?" Dolly asked. "Why move away? You've got a comfortable room here with us Mum."

"That's just it. Lily should have her own room now and you need the place to yourselves. No, I'll be quite happy in my own place."

A few weeks later, Gran left a note on our kitchen table to say she was moving again, this time, to a room in a house out Hove.

Thought the War was over,' she wrote. *'Can't think why they need to keep firing those guns on Dyke Road Park.'*

Mum and Dad were baffled. Gran didn't say anymore about the guns when Mum went in to see if she could help her mother with her moving arrangements. What she found was Gran having a real clear out.

"What are you going to do with all these letters?"

"Ah well – you might as well throw those old things away now Dolly." Granma was unpacking some things while packing others. Mum held out a handful of loosely bundled old letters. One fell to the floor open so, as she picked it up she read a few lines. Turning to her Mother she said,

"These letters, they're from Frank. This one's dated 1890."

"Yes." Gran answered, absorbed in clipping the latch firmly closed on a small oval tin trunk. Dolly read some more.

"He says here, *'Marigolds grew like a golden sea, way into the distance and tall white lilies waved like splashes of foam.'*"

"That's when he was first in South Africa." Gran replied. Mum carried on reading,

"*'Watching from up on the berg I could see far across the plain where spumes of smoke were drifting long and high.'* He says here that his guide told him the Kaffirs were burning off long Tumbuki grass. He makes you feel you're there beside him."   "Yes, that's just what I felt when I first read each letter." Gran said.

"But there's so many letters. Oh, and look, here he says how his guide was taught English by a Scottish Missionary because the man told him they, *'could cool themselves and take a drink from,'* the brawling mountain stream.' Frankie speaks like that now doesn't he? Oh and goodness, bananas grew wild in thick clumps. We haven't seen a banana for five years here." My Mum remarked, "Sounds like a paradise. Why didn't you go out there to him?"

"It does look like paradise," Gran said, as she unbent herself and turned round to face Mum. "But you know Dolly, it would never have worked."

"Why? You knew he loved you. By the look of what he says in this letter he was heartbroken when he finally realised you would never join him. He said he'd had such hopes. He calls you his darling, 'Clara Ann.' I've never heard anybody else call you by that name." Tears shining in her eyes, Mum put the letter back in its envelope.

"Yes I know, only he and Granf and Granny Pilbeam used my full name. Frank's letters look so romantic. But Dolly, I wouldn't have fitted in. As soon as the women knew I had been in service, and in Frank's own parents' house, I would have been cut dead."

"But not out in Africa surely?"

"From what I heard it would have been far worse. What women friends would I have had? Class means everything especially in Colonial communities".

"You would've had baby Frankie."

"Frank had his work. If you read all those letters you'll see he had to travel and be away for weeks at a time. I knew that from what I saw of his father's long absences away from home to keep his business going. We would be in another country, I'd have no friends. It would have been a very lonely life. No Dolly, I can't think what came over me with Frank."

"You loved each other didn't you – you said you did?"

"Yes, there's no doubt about that." Gran sat down on the edge of her rolled up feather mattress, the thoughts of all those years ago running through her mind. "We were young and full of life. When I think back of how we marched into the Grand Hotel for tea that afternoon, so full of ourselves. Well, the cheek of it. You could only do that if you were very young and carefree."

"What d'yer mean, you grew up?"

"Yes, just that, it was a pity I'd succumbed to youthful emotion. I really hated leaving my job with Mrs Charlish."

"Yes, but then you wouldn't have had Frankie."

"Or you." Gran laughed. She was a past master at changing the mood. "Come on now. We've got to get these things together. I want to get my bed made up before tea time."

When my Father got in from work at midday he humped Granma's roll of bedding on one shoulder took the heaviest case in the other hand and Mum carried two cases, one included the bundles of letters. Granma and I followed with the last few bags.

We began to visit her each afternoon to make sure she was alright and she dropped in regularly as she said she was used to doing before the War. "It was just like when your Gran first retired," my Mum told me.

"Now you don't have to keep visiting me Dolly." Granma told us, "I'll be alright. You get out with the other young Mums."

Granma had always been determined to live life the way she wanted. Mum and Dad had told her she could stay with us because Jim and Hilda had her Dad living with them; the evacuees were home and they had taken Hilda's toddler nephew, Tony, into their home, after his Mummy died. Jim told Dolly,

"Stop worrying. There's no way we can change our Mum's mind. We'll just have to keep a close eye on her where ever she decides to be."

Granma always made her little home comfortable with her feather mattress and quilt; her wicker armchair, table and chest of drawers; tea kettle and bits of Willow pattern china. When I visited, her story telling filled a major part of our time together, as it always had, with a new story on every occasion.

6

Summer visitors

That first summer after the war it seemed all the houses in the street buzzed to overflowing with young vigorous relatives down from London and places beyond, taking their holidays at the seaside. Relatives I never knew we had came to stay, each family group bringing with them a case full of their favourite sauces and chutneys, along with horded food, because we still had rationing. From which of Gran's siblings these cousins were descended I've never known?

At first the turmoil in the house was fun. Beds shoved together, mattresses on floors, lively teenagers and toddlers, bodies flew everywhere. The house was crammed full seeming to shake with shouting and high pitched excitement. Up all hours, sleeping in late, no regularity. Similar chatter, clatter and laughter could be heard in gardens all along the backs from other families. The houses were full of women, girls, young boys and babies, the Dads came down to Brighton on the train at the weekends. My Dad picked his way through the sleeping bodies going to work at eight every morning as usual. He never had a holiday. The only official holidays everybody could take were Bank holiday Monday, on the first week in August and Boxing Day, the day after Christmas.

In four years I had only seen the sea from afar. My first visit to the beach was a real disappointment. We walked on horribly wobbly uncomfortable big and little stones that rolled and slithered under your feet, and they were very dirty.

A photo (shown opposite) taken on that first visit shows crowds of families behind us as we stared into the sun; the Brownie Box camera user guide said, '*face the camera away from the sun when taking a picture.,*' So there we were, sitting on the pebbles squinting into the bright sunlight, our hands held against our foreheads to shade our eyes, proving by our dirty palms, the war had left the beach above the tide line absolutely filthy.

Although I enjoyed having children in the house to play, I had never before experienced the bickering and sneaky whisperings that went on behind each other's backs. The youngsters were so excited and rumbustuous and space so tight that one or two of my parents' bits of china and ornaments, including my own books and toys disappeared later to be discovered broken and buried in the depths of my doll's pram and toy box.

Without his wife knowing, an 'Uncle' had secretly wheedled money out of my Mother, 'just a loan,' he'd said, after losing heavily on the gee-gees. What my Dad later referred to as 'losing his shirt'. I thought he had been wearing a shirt when I saw this man with a smug look on his face, lolling lazily back in my Father's armchair.

Whilst I was a bit sad to see my playmates go, my parents thought differently. Mum had spent most of that hot summer cooking for a tribe, trying to make the food stretch to fill the stomachs of constantly hungry young teenagers and their parents. At weekends Dad found himself caught up in reciprocating unwanted rounds of drinks down the pub. The locals never bought each other drinks. Rounds were far too expensive for working men. Buy your own and you can drink as little or as much as you can afford, that was their code.

Finally, the school term imminent, all the houses but a few returned to the peace and quiet of the 1930's. You would never have known all those extra bodies had been there; except for the havoc caused by a passing hurricane on our carefully preserved pre-war furnishings. The house looked as if we had had our own personal invasion.

Dad's initial light hearted comment about the episode when Mum's cousin's husband, 'lost his shirt', had annoyed my father more than I knew at the time. He said, the so called 'uncle,' was the worst kind of 'sprucer' he knew. Mum said,

"But he said there were two of those Bookies waiting, 'to get him' at the end of the street."

"Oh Doll!" Dad sighed.

Mother never got her money back and Dad would not hear of family visits en masse again. That was the last time we got 'put upon.' Mum had been saving a couple of bob a week from the housekeeping so that we could have a summer holiday. That money was gone so Dad made a slot in an old Cerebos salt tin and soldered the lid on so that Mum's savings would be untouched until we needed the money.

BOOK THREE: 1941 – 1952

7

Pre-NHS

Since I was three years old, a cyst on my neck grew and constantly erupted. Dad cleaned and dressed the nasty abscess each evening before he rushed off back to work or fire watch; keeping wounds clean and well covered was something he did well. He felt very responsible for our health. My visits to the Out Patient's clinic at the Children's Hospital on the Dyke Road became a regular event. When Mum found Granma had moved to another room, this time in the Buckingham Road, close by the Hospital, it gave Mum an excuse to drop in for a cup of tea and keep a eye on her mother. As I turned five our lovely lady Doctor, Grace Vance, decided it would be good sense to operate to clear the cyst before I started school in the September, so an operation date was arranged. This coincided with Mum and me arriving for tea at Granma's to find she had been asked to vacate her room. Granma it seemed had woken the whole household on a number of preceding nights by knocking on the ceiling and walls with a broom, calling to the other residents to, "stop clattering about and go to bed." They were already in bed. It was 3 a.m. in the morning. It now became apparent poor Granma was hearing noises in her head, which at first, she had thought were bombs still being rained down on Brighton in night time raids. When she was firmly reminded the war had been over for a year she transferred her annoyance thinking the bangs and crashes were noisy neighbours.

This time Mother persuaded Granma to come back to live with us because she would have to spend more time taking me to the hospital and wouldn't be able to trail across town daily to check up on her Mother's welfare in yet another house. So Gran relented and came back.

"Just for a while Dolly." she agreed.

As I lay on a high table I clearly remember seeing something dripping from a small bottle onto a tea strainer, held above my face. I was later informed that it was Ether and I found the smell invaded my whole body for many months afterwards. Following the operation I was trussed up like a chicken with swathes of cotton bandaging wound across my neck and under my arms and round my back, stopping me lowering my arms, just to keep the one small dressing securely in place at the front of my neck. Dad changed the dressings but the hospital preferred to do it so I had to visit the hospital more often, only this time it was two twelve inch long, one and a half inch wide strips of the new sticking plaster criss-crossing my five year old chest and shoulders; un-sticking this clumsy stuff was a nightmare. Sixty years later a five cm. square of plaster would do the whole job.

For a 9.30 a.m. appointment at the Out Patient's, Mum and I would wait on hard wooden benches that faced away from a window looking straight at a blank wall. There were no newspapers or magazines so I took my Mickey Mouse comic that Aunty Hetty gave me from her newsagent's shop each week. Rarely was I seen by the Doctor before 1 p.m. or even 2 p.m. Mum was glad to have Granma at home to have a meal ready when we returned.

My Gran seemed happy to be back in the kitchen and part of the family again, telling her stories and listening to mine, over her Willow pattern tea cup and dish, or up in her bed with the short blue and white candlestick.

8

Coming home

Roy's girl friend, Mildred, whose family lived in the Prestonville Road since the end of the 1930's, told how she and her brothers would often dawdle along to school knowing that if Mrs Volks saw them as they passed the end of Park Terrace, she would get her car out, call all the children into the back seat and drive them along to Stanford Road school gate. Mildred said, "It was my cheeky young twin brothers that worked out that little weez. They knew Mrs V just loved children and she didn't like to see them late for school."

Mildred joined the WAAFs straight out of Varndean School in 1943. She did her training in the latest Telegraph system and became a supervisor at South West Central, sending the incoming telegraph communications from Europe to points all across Great Britain.

At the ending of hostilities Mildred's unit processed the demobilization signals, so when she saw Roy's name on the list she knew he would soon be on his way home, so tipped the family off. They all knew he was coming home before he knew himself. He'd been at the Valley base on Anglesey with a Polish Squadron where he and his pal Tich, from Wolverhampton, were in a band on the base. The family were excited to see him again. Roy brought me back a beautifully engineered child's sewing machine and gave me some German coins out of his pocket, including a heavy gunner's cap badge. He also gave me two pairs of Tank Commander's goggles, much to the envy of the little boys along the street.

Mildred before she became our Millie

9

Voices of experience

"Got anymore of that nice jam left Pop?" Roy's voice called. Silence followed, a kitchen cupboard door banged hard shut against a string of roaring expletives. I was only five and a half but my tender years did not prevent me from feeling the air vibrating with an explosive vacuum – seconds later my cousin was at the piano in the front room playing furiously banging out harsh sounding jazz rhythms. It went on for a long time.

The house fairly shuddered. Something sounded very different. In the room above I carefully replaced Aunty Hettys' 'treasures,' back in the top drawer of her dressing table and trotted off downstairs passing my father, who was in the lavatory on the landing, coaxing the old overhead iron water cistern to work to its ordered chain pull. It was a regular job for him, his sister calling round to 'come and get Arthur out of another muddled household job.' The tone of Roy's playing had slightly changed so I sidled into the room and sat on a low stool tucked between the piano and the bay window to listen. I liked to hear my cousin Roy playing the piano. Following his usual morning routine, Uncle Arthur, had been in the back yard, feeding the chickens when the eruption of expletives broke out in the kitchen. It was his breakfast break from the newsagent's shop, a time when Aunty Hetty took over for her stint behind the counter until midday.

Roy played on. He hadn't stopped. His fury carried on the air like a great storm. First Arthur, then my father wandered in to listen to the now beautiful strains of a calmer romantic tune. Arthur was holding a drying up cloth whilst Dad stood wiping his greasy hands on a rag. After a while Roy, still wearing his smartly creased RAF blue trousers and crisp cotton shirt with the sleeves rolled back, took a deep, deep sigh and swiveled round on the piano stool to face them. The two men obviously had some inkling of the reason for Roy's actions. Arthur sank onto the arm of the settee and my Dad leaned against the door frame. Neither spoke.

Words poured out from Roy under a barely controlled releasing of built up head of steam.

"If Mother only knew what we saw." he seethed, "Jesus Christ if only she could have seen those poor souls; walking skeletons; living corpses – an' she's got that cupboard full of stale bread. Food Wasted." The words came bitten through his teeth. He was SO ANGRY.

Agh! He realised his Dad and Uncle knew how his Mother went on. She'd buy herself a Vienna loaf, cut off two slices from the soft centre, spread them with butter and sit at the kitchen table with a cup of tea, then just forget the rest of the loaf. Or she'd open a jar of Shipham's paste for Sunday tea then forget it and buy a new one. They all knew how Grandfather Smith had railed at her for wasting food in the years after her Mother died, when she'd had to take over running the house. How she'd roast a shoulder of lamb for Sunday dinner then leave the remains to go off in the cupboard. She had no sense of household management. Her Mother had done it all so perfectly. When Ada died in 1929, Hetty just went out and bought fresh food for each meal forgetting everything that was started, or half finished left in the cupboards until one of the men heaved the spoiled food out into the pig bin. Roy just couldn't stomach seeing that wasted bread after what he'd seen over in Germany where he'd witnessed the horrendous sight of so many emaciated bodies; human beings half alive.

Nobody noticed I was sitting at the end of the piano. Along with my father and Uncle Arthur I too listened, taken up with Roy's heartrending account of the sights and smells that surrounded him and his mates as they carried out their orders to round up the people who lived in the nearby village and march them into the gates of the prisoner of war camp, that I later overheard my father tell Mum was, Belsen. Roy said he and Tich couldn't believe these people said they had no knowledge of the horror happening so close to their homes. 'Bloody hell, surely the stink must have made them wonder?' Tich in his rich Black Country, accent had barked, choking in his state of disgust and shock. Roy told how these civilians were made to dig graves along the roadside while he and the crew kept guard to be sure nobody got away with not doing the graft. The women held scarves over their noses. He and his fellow soldiers could see, amongst these people were those who had worked as guards in the camp.

"You could tell," Roy said, "it was bloody obvious, they were so arrogant."

Roy's horror went deep. He talked and talked, at times tears streaming down his face until his voice trailed away.

At teatime back at our house I heard Dad telling Mum that Roy said he had seen a young British soldier sketching those poor people and the awful scenes inside the camp. Fifteen years later I discovered that young war artist was Leslie Cole, one of my teachers at Brighton Art College.

10

School Days Begin

After watching all the excitement in the school playground from my bedroom window at the back of our house in Coventry Street, I was looking forward to going to school. On the first morning I couldn't get into the playground fast enough. But when I got into the classroom I cried every day for a week. I had no idea the children, so happy in the playground, had to sit still at tables after they walked in through the big green doors. And although the 'babies' room was spacious, taking up the entire width at the end of the building, I did not like being made to sit still in one place all day.

Through my sniffles at the end of each day I told Gran my good reasons why school wasn't such a fun place to be. Some of us were given blackboards and others had slates for practicing writing and numbers; and we each had a tin of little pieces of chalks that were so mucky you couldn't see what colours they were and when you made a mark on the board it gave a sharp squeak that hurt your ears. The chalks made a nastier noise on the slates than on the blackboards. Some boys kept making their chalks squeak because they knew it made two little ones cry, and the teacher had to keep telling them off.

Monitors came round giving out short stiff wire rods; each held ten dull looking cubes of wood. We were told these were to be used for counting. They were ugly rough things. The cubes were packed tightly and couldn't be taken off the rods. I dropped mine into the cotton bag hanging on the side of my table and forgot it.

I was expecting to be given orange juice and cod liver oil at playtime, like I had seen given out during the wartime, but instead we were each given a little bottle of milk with a straw pushed through a hole in the round cardboard top. On hot days the milk was sour; having been left out in the sun from the time it was delivered about 6 in the morning until our 10.30 playtime. I was made to drink it until it made me sick. I couldn't drink a glass of milk again for twenty years.

I enjoyed reading and practicing writing, when we could write on paper with a pencil instead of using the dirty chalk on black boards. As I was 5½ in that September I wasn't allowed to sleep on one of the little beds in the afternoons, "You're not a baby." The teacher told me, but I still wanted to lay my head down to sleep. By the afternoons the room was very hot and stuffy. I knew then why I had seen the children burst out into the playground at the end of each day. I loved the teacher, Miss Timpson, she wore a flowery patterned smock and little round glasses that made her look like a wise old owl. She was a tall gentle lady who led us out of the back door, of what she called the 'babies room,' just a few minutes before the bell at end of the afternoon, this allowed us to run to our Mothers at the school gate, to avoid being knocked off our feet when the older children came helter-skelter out of their door.

11

The Shock of colour

It was a grey afternoon when we were walked in a crocodile from Stanford Road School down the hill and along the London Road to the Royal Pavilion. Our school formed a group along the pavement to the North of the main doorway and being the smallest children we were in the front row.

'Stand still', 'be quiet,' we were told before we were each handed a little Union Jack on a stick to wave at the two ladies visiting our town. 'When you see them you may shout Hooray' our teacher said. After what seemed a very long wait, for us five year olds, a big black car came slowly along the road towards us and it was at this moment that I suddenly became aware of just how dull the world was around us. Inside, the car was bathed in bright glowing lights aimed at two smiling and slowly nodding ladies. One dressed all over, hat, coat and dress in lavender, the other all in sugar pink, their faces rouged and lipsticked. Two white gloved hands waved gently backwards as the car passed close by stopping a short distance away under the stone porch outside the main entrance. Even when the two figures stepped out from the bright interior they still seemed to glow with colour making the background stone walls and hedge plants look dull and dustier than ever.

I know, for my part, I made the long slow walk, in what seemed a dazed crocodile, back along the London Road and slowly up the steep incline that is Hamilton Road. I knew from the black and white pictures in the following day's issue of the Daily Mirror that the two women were Queen Mary and Queen Elizabeth, but before that day I had no idea colours could be so stunning.

"That lady in Lavender didn't get my chicky brooch." I reported to Granma.

"I expect she's got a lot of nice broaches of her own." Gran replied.

"What lady's that?" Mum asked.

I answered, "The older lady that was in the car."

"What older lady?" Mum queried.

"Yes, you know, the two Queen ladies."

"Oh yes. No, what brooch are you talking about?"

"You <u>know</u> my brooch Roy's girlfriend Mildred gave me. It's got a chicken coming out of an egg an' the egg's a real pearl. I heard Mrs Hollis at the second hand shop tell Hazel's mummy that when the Old Queen Mary went on a tour round the antique shops in the Lanes, if she saw something she liked, she expected it to be given to her. So I put my chicky brooch inside my coat then she couldn't see it."

"The child's got good sense Dolly." Granma told my Mum as if I had avoided a tricky situation.

"What the eye doesn't see the brain can't 'crave' you mean?"

It was a sunny day when we arrived in the hall for morning assembly on the first day of May. Our teacher had made us put our plimsoles on, which we only did if the lesson in the hall was PT. In the centre of the big hall stood a tall pole with colourful ribbons wound tightly round from top to bottom. The previous week we had been told stories about the month of May heralding the start of spring time; little birds came out off eggs, lambs were born and a green haze frothed all over the hedge rows and trees. We had voted for a may queen to lead the celebrations but we did not know our school had its own may pole; that was a big surprise.

"This morning you are going to learn how to dance around the may pole and this afternoon we are crowning the may queen and your mothers are coming in to watch you dance."

Standing in a wide circle around the pole we were each handed the end of a colourful streamer; holding our ribbon away from the pole we skipped round the pole beginning to weave the colours down the pole. From all around the room voices started shouting urgently,

"He's going the wrong way." One boy could not understand which way to skip. No matter what our teacher said or the way she pointed him, he still turned in the direction he wanted to face, causing the ribbons to get into a tangled mess. Our practice seemed to take all morning. When the afternoon came, the boy was nowhere to be seen; the dance progressed, parents clapped as we wound the coloured ribbons round the pole smoothly making a very colourful sight. An 'encore' was called for, so we were allowed to dance round the pole in the opposite direction to unwind all the ribbons.

Come to think of it, from then on I noticed that boy, who went his own way, always seemed to get; what my Gran would have called, 'the wrong end of the stick.'

12

Seen from my eye view

Since witnessing such bright colourful sights I thought the buildings in Brighton looked like a mouthful of jagged broken bad teeth. After the ending of the war I had seen so many people laughing, their mouths wide open showing great gaps in grey broken teeth that it made me describe how our bomb damaged town appeared to my eye. In almost every street there were piles of brick rubble, mostly cleared to within each buildings boundary,' occupied by groups of people picking over the debris. People who looked really down at heel and at the end of their tether, some pushed broken down perambulators or trucks laden with their possessions. One lady I remember well, because she looked such a strange sight. She had a scarf wrapped round a lump on the side of her head nearly as big as her head itself. Whether it covered a huge amount of bundled up hair or, as some said, it was where she kept her life's savings – impossible of course – except that the bundle appeared to be quite heavy. Goodness knows how she managed to balance it all. I heard my Father suggest it might be some kind of growth, but it was enormous. Years later, after reading Sir Frederick Treve's account, I compared it as a bit like the Elephant Man must have looked.

We never stared. She never seemed to notice anybody around. Mum told me she thought the lady must be searching amongst the remains of her own house maybe she had lost her mind poor thing. Although she was sometimes in tears as she sang intermittently, sometimes doing a little jig as if remembering happier days although she always acted very dignified, the scarf wrapped protuberance shook, even wobbled, but never came loose. One day we passed through her narrow street and she was no longer there.

Small groups of men and women sat around or rummaged on the bombsites and slept amongst the rubble. Large areas of the town looked very forlorn.

I don't think we saw many poor souls at the bombsites after the long hard iced up months of 1947. Nobody made so thin by war could have survived out of doors in a winter as long and severe as that winter.

My parents and our neighbours had to delve even deeper than ever into their, by that time, meagre resources. Everybody threw their ashes from the grates out along the icy pavements and down their doorsteps. I had no wellington boots so mum pulled a pair of Dad's thick socks over my shoes and socks to help me get a grip on the ice as I walked to school. It only helped a little because the wool gathered a solid layer of ice under each foot before I had gone a few yards. There was nowhere to dry clothes and other outer wear other than in the schools' crowded cloakrooms, so our coats were as cold wet and clammy when we left in the afternoon as when we arrived that morning. The general temperature stayed below freezing point every day, the cold was relentless for about three months, but school never closed throughout that winter term.

Mum scraped the coal dust up from the floor in the coal shed and mixed it with cement powder. Dampened a little she pressed the mix into cardboard sugar cartons. Placed on top of the embers of the one fire we had in the house, last thing before going to bed, one of these blocks would burn slowly through the night keeping the room warm and helping to dry our outer clothes. I went to bed with a hot water bottle and a woollen scarf tied round my feet to avoid getting chilblains.

Mum worried a great deal about Granma but Gran had acquired a Valour paraffin heater that kept her very cosy. There was even a paraffin roundsman down her road so she didn't have to carry a heavy paraffin can from the hardware store. Before she got the paraffin heater her one window was blinded with ice. The landlord even tried to charge her extra rent for a new electric light bulb when the first one blew. Granma said she didn't worry because she was used to ancient lights. Electric light was too harsh for her anyway. No, you couldn't try anything sly on Gran she had her answers.

Along the narrower roads the trees in the verges were sheltered by the closeness of the houses. In some of the much wider tree lined roads, and exposed areas in the parks the trees didn't fare so well. Many branches cracked and broke off, even whole trees split from top to bottom in the sharp cold. Frost patterns that spread across window panes in January remained without a smidgen of a thaw all day long well into March.

Our house was filled with a milky light during the daytime for so many weeks I began to wonder if the world had changed forever.

Dad was constantly called out to mend burst pipes but when the thaw came in April the floods came too turning the cold calm atmosphere into a mad rush of people calling him out day and night. Thank goodness by 1948 there were many more Plumbers available to respond to the call outs, because Dad himself seemed to be working day and night, with very little let up for almost three months, at a greater rate than his wartime fire watching nights. It was mostly the big old houses where nobody had suspected split pipes, the icing being so hard, that when the thaw came so suddenly, flooding followed immediately because the temperature change was so extreme.

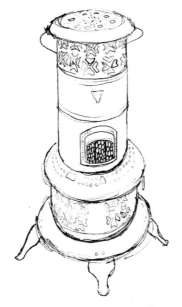

Valour paraffin oil lamp

13

From the artful –

Sitting in a half circle on the floor around the teacher's chair, we gazed up into her face expectantly; it was a Monday morning. She waited, we were all quiet.

"Now, what did you do at the weekend, my dears?" Miss Timpson asked with an air of mystery. Looking directly into our eyes she really listened just like my Granma listened. The first two or three Monday mornings started off rather subdued and tongue tied. Most five year olds had been seen and not heard and never been asked what they did, or thought, so it took some coaxing. As an only child I was used to hearing and telling stories in the company of adults, while most childrens' mums were deep in the washing on a Monday, their pre-school children were used to being told to, 'run away and play'. For a growing number of children, whose father's had been away at the war, there was the frightening addition of a smelly man in the house who, they were warned, 'you mustn't upset.' The routine was the reverse in our house because my father was now out working even longer hours.

As we got to know each other Miss Timpson gradually tapped our tongues until there was no stopping us. But there were the exceptions. They were the reticent ones, who were afraid of looking silly in front of the others because they did so little at the weekend, who finally managed to offer only, 'Played ball Miss.' But that was enough for Miss,

"Did you Tommy, where was that?"

"Dyke Road." Tommy slowly replied.

"What colour was your ball?" A frown came with the flummoxed answer to that question, "Doesn't have a colour Miss."

"Brown, Grey?" Our teacher probed.

"Brown Miss." he replied being relieved by her prompting.

"Does the ball belong to your brother, Tommy?"

"Yes Miss, he's eleven Miss."

"Yes, and I expect it's a hard ball isn't it Tommy?"

"Yes," Tommy gave a questioning look, "Bob calls it a cricket ball."

"That's right Tommy, and has it got a pattern on it?" Miss Timpson asked.

"Well yes, but not a pattern Miss." the quizzical look grew.

"What would you call it then?" Slowly Tommy's quizzy look changed.

"They're stitches Miss." Miss smiled.

"'That's right and Bobby's very proud of his cricket ball because your Daddy played for Stanford Senior Boys, didn't he?" Tommy jumped up smiling. Teacher showed she had recognised him, filling him with pride and confidence. She got us all to take notice of the things around us, the everyday things that with a little thought we could describe. Miss Timpson was calm, patient and kind. She coaxed our minds with care, she opened our shells very gently teaching us to see and describe. We were a generation looking through dirty air at beige and grey. Many of us had never been to the pictures, too young even to have seen 'Snow White and the Seven Dwarfs'.

Miss Timpson knew our siblings and our relatives. Although an only child I, nevertheless, was one of eight cousins who went to Stanford Road School; oh yes, there was no doubting it, she remembered our connections. By the end of our first year with Miss Timpson, we could each talk about something to interest us all. I discovered writing was my favourite activity. Making meaningful shapes with a pencil was thrilling.

On Friday afternoons Miss Timpson read us a story. It was just like a calming gentle farewell, before leading us quietly to our mothers waiting at the school gate.

14

– *to the, broken, heartless?*

Moving on from class one meant leaving behind our babyhood along with the blackboards, tins of chalks and the square beads on rods for counting; and for most of us, our centre front milk teeth.

"Try not to smile." Mum said, as she deposited me at the school gate on the morning our first school photos were to be taken. I still have the one inch square black and white picture of myself looking into the camera, desperately trying not to smile.

No more afternoon naps rolled in blankets on the floor. No more playing in the Wendy House on Friday afternoons.

Familiar faces were divided, sending some to fiery Miss Daniels' class and those who were a bit behind, not quite ready to write with pencils went to stout motherly Mrs Goodall's classroom; they were the lucky ones, but we didn't know at the time. While they still sat round the teacher and drew pictures, we sat in regimented lines at carved up ink splattered old double desks. I had been at the back of the queue when we were marched in from the playground to our new classroom and found I was sharing the only table. My table partner and I each had a chair and kept our books and pencils in our own cotton bags hanging on hooks at either end of the table. It wasn't long before I realised my luck; even though Billy Turner fidgeted, picked his nose and sniffed horribly, at least we had our own freedom of movement. The other class members shared single plank seats and a single long desk lid. If your desk partner forgot to get something out of the desk the whole shared lid was flipped up sending books and pencils boxes cascading to the floor. However, the desk lid opening was soon curtailed.

"Selfish child," screeched Miss Daniels, from her place at the front of the room. Every child jumped; the whole room seemed to jump. Eyes popped out and books slithered off desks slamming to the floor, pencils clicked against wood, breaking off their tips. Bottoms returned to seats with hearts beating faster, breathing coming erratically. We were six year olds, never before had a teacher shouted at us. The noise was startling.

Not everybody could remember their pencil or ruler was needed so inevitably one child would be seen desperately holding onto their books whilst their desk partner scrabbled under the lid prompting yet another sudden shriek of, *'selfish culprit'.*

We were jumpy as fleas by the end of the first day. I will always remember how we ran as fast as our legs would carry us out of Miss Daniel's classroom when, at the sound of the bell she released us. But worse was to come. As the days unfolded I related to my Granma what happened each day in that classroom.

Miss Daniels told us she brooked no talking – or fighting.

"Look at the board. Now copy what I do onto the lines." We had been given our own book of pages with four lines ruled in pencil on each facing page. The first page had a small letter '**a**' written by the teacher in heavy pencil at the beginning of the top line. Miss Daniels turned half her body to the blackboard and wrote a large letter '**a**' on a chalk ruled line. She formed the '**a**' telling us where to start and curve the line up and over backwards, and straight down along the bottom back up to the top and down again ending with a little tail flipped up to the front. Just like a little fat cat with its tail flicked up in front of it, "Now you do it." She ordered.

Some of us were quite used to seeing letters and words in books and newspapers, some children had no books at home. Some families didn't talk to each other except to argue and shout. Those who had already copied their '**a**,' were told to fill the rest of the line in with more '**a**'s,' while Miss Daniels marched around the desks poking those she called the 'lazy ones'.

"Don't suck your pencil, dirty boy. Did you see me suck my pencil – right – good, write, the way you saw me make an '**a**.'" Going briskly back to the blackboard she wrote another '**a**,' next to the first one.

"Now, go on, you do it like that." Coming to our side of the room, teacher pointed to us saying, "Good Billy, that's right and his table partner has hers right too. See, these two can do it."

"She's not my partner," Billy retorted firmly, "She's Skippy."

"No, that girl beside you is Lily." Miss didn't like us answering back.

"She's Skippy." Billy was adamant, "I heard her dad call her it." I was mortified that a family nickname was being shouted about me.

"And anyway that's wrong," I blurted in annoyance, "it's Skipper not......"

"Oh dear now I presume Lily is a sea captain." Teacher replied sarcastically, just missing flicking Billy's ear because Johnny Perkins, in the desk across the aisle from me distracted her by wailing, "I'm all wet. She's wet the seat Miss." a shiny pool of urine was forming a trail along the bench and beginning to drip to the floor. Johnny stood up abruptly, his short trousers already soaked down one leg and into his sock. "Oh yuck." He yelled.

"Get out to the lavatory and clean yourself." Miss Daniels barked. Before he got through the door the teacher shouted, "And bring a mop and bucket to clean up this mess."

A tiny girl sat on the other end of the bench, her curly head bowed, covered with both arms as if waiting for a good beating. I was mesmerized I hadn't seen anybody cowering like this before. Her name is fixed in my memory, she was my friend, we had shared a table in the baby's class and I knew that her Daddy hadn't come back from the war. Miss Daniels seized the back of the little girl's collar and using it like a handle lifted her off the wet seat; holding her well away from herself the teacher dragged my friend, to the front of the class where she stood, head bowed, body withering. Stunned, but thankful it wasn't any of us, we stared.

To this day the vision of that navy and white polka dot dress with its neat white peter pan collar half ripped away from the neck and the tears that seemed to run down the little girl's fiery red cheeks into her soggy socks has never left my memory.

"You see children. This is a filthy dirty child. None of you will do that will you?" We didn't answer, "WILL YOU?"

"No Miss." 39 whispers replied.

"Get out, go and clean yourself up." Mr Fox, the caretaker, was standing outside the classroom door. It had been slightly ajar after

Johnny's departure so he must have overheard as he came along with the mop and bucket. Seeing him Miss Daniels barked,

"No John is doing that Mr Fox." But Mr Fox didn't answer. Looking straight ahead, he walked quietly across in front of the teacher taking no notice of her protests. He mopped up the puddles, wiped the seat and floor with disinfectant and dried the seat. Then laying a clean towel out on the seat he turned to Johnny, who had followed him back into the room dressed in a pair of big boys' trousers, saying,

"There you are Johnny you sit on that you'll be OK now. Mrs Fox'll get yer trousers dry in a jiffy."

"None of that Mr Fox the boy's alright he doesn't need your sympathy."

I don't think any of us even breathed as we witnessed all this, our eyes watching as Mr Fox walked back past the teacher shutting the door quietly behind him.

"*'I thought we'd just fought a war to get rid of Hitler, seems 'e left 'is bloody sister in that classroom!' *That's what he said." Mum told dad at the dinner table that evening. "I was just going in to the canteen when I caught sight of Mrs Fox in the caretaker's cubby hole, under the stairs that lead up to the Head's room, she was changing a little girl out of her wet undies. I thought something must be up; what with hearing Miss Daniel's shouting, and her well known for not letting children out to go to the lavatory during her lessons."

"Oh that's unkind." Dad said through a mouthful.

"Well, the Head was just looking in asking what the noise was all about when Mr Fox came out of the classroom. Aw he did look annoyed when he said, what I said, 'I thought we'd just got rid of Hitler.....; "

"Thank you Mr Fox, I'll speak to Miss D later. - Oh she's a lovely kind woman."

"Who is? Asked Dad another forkful poised mid air.

"Mrs Arnold, you know I told you, the headmistress. She stroked the poor little girl's cheek gave her such a kind smile and a jelly baby; called her sweetheart, saying, 'There, now let's find Mum shall we?' and asked Mrs Fox to take her home."

The seat beside Johnny was empty the next day in fact it remained vacant for the rest of the term. When my friend returned she had a different surname.

I was telling Granma that my friend had a new name when Mum came into the room and filled in the part that had happened on the adults' side of the classroom door. She told us how Miss Daniels later stumped down the spiral wooden stairs from Mrs Arnold's room. The canteen helpers had heard, both women's faces were looking drained. Miss Daniels had been reminded these were very young children she had been given into her charge, her unkindness wouldn't help them to learn. On the other hand Mrs Arnold knew Miss Daniels' background. Losing her fiancé in the skies over the Channel had made her bitter and lonely. Taking her hurt out on her young pupils was unforgivable. It had happened before. It wasn't something that could easily be wiped off their young memories. Her behaviour would have a lasting effect on some just like her own loss had on her.

"That girl's come back to school," I told Granma, "but she's got another surname." Although I had heard my friend's daddy had not returned from the war I was still puzzled. Mum said to Gran, "It seems an old naval friend of her Dad's had called in on the Mother saying her husband had asked him to look out for her and the children for him. "I hear she was persuaded to marry this 'friend,' and since then her two boys, who are 10 and 12 years old have run away. Of course all this part of her story came from my Mum and school gate gossip.

Her story and her name remains clear in my memory all these years; plus something else I recall. Her Mummy stood out from the crowd of mothers at the school gate, because she was like a little doll; always neatly dressed, teetering on high heel peep toe shoes and her raven black hair in a small bun fixed with a large bow on top of her head. In marked contrast other mum's wearing wrap around aprons over old ratty cardigans, their feet in slippers or run down old shoes and stockings rolled down to their ankles. While little Mrs doll, seemed all perky and bright, many of the other mums leaned against the school railings, arms folded and invariably a fag hanging out of their mouths.

Later that little girl was given her own chair beside me at a double table. We shared coloured pencils and both enjoyed the writing and drawing.

On Monday mornings Miss Daniel's didn't listen to our stories, she told us to write about what we had done at the weekend in a 'Monday morning diary.'

That was when I was the next one to stir Miss Daniels into one of her rages..

15

My Monday Morning Diary

"'ere Artie you'll never guess what 'appened today."

"No what?" Dad replied, a forkful of dinner halfway to his mouth.

"Lily's teacher came right into the Canteen just as we were clearing up, and straight out told me off. She said I was immoral for taking a child to the races."

"No, she never did," Dad said. "You, immoral, that's a bit thick. What made her come up with that lot of old tosh, eh?"

"Miss D waved Lily's exercise book at me saying Lily had written this story in her Monday morning diary. She said a six year old shouldn't be writing about horse racing, Bookies and shootings. Said I was taking the child into bad company. Right old ticking off I got, just like I was a kid." Mother got red in the face at the recollection. "I felt such a fool in front of all the other women they were holding tea towels in front of their faces giggling fit to bust. Well, them giggling made Miss D worse, and she said the Head would tell the Schools Inspector."

"Did she show you the book luv?"

"Hmm, no not really, I had to pull it out of her hand. Then she went,

"Humph!" all puffy like, "I suppose you might as well see the "damage" Mrs Smith, it's not pleasant reading."

"Damage indeed, I'll give 'er "damage.""

"What had Lily written then?"

"Went to the Races and saw Gordon Richards horse shot." Mum told him.

"Is that all?" Dad asked.

"No, Lily's drawn a nice little picture of a man in a coloured shirt riding a horse."

"Lily must have been pretty close to see that. Did she really get that close?"

Mum didn't reply and I kept my eyes down in my tea, both hands cradling the cup as usual.

Being the youngest in a family of older brothers and since her father died Mum had grown up as an only child but she was never lonely. As she said, 'you've got to make your own fun nobody else is going to make it for you.' Now married she still spent her days and even most of the nights on her own. Although Dad was at home in a reserved occupation during the war years he worked l ong hours and then many nights on fire watch duty. When I came along Mum finally had a pal to keep her company. She knew Brighton and Hove like the back of her hand so with me in the pram she walked everywhere telling me about the places we passed. When I could walk beside her we would often swing along the cliff top at Black rock singing the latest songs, the wind blowing in our hair. On race days we went to the far side of the Course. Brighton Race Course on top of the hill always seemed to be in a glowing halo of light with wonderful views all around. I could see the glittering sea and the blue green Downs before it got too crowded. As the crowds gathered I was surrounded by a tangle of men's trousered legs and women's bare legs tottering on high heels in the slippery grass. I noticed the ladies had brushed their hair down and full like Deanna Durban and Margaret Lockwood. Until then I had only seen women with their heads wrapped in scarves. Some of the men were hollering, waving their arms and clicking their fingers. Few people bothered about a small child amongst them, they were too excited by a tall dusky man calling out, *"I've got a horse. I've got a horse."* his voice sounded as if it was surrounded by my Granma's thick velvet coat. Anyway, folks were gathering round him pressing small silver coins into his hand and he gave them little tickets.

"That's Prince Monolulu," Mum whispered in my ear. "He's giving tips for what horses to put money on." I must have stood there with my eyes glued to this giant waving a handful of tickets. He looked hugely tall; made the more so with the high waving ostrich feathers he wore in a crown on his head, and bright in the impressive silver blue embroidered waistcoat. Noticing me, he smiled and touched the top of my head saying,

Monolulu 'n' me
he seemed to be holding up the sky

"Another seer I see." That seemed to me rather strange. Moving on he called again, *"I've got a horse. I've got a horse."*

Soon after, a slow rhythmic thumping sound made people urgently tell each other, *"They're coming."* The horses were cantering down to the start, their jockeys standing up on the stirrups. I thought the riders were very little men, Mum said it was because they had to be lighter weight for the horses to carry.

"Come on let's get near the rail, the 2.30 will start soon." The crowd moved towards the railings. I squeezed between the legs and got right under the barrier, and as Mum was small herself, the men let her get in front. The babble seemed to hush. Then the shout went up. *"They're off!"* Mum held me tight as she leant against the white fence bar. The great horses came thundering past, their hooves churning the turf into flying clods. I was only inches away from the snorting breath and flashing steel shoes. "Where's Gordon Richards?" voices started asking.

"He didn't go by."

"Damn it, I backed his mount."

I didn't know some of their words they were just another experience to my ears. But where WAS Gordon Richards? All heads were craning back along the rail. Voices were tossing information over the heads and across the crowd saying that his horse had fallen near the bend.

As a truck drove up the opposite side of the Course I sidled under the rail and along to where I could see a man in a lovely bright patterned shirt and cap standing looking down with a sad face at a horse laying silently on the ground.

The men from the truck began raising a big green cloth around the horse and the brightly dressed man.

"Oh! Where's Lily. Lily where are you?" My Mother called anxiously, followed by shouts from the crowd.

"Lily, yer Mother wants yer." It was then that the men with the big green cloth noticed me watching events.

"Go on yer Mum wants yer. Be off with yer, you shouldn't' be 'ere."

As I turned away back towards where Mum was standing a loud thump made me jump. Somebody nearby said, "They've shot him!" Voices were silenced at the news.

" 'oo, Gordon Richards?" a voice asked.

"No, you silly date, the horse, it broke its leg." replied the first speaker. Most of the people in the surrounding crowd laughed at the repartee but it did break the tension.

At school on Monday morning our teacher in the first class used to say, 'Gather round children. Sit down on the floor, hands in laps and cross your legs. Now, tell us what you have been doing over the weekend. Who is going to start?'

Hands would to go up and voices say, "we went to our Gran's for tea on Sunday Miss." another would add, "We played football in the Park." Some sat looking everywhere but at the teacher because they didn't have anything to tell. I had usually done something quite different but I sat quiet too, because they never believed me. The teacher always looked at me out of the corner of her eye and the kids would say 'she's telling whoppers.' But now on a Monday morning we didn't have to say what we did we wrote it in our diaries. That morning I wrote what I had seen at the Races.

It seems Miss Daniels marked the diaries during the lunch break. When she read what I had written, she said sharply that if it was true, in her opinion the Races was no fit place to take a child. So down to the Canteen she promptly marched to confront my Mum who was a WVS dinner volunteer at the school. Words like irresponsible and unsuitable were hurled across the room.

"Never you mind Vi," one of the other WVS ladies said to Mum, as my teacher snorted her disapproval of their giggles and stumped out of the Canteen. "Take no notice of 'er, she's jealous she doesn't do such excitin' things."

My Dad never did get the full story of how close we were to the scene. Mum told him how good my reading and writing was getting on in my second year at school.

My next entry in the Monday morning diary was about my Aunty Hetty who drank Yardley's Lavender Water. They didn't believe that either, but that's another story —-"Isn't it?"

"But Granma, why did my teacher tell Mummy off. I wrote what teacher asked."

"Yes, of course you did sweetheart. You did well."

"Why did she say Mummy's immoral, what's that mean?"

"Your teacher doesn't think small children should be taken to the Races." But I countered by telling her I saw lots of children there.

"It's not the races and the horses it's all the grownups that do bad things with money." My questions wouldn't be stopped so she told me the story of the Wagoners who came to her grandparent's Inn every year. They sounded like some of the people up at the race course who sold Hokey Pokey and told fortunes.

"Your teacher would have said the same about my Gran and Grandad allowing us children to join in the fun at the Wagoner's camp on those few hours they stayed at the Inn yard. She would have said they weren't the right people for us young children to be amongst, but how else would we meet people from other lands bringing their different ways. You keep watching and listening. Life is everything that happens all around." What made us laugh was Mum's shrill telling of the tale to Dad.

"'- and in front of everybody else," Mum kept repeating. "Telling me I was immoral. Well! I felt awful."

"No, you don't expect to be given a thick ear by your teacher when you're a thirty five year old Mum." Dad chuckled as he said this but he did say to Mum not to give it a second thought, "None of us think you're immoral." He wanted to help her get over her discomfiture.

The rest of the family laughed it off. I always saw my family as bright and breezy, ready to look on the lighter side of life.

And Granma's own stories did help me to understand why adults have different ways of doing things.

16

Keep on watching and listening

The incident on the Race Course happened when I was six. At that age I had no knowledge, or understanding about Brighton's sleazy reputation. After hearing about the furore the few words in my school diary had caused Granma, asked me,

"What was it that man on the race course said to you Lily?" I didn't have to think about it. His words were quite clear then, and have been all my life.

"Another seer I see."

"That's worth remembering. You keep watching and listening." She was right. Life is full of exciting pictures and engaging stories.

Gran stopped going with Mum on their regular Saturday outing to the cinema. She could no longer see clearly what was on the screen so I took her place, I went with Mum every Saturday afternoon to the Academy Cinema in West Street. We caught the number 38 bus down town from the Seven Dials. On the return journey home I bombarded Mum with questions. Why did that happen? Where did he/she go? Why did they say that? I wanted to know it all.

It wasn't until the early 1950s that we saw Richard Attenborough in 'Brighton Rock,' and I found Graham Greene's book in the library. I realised I did know something about Brighton's seamy underworld. Betty's story came into my mind and I started putting two and two together. Betty was Aunty Hettys' 'Daily,' who came to 'do' each morning, often arriving on Monday with a black eye, especially after a Race weekend; many more bruises came into view when she rolled her sleeves back to do the washing up. Betty's husband was a Bookie at the Race Course. That's yet another story to be revealed later.

In the days directly after the war I saw my Mum dressed up looking young and glamorous when we went to the Races. Dad was never there, he was always working in those days. Mum and

Dad never did anything social together except she might join him down the pub on a summer Saturday lunchtime when I could stand outside on the doorstep.

On Race days Mum and I would both be in our pretty frocks, Mum wearing the Cuban heeled sling backs she had kept carefully wrapped in tissue paper from the 1930s; they were turquoise and matched the leaves among the flowers on her silky dress. On her heels she looked like a young girl and with her homemade hat in the latest style like a tea plate tipped over one eye she appeared even cheekier.

Mum made me one particularly memorable frock from a length of material she had retrieved from a bag of what Dad called 'cotton waste.' He was working in one of the new department stores in the Western Road and asked a passing backroom assistant for a bit of cloth to wipe his hands on, the young lady turned out to be a window dresser who gave him a whole bag full of used display cloth. Dress materials and clothing were still on points rationing, so the length of soft white cotton muslin with orange and yellow cotton dots, Mum pulled out of the bundle was an exciting find. When washed it came up so well she soon got down to sewing, and in what seemed no time at all, I had a pretty dress trimmed with orange satin ribbons and all without using any of our points. Mum said my dress reminded her of the Clarice, 'something,' china she'd been planning to buy at the Co-op with her next divi payout.

Going to the Races gave Mum a carefree day out after all the greyness and worry of the previous years. For me the sweeping view from high on the hill was the biggest attraction. The midday air was so clear, golden even, from the angle the sun lit the sweeping bay from Saltdean to Worthing fading round behind the hills into a silhouetted edge of town tops, from the Good Shepherd on the Dyke Road, down to St Paul's pointed tower at the bottom of West Street. I could only visualize the Pavilion hidden deep in the Steine valley before my view swept up over the arc of the Race Course backed by the rolling green Downs hazing away into the distance.

Standing in the crowd, I remember within my six/seven year old self, the atmosphere of expectancy catching people like a contagion, generating a thrill to the system you could hear in the rising voices.

Hope mounting before each race; 'They're off,' starting a crescendo of noise; then the roar subsiding into thrilled excitement and head shaking gloom. But few people were glum for very long. Although Mum and I were only the two of us we were never alone. Strangers were not strangers for long.

Mum would choose a spot, a short distance from the ever moving body of the crowd, where we could sit on the grass to eat our picnic. One particularly happy time near a family; Mum Dad and four children, who were speaking in a language I had never heard before. Mum said they were French. I listened as I ate my cheese and lettuce sandwich thinking how clever the children were because they spoke French too. Their Mother sat cross legged, a huge long loaf of bread held against her large bosoms cutting, with a large sharp knife, in toward her chest, distributing the slices as fast as little hands could grab them. I heard my mother wince at the sight of little hands so close to the Mother's sharp knife. The two Mums smiling in friendly union. All comers talked and laughed freely together giving knowledge and advice, Mum having small bets, her joy and disappointments shared with whoever were neighbours for the occasion.

"Have another go." "Try again." people advised each other.

Wherever you looked through the crowds there were arms telling the odds with their fancy handwork, or 'wide boys' pointing out a mug worth pick pocketing. Mum told me her employer, Noreen, had shown her the signs when they came to the Races together back in the early thirties.

Side show callers shouted their wares to entice you inside their tents. Booths for the Palmist, or to 'Have your bumps felt', or 'Come inside and view a heart stopping sight' like '**The smallest man**', or '**The fattest woman**;' '**The hairiest feet**'. 'Only sixpence, you'll be amazed, worth every penny'. But Mum would never venture inside; she just loved standing in the crowd, hand firmly on her purse, watching the reactions, listening to the backchat between the sharp salesmen and the larky punters. That's how, by chance, she won the best piece of china from a stall where it had been on the top of a pinnacle of 'star gifts,' but only for show. A 'bystander' had been goading the salesman with the patter asking if, 'the china egg had to be smashed to get the chocolates out?' The salesman didn't want to say, suggesting any asking price was too high for the likes of him down in the crowd. Suddenly the repartee got overheated. A breeze blew up taking Mum's little hat high off her head sending her hand up to hold it on. In that second the sale was made, "Gone to the little lady in the saucy hat." the salesman cried.

"Aw my gawd," I heard Mum shriek, "I can't afford ten quid! No, I wasn't bidding." she cried out. There followed a lot of argy bargy with the salesman getting nasty, when the bystander, who'd been goading the auctioneer, stepped in saying he'd had a good day. He paid over two new big white five pound notes then gave my Mum the china Easter egg. It was printed all over in the blue and white Willow pattern. On the way home Mum asked me not to tell Dad because he might wonder how she came to pay for such an item. At home the china egg went to the back of the cupboard until she gave it to Granma at Easter the following year. By then the chocolate had seen better days. When Mum got her coveted piece of colourful Clarice Cliff china with the next divi payout, Dad said it was a waste of money, but Mum and I loved it standing in our front room bay window filled with hyacinths bulbs. Mum needed those bright cheerful chummy days. For many in the crowd, like Mum and me, they were innocent days. On the other hand, for many the dark under belly described by the author of 'Brighton Rock' caused a lot of hardship. I saw some of that side of it too, in dear little Betty's life, before I understood what it was really all about.

For me, as a child wanting the freedom to walk to the shops at the Seven Dials on my own, the dark side of Brighton was all the stray dogs roaming the streets. Dad said they were mostly abandoned animals, where people had lost their homes during the bombing and were lonely. So when a child came in to view some trotted across hoping for a game, or as for me, being small, it meant they bounded across into me frequently knocking me over. I would never walk down tree lined Lancaster Road if I could help it because there were always more dogs and consequently more mess. It didn't help when one parent said, 'keep away from those dogs, they might have Rabies and dogs with that disease always run towards you wanting to play.'

"Silly man," my Mum said, "frightening children like that. The Council will soon round up the strays. Dogs rarely manage to find a new home like cats who wheedled their way into people's houses as if they've been there forever."

BOOK THREE: 1941 – 1952

17

6th birthday tea

Mum put a threepenny bit and a penny in my hand; I didn't give her a chance to say what it was for, I said, "It's only thrupence Mum."

"What is?" she asked, looking puzzled.

"Dinkie Chop sauce." I replied, wondering why she had forgotten my favourite sauce.

"No it's not for that. Run along the shop an' get a toilet roll, they're fourpence. Can't have children going home telling their Mother's we don't use toilet paper." I didn't argue because we didn't use toilet paper, we had always kept the Daily Mirror on the bench beside the toilet pan and tore a couple of pieces off for wiping bottoms. My Mother had relented and was giving me a party for my sixth birthday. Other little girls, in Coventry Street, had Christmas parties with loads of kids pressed tightly together along forms at tables, butted together down the length of their parents' sitting rooms; so did others in the surrounding streets. Grandmothers and Aunties served the food and poured squash. Only one boy had a party, he lived up at the Barracks opposite Dyke Road Park where there was plenty of space to have tea and run wild on the overgrown parade ground.

Mum said she would do tea for six of us. She had trawled Woolies in the London Road and Western Road, finally getting six coloured plastic party desert bowls with matching spoons and six fluted glass tumblers for orange squash. We had the table pulled to the centre of the front room with Mum's best table cloth spread with plates of sandwiches, jelly, blancmange and a cake with six candles. While Mum was fetching more juice from the kitchen the food was shovelled down in no order, without any ceremony by the three boys and three girls, which included me. Too full for birthday cake and with nothing more to do the boys slid down under the table and started playing at fighting in a dungeon, watched by the two girl guests giggling and squealing in delight – not me – I could see my Mother's face. In the nick of time Dad came home and suggested he would put some records on his grammaphone. The first record he selected was, the 'Skater's Waltz' blaring out loud, setting one little girl dancing round the table saying she was having skating lessons down at the ice rink in West Street. When dad got the next record going, it was the 'Rustle of Spring' making the girls go floating around as if they were fairies, so of course the boys had to set about cheekily mimicking the girls. Father having sorted out the boys for Mum, went off leaving us playing, again under the table. Mum was washing up in the kitchen when we erupted from the front room and up the stairs in a cowboy game, the boys lying along the landing shooting us girls through the banisters. Our squeals of delicious fright mingled with a mighty holler as my Father came out of the lavatory on the darkened landing stepping straight onto one little boy's fingers as he lay with his imaginary gun between the banisters. For my Mum the parents coming to fetch their offspring at seven o'clock couldn't have come soon enough.

Mum had always been reluctant to have any children in our house. If I did venture to bring anybody in to play Mum would always say,

"Don't let them think they're staying for tea because they're not."

18

Downs and ups

Mum could not hide her concern for Granma's moving from one rented room to another or that the operation performed on my neck hadn't solved the problem as hoped. All the worry added up to Mum's lovely dark hair falling out in handfuls. The Doctor called it Alopecia saying it was caused by the strain of the war years. Nothing seemed to stop the one or two small bald patches spreading and that was making her worry grow. I can only just remember, in those days my Mum's thick shiny, almost black hair. She had it set close to her head in deep waves.

Arthur Ovenden, a friend of the family who used to have his men's hairdressing saloon in the backroom of Uncle Arthur's newsagent's shop, had recently retired and closed the business. However, it turned out to be a bit of luck for my Mum because Mr 'O' still obliged a few old clients one of whom was my Father, whose hair he came to cut at our house once a month on a Saturday lunch time. Knowing how unhappy Mum was about her hair loss Dad mentioned it while Mr O was giving Dad his monthly 'tidy up'. Much to Mum's embarrassment she had to remove the scarf she had taken to wearing to cover her scruffy looking hair.

"I'll cure that for you Dolly." Mr O said with gentle assurance. He came the following Monday morning; then every other morning before Mum went to her job at the school canteen, and massaged his own made ointment into her scalp. Within three months her hair loss had ceased and new hair was growing strongly and almost as dark as in her youth. It made her feel so much better in every way. We never knew what was in his special ointment. I never mentioned my observation to Mum but I thought what I saw in the bowl looked like the chicken droppings in Uncle Arthur's chicken run!

Mother had her regular routines. One of her pleasures was to smoke a cigarette while she did the cooking all alone in the kitchen with the door shut on the world. In the afternoons she did the ironing with the iron plugged into the single central light fitting hanging from the ceiling in the dining room. In the evenings she mended Dad's socks, sitting under the single electric light, while they both listened to the wireless, although he always stood up at nine o'clock, put his jacket on and went out to the pub. But best of all Mum liked to be out during the day time even, if it were just looking round Woolworths and Marks & Spencer's; they were what she called, 'the Bazaars.' There was no extra money to do anything but walk and people watch. A seat at the pictures for one shilling and two pence (6p) on Saturday afternoon was as far as the money would stretch. Before the war, before she became a Mother, she would sometimes join Hetty, who would grab a handful of cash out the till, calling to Arthur, "Just off for a bit." Then, Mum said, they would spend hours trawling through silk scarves in Hannington's where women like Mum, who being only a servant in the 1920s and 30s, would never have ventured inside. Hetty took an age trying to decide which scarf she wanted, this or that or maybe the other one. Would it be the first one she saw or should she get another pot of rouge – never lipstick, always rouge and big bottles of scent? Then she would always want to go back to the scarf shop and another interminable time would be spent saying, "hold this one up Dolly," or "no, this one." Mum stopped going shopping with her sister-in-law saying, Hetty wasted too much of husband's money and her time.

The likes of Dolly and the other canteen workers needed their wages for everyday essentials, but when Joe Tennant sent the message via his Mrs that he would be having a few pairs of new sheer nylon stockings on offer, would the girls from the school canteen like a pair a piece?

"OY oy, things a' lookin' up girls." Bib Cannon cheered.

"Yes please." They all chorused, swiftly followed by, "How much?"

"Joe said, nine shillings (45p) a pair, to you girls." Mrs Tennant's reply was met with silence, but not for very long. "Go on let's spoil ourselves. It's only a shillin' (5p) a week till the end of term. So it was decided to each save shilling a week they would all be hard up together.

"Give up your weekly library book." Dad suggested, "There's plenty here on the shelf."

"Yes I know, but they're yours. I don't like 'The Count of Monte Crysto' and 'The Hunchback of Notre dame,' Mmm, s'pose your right though. Be lovely to have something glamorous to wear for a change. Where do you think Mr Tennant gets all the things he has to sell?"

"Up at the Barracks I should think. The lads pass on all sorts of unobtainable items to Joe, he's got to earn a living somehow, left a leg somewhere on the other side of the Channel.

BOOK THREE: 1941 – 1952

19

The Street

Two elderly ladies dressed all in black; double breasted ankle length coats, wooley gloves and round felt school girl hats, came marching along the centre of Cov. One was rotund and very short, the other tall and skinny. Dad called them the Misses North 'n' South but I knew Uncle Arthur called them Miss Arse 'n' Pockets.

We were used to seeing these two sisters collecting for the Church but this was something different, they held a board high in the air between them, the words on it read – No VICE on our STREETS. The pair stopped, turned to face the house of a neighbour for a few moments before moving on.

"What's it say?" my friend Sandy called out as she and the girls skipping in the road ran across to the pavement to clear the road for the two marchers.

"Vice in our Streets." I read.

"What's that?" Jennifer asked. Jimmy and the older boys playing tab cards smirked.

"What is it?" Sandy nagged her brothers.

"Things - -." The boys answered, "wotch it the o'l girl's are after yer!" We all scrambled each towards our own homes.

"Go indoors children." Miss North ordered as the pair walked forward. Her command even scattered the lazing fur licking cats. We children slowly re-gathered following on behind to see where the banner carriers would stop next. One or two adults came out on their doorsteps for the same reason.

"Whoops," hissed my Mum, "That's Mr Doodar's house."

"Who's Mr Doodar?" asked my Father rolling himself another cigarette as Mum craned her neck to see down the street.

"Can't remember 'is name," answered Mum. "He stands along the end of Prestonville you know." Mum coaxed Dad with her elbow as if I shouldn't know who she was referring to.

"Oh him, 'es the Bookies' Runner." Dad blurted out as he realised who she meant.

"That's it. Quiet little man."

"Well he has to be." said Dad going back indoors losing interest in the two elderly spinsters. He hadn't just lost interest, he wanted to eat his dinner and read the paper.

By the time our little band of pals, skulking along behind the banner turned the street end by Alf Eve's Dairy, there were quite a few doorstep watchers and twitching curtains. The ladies' marched on round into Exeter Street while most of us stopped to gather round the back of the Dairy. Mr Eves was one of our joys; he entertained the children at Christmas with his conjuring and clowning. The boys fought to get jobs helping him with his milk round. Alfie Eves was my parents' contemporary, one of the young men who had missed the first war and been among the young men who frequented the Regent Ballroom; he worked in his Father's Dairy all through the last war doing his bit for the community.

The last of the merry band of following children dispersed round at St Luke's Church Hall in Exeter Street. That hall always smelled of stale cake to me.

When I reported this latest goings on in the street to Granma, she said, with her usual little chuckle,

"It takes all sorts. They're just playing their part in the community."

"I know what made them do that banner." Mum told Gran. "Arthur took Betty round to Miss North and South's house last week after she'd turned up for work with a black eye and all those bruises."

"Oh, Dolly, not again. Poor, Bett."

"Yes, well it was worse this time. Betty's son had come home last weekend on leave from the Navy you know. He actually caught his father in the act. Arthur said he knocked the livin' daylights out of Fred; then brought his Mother up here for Hetty to look after. Anyway Arthur said he'd see Betty was somewhere safer because the first place her husband would look was their house. So he took Betty to stay in old North 'n' South's spare bedroom. He advised Betty's son to hop it back to sea. He said he wouldn't put it past Fred to get 'is razor pals out after him, although he was his son."

"They're good ol' souls those two women." agreed Granma.

"Betty's safe at their house for the time being."

"Well, she's certainly got the right pair on her side." Granma chirruped. 'Live up to their Christianity they do."

My Father was a quiet man. He listened and certainly had his own opinions mostly based on the practical side of any argument. He was self contained, at times funny, but always kind. He may have made a sharp derogatory remark about a person who deserved it, but he'd always be there to catch and help if somebody tripped. The people he disapproved of and showed his contempt for were the shirkers; those who got out of any war service; who never even did a fire watch duty; who borrowed your tools, took them to do a job for somebody else for payment, then brought your tools back damaged – never expecting to repair or replace. We had a neighbour like that. He stayed in bed late, his wife complained so we knew what he was like. He drank alone, nobody wanted to be associated with a Fascist. When he walked up the street he was like a weasely animal looking this way and that as he slunk against the wall. The only time he was seen strutting was in the centre of town along with his friends all dressed in their shirts their hard bullying voices beneath their billboards.

The first time I heard the phrase 'Moonlight flit,' Mum was telling Dad that Patti and her daughters had upped 'n' left their house. It was the one where the two ladies had pointedly halted outside. Husband dead on the beach at Dunkirk; Canadian soldier boys all shipped off home; she'd done what she'd had to, to survive.

"Poor woman," Mum said, "hope she finds her feet."

Shortly after, I saw a man piling old lead piping and broken tiles in heaps with brick rubble out on the front garden topped by a water cistern and cracked old lavatory pan, I did wonder if he might have found Patti's feet but I thought I better not ask.

Dad said he'd heard the new owner had put his demob money into the house. The man worked every evening and all weekends before his wife and two children moved in. It didn't seem like they had been there more than a few minutes before a, 'For Sale' board went up on the front post. It was the first 'For Sale' board I had ever seen, before then boards always advertised the houses, 'To Let.'

One Friday evening the man had all the little coloured tiles up off the front step and spent the rest of the weekend relaying the pattern.

"He's made a lovely job of that step." Dad reported. Monday afternoon the board was changed to, 'Sold' and the family disappeared. We children had hardly had time to get to know the two children.

So many of the family's in Coventry and the surrounding streets had known each other for years now the neighbours were moving on and new faces were joining us.

Peacetime allowed time for oneself; gave way for new possibilities heralding changing aspirations.

"Just a leetle touch more that way boy!" Three elderly men were hunkered down comfortably on our front step watching Dad who was wood graining the front door. Feather in hand, he was carefully dragging it across the wet surface pulling the darker varnish away to reveal the lighter under colour. Two or three retired craftsmen who lived along the street had stopped to admire Dad's patient work, one or two stayed to watch and one offered guidance. It was a long concentrated job, watchers stayed and moved on. Finally with one still down on his hunkers and another two leaning on the wall, Dad stood back looking to see if any further strokes were needed.

"Lovely job." all sighed in unison as they stood up stretching as if it were they who'd done the work. Moving off home, each called out, "Cheery bye lad."

Dad hadn't spoken a word he'd been too engrossed in his job.

The front door stayed propped open until very late that night. Although it was cold the varnish had to dry before the door could be closed, and a cold evening made it all the better, there wouldn't be flies around to get stuck on the tacky surface.

A couple of days later a neighbour asked Mum where my Dad got the lovely new oak door,

"S'pose it's becoz 'es in the bildin' trade?" the woman commented.

"No, he painted it himself on our old door." Mum told her.

"Never!" the neighbour replied, "That tak's an artist ter do that, 'es a plumber not a painter ain't 'e?"

Dad had been inspired to have a go at doing our front door, after he had watched one of the painters from his firm doing some wood graining for a big house up in the Dyke Road.

It had taken him a week or two to get the door ready, as he said it had to be prepared carefully. "We can't have anyone going in and out while I'm working on it." He had told us, "Keep the cat out of the way." After all the long hours he worked for other people Dad thoroughly enjoyed doing such a gentle patient job on his own front door.

"And the neighbours enjoyed it too." Mum commented.

"Ah well they're old craftsmen," Dad said, "Made me smile when Jack Sage starting giving me instructions where to place the next grain line."

"Yes, I noticed," Mum added, "Syd gave him a flick behind his ear to shut him up, nearly knocked his cap off."

"Ha! I didn't notice any of that." Dad laughed.

"You hadn't got the time," Mum agreed, "you had yourself well into it. Don't expect you noticed the cat sat at the bottom of the stairs all afternoon watching you."

"No really. Dear old Chu Chu. He must have thought I'd lost my marbles kneeling there in front of the door all day!" By then Chu Chu was then 10 years old and passed his giddy kittenish days when he would have galloped across the room ready to play.

Satisfied with his door painting artistry, Mum said Dad went off down the Porthall for his usual pint that night with a new spring in his step.

For the elderly retired gents who watched my Father wood-graining the front door that day, some things would not change in their lifetime. They still said, "Good job you did there, boy." as they greeted my Dad in the street. They had known him when he was a young Apprentice Plumber. He always greeted them, saying, "Evening Squire." When their generation was gone those greetings were rarely heard in the street again.

BOOK THREE: 1941 – 1952

20

First family wedding in 21 years

Christmas week 1947, the date had been set for my cousin Roy and
Mildred's wedding, and I was to be a bridesmaid. Six months before
cousin Roy and his young lady, Mildred had come round to our
house to ask if my parents would allow me to be a Bridesmaid at
their wedding. They had sat side by side on two dining room chairs
explaining their plans.

It was decided I needed my long hair cut making this my first
ever hair appointment with a hairdresser in Surrey Street, near the
railway Station. Mum had a wash and set sitting, what seemed like
ages, under a great domed hair dryer in a curtained cubicle next to
mine. The hairdresser said she would have to wash my hair before
cutting and then found my hair so thick she had to dry it with her
latest hand held hair dryer. It was an ugly brown Bakelite thing like
a gun and the hot air blasting against my head hurt so much the
hairdresser had to stand further and further away from my head
back into the cubicle opposite. There was only one temperature on
the dryer. My hair looked awful and Mum was very cross. She tied
a huge bow on the top of my head, hoping it would hide my awful
rough mop.

Mildred's parents had moved away from Brighton to Croyden
where her father had got a new job. While Mr.O, the retired Barber
took over Uncle Arthur's newsagent shop for the day, our family
gathered in Preston Road at the bottom of Lover's Walk, to catch
the London bound double decker bus. We all, except my Dad who
could not get the day off work, climbed to the upper deck in our
wedding finery, including Roy and his best man Jimmie, who both
slept and snored all the way only being firmly roused when the bus
stopped to drop us right outside Mildred's parents' house.

Measurements had been taken weeks before and a length of
Lavender coloured crepe material was purchased by a friend who
worked in the East End rag trade. Hanging along the picture rail in

the family front bedroom were six Lavender coloured bridesmaid's dresses. When they came to place the Alice band of rosebuds on my head the faces of all the Aunties looked decidedly glum. I was hustled down to the kitchen in my long frock, stood on a box beside the gas stove. Not having seen curling tongs before I felt rather alarmed watching the spits and sparks popping off, what looked like large metal scissors, heating up on the gas ring, but the Aunties stood round me determined to succeed where the hairdresser had failed. Their first go at curling my hair with the hot tongs failed miserably.

"Need to be much hotter." One of the Aunts ordered, so the gas was turned up resulting in a terrible smell of burning hair and finally success. The black and white wedding pictures show me with curls looking as if I had the fingers of a pair inflated rubber gloves sticking out, on either side of my head.

The day was extremely cold so the Mother's-in-Law wore their fashionable fox furs thrown over their wool two piece costume suits.

Mildred's Mum had a double silver fox fur, one over each shoulder. Nobody had warned my Aunty Hetty that the bride's mother owned a 'double'. Aunty only had a single silver fox and looked daggers at her new in-law.

We bridesmaids preceded the bride to the Church in a taxi. No sooner had I sat down on a little seat behind the driver when he stopped and the door opened. We had only just crossed to the Church on the opposite of the road from the family home. I was very proud of my bridesmaid gift, a silver cross prettily engraved with a flower design, on a fine chain and a muff to keep my hands warm. I had to lead the group of bridesmaids down the aisle. Later I told my Gran how embarrassed I felt when I had followed the bride and groom into the vestry for the signing, leaving the other older bridesmaids standing in their positions in the aisle where I should have stayed. I was too young to know better.

Outside the Church on that freezing cold winter day, the newly related Mothers eyed each other's fox furs; Hetty, in her single silver fox looked 'daggers' at Ruby, who was sporting a double, then quickly changed her face to a smile for the camera, while we bridesmaids shivered in our short sleeved thin frocks. Mildred's twin brothers stood proudly in their new uniforms, having just been called up to do their National Service. Alongside them was their older brother who had served during the war on Halifax's as a Navigator and decorated by the King for the part he played in our victory. However, in all the excitement, and no doubt urgency to get back in the warm, Mildred's brothers never featured in her wedding photo line up. Much against Government rules Mildred's Mum had hoarded and saved food to give all her guests a good ham and tongue tea.

The only memento of my outfit I was allowed to keep was the muff as the dresses and rosebuds were destined for another Bride's wedding.

I'm told I fell sound asleep when Aunty, Uncle and the best man, my Mum and I travelled back to Brighton on the last bus. I must have slept all the way as my next memory is waking up in my back bedroom in Coventry Street. Dad had met our bus at the bottom of Lover's Walk and carried me up the steps and all the way into my bed.

After I told Granma all about the ham and tongue tea, she told me about the day she married my Grandfather Thomas Cowley. She told me the first meal after a wedding is called, 'a Wedding Breakfast,'

It was impossible for young newlyweds to find a home of their own in the years after the war, so like many others Roy and his new young wife were given the two top rooms in Aunt Hetty and Uncle Arthur's house, whilst the two generations shared the kitchen for cooking and eating along with the back kitchen bathroom and the lavatory on the landing.

As soon as he could find time from his new job at home in Wolverhampton, Tich, Roy's war time buddy, came to Brighton to meet his old mate's family. And what an introduction to Southern life that turned out to be.

Tall and long in the leg, Roy was a younger version of my Dad. They were the kind of chaps, so full of energy, who took the stairs two at a time; the family were quite used to that. One other thing that seemed the norm was Aunt Hetty's way of sitting in the lavatory on the landing, with the door wide open. She didn't like being in small enclosed spaces.

Roy, having walked Tich up over the hill from the railway station to the house and dumping his bag just inside the front door, said to his pal,

"Follow me. Milly'll be up in our sittin' room, top front." And off he went at his usual pace, up the stairs two at a time with Tich hurrying to catch up one stair at a time like a normal person. At the turn of the landing Roy's visitor came face to face with an open door and Hetty sitting on the lav', knickers round her feet, reading the paper. At the sight of an unknown face she slapped the newspaper over her head which didn't do her modesty any good at all. While Tich, quick as you please, said,

"Mornin' Mrs Levett." and carried on up the stairs without missing a step.

So another humorous turn of Hetty's character entered our collection of family stories.

"You haven't met her brother yet." Roy laughed as he and Tich marched round to the Port Hall Tavern where Roy knew he'd find his Uncle Artie on Saturday lunchtime. Standing on the doorstep with my glass of orange squash I had never heard so much telling of events and tales that generated such laughter. Miss Cole warned 'the boys' to watch their language, "There's a little lady in earshot." she said. Nevertheless when closing time arrived at half past two the company from all bars stood outside reluctant to leave, still listening to the two young recently demobbed airmen telling about their jaunts with their dance band on the airbase.

Looking at his watch somebody said,

"Here, you'll have that new young wife of yours after you Roy!"

"If she's got any sense she'll have put 'is dinner in the dog."

Chortled Mrs Wood as she locked the pub doors behind them all.

BOOK THREE: 1941 – 1952

21

Premonition

Something unusual stood in the sunshine, out on the pavement, in front of our neighbour's house; a big high up modern baby carriage. We children gathered round, some standing on tiptoe, to peep at the baby. Its' Granny came out on the step to watch us, the usual tab of a cigarette hanging from inside her upper lip, it waggled as she spoke. The baby's young Aunty, my school friend, had her finger clutched in the baby's tiny hand, its little feet drumming happily on the pram's mattress. I ventured my hand into the pram to touch the baby toes,

"Don't do that you silly girl." I withdrew in shocked haste, "You'll make the baby cross-eyed." The Granny barked. Her roaring voice took my breath away. My heart felt like water and I was for a moment rooted to the spot. It was just a little tickle. The other children either hadn't noticed as the bark wasn't directed at one of them or they had taken in the information as a fact.

After everyone else drifted away to skipping and bead swapping games I wandered back inside our house.

When I next saw Granma she was stooping beside a low fire stirring her midday soup. She waited, she was a good listener but I wasn't quite ready to put my query into words. Granma ate her soup with a touch of salt; I had watched her ways so many times. Mum left us to talk while she did a bit of shopping, to save Granma having to go out in the cold winter weather.

Sitting together beside the fire and I told her about the baby, the tiny toes and the neighbour with the hanging cigarette that left a white smudge on her top and bottom lips when she threw away the end.

"Cross eyes!" Granma's chair nearly tipped over backwards as she threw back her head laughing so much. "Wherever did she get that old wives' tale from? Take no notice, that's not possible. It's her first grandchild, I expect she's just jealous, wants all the joy for herself."

"Granma," I ventured slowly, for I had to tell someone, "Granma, I'm going to have a baby one day but it's going to be wrong and it's going to die." In my child's mind I could only picture the 'wrong,' as if the baby was going to be – like – a – *donkey*, something very different. Far ahead, into the future, my thoughts told me I would then have two more children, a boy and a girl. Granma, never fazed, listened thoughtfully,

"Well, my sweeting you are very fortunate to be forewarned." She smiled a knowing smile. It was quiet in her room beside the comforting fire and the bed quilt, made from all the years of family remnants.

After she had poured the boiling water from her little black kettle on the leaves and given the tea in the pot a stir, she sat back in her chair.

"Keep what you know to yourself," she said quietly, then after a pause, "until it's resolved." Sipping her tea from her old tea dish, she added, "There are people who won't understand."

Part Four

BOOK THREE: 1941 – 1952

1

Keeping Gran in the picture

Mum and I went frequently to see Granma. We could see Gran's eyesight was failing and although there hadn't been any further episodes of waking the household in the nights, Mum realised Gran was still experiencing noises in her head. It seems Gran had come to terms with the fact that the noises were not other people's thoughtlessness or even bombs going off. She was also sensible enough to know if she wanted her freedom she had to keep her own counsel. She never complained and never seemed to mind being alone. One of her great escapes was still in telling her stories and listening to mine. I now took on another role of bringing her up to date with the happenings in Coventry Street.

"You remember Muriel Stebbings, Mum?" My Mother began. "The couple across the street, they've bi'n there since 1937. He works in the offices at the Railway, you know." She pressed on, because Gran was looking a bit vague, "You remember, Mrs Stebbings' Grandparents came from Glasgow, you met them in Queenies' shop and he told you about Frankie's Hotel being used for soldiers."

"Oh yes, I know who you mean, the man who told me that he and his wife worked at that Pottery making Willow pattern china."

"They told you they were both born on St Kilda." reminded my Mum.

"Ah, yes, so they were. Your memory's better than mine."

"Mr Stebbings is home." I cut in. "I can tell you all about it Gran."

"Can you?" Mum looked surprised but carried on, "I was going to say Artie and I saw him walking down the street."

"Who was dear?" Gran asked.

"Mr Stebbings." Mum laughed at the tangle she was getting her Mother into.

"Oh that's nice." answered Granma, "What a relief for Mrs Stebbings to have her husband home. Ah, I'm so pleased for them." Gran added with real feeling.

"But I can tell you all about it." I said eager to tell what I knew.

Gran relaxed back in her wicker armchair while Mum lit the small paraffin stove Gran used for cooking in the summer months, when she didn't have a fire in the grate. Summer days were not bright in this latest rented room at the front of the house, where the passing buses made the window frame rattle. I could just remember the first high bright airy back room she'd had in Buckingham Road, the sun shone in all the afternoon. Mum said that room cost 2/6 (two shillings and sixpence, 27½ p) and this one in Hollingdean was only 2/- (two shillings, 10p) a week and the lavatory was close by and not two floors away and shared with six other lodgers. But here, on its convenient bus route, the sun only shone through the curtains in the very early mornings.

"What's this all about then?" Gran asked, peering over the steaming liquid in her tea dish.

"We've got a fish shop in Upper Hamilton." I reported.

"It's Harry an' Connie Cutter's, they've opened a wet fish shop with his demob money." Mum added.

"And they're selling shrimps too!" I told Gran.

"Mm, I love shrimps." Gran said as she dreamily took another sip of tea.

I knew how she loved shrimps because she had told me how her Grandmother used to take all the grandchildren collecting shrimps and shellfish in the rock pools in Pevensey Bay and how they would make a big soup in the kitchen at the Lamb Inn. "Tell us about the shrimps, or was it Mrs Stebbings?" Gran prompted.

~O~

Granma was right, as it turned out the story was actually about Mrs Stebbings.

2

Shrimp Feast

"Mr Cutter lets us have a big bag of shrimps for threepence – cos that's all the money we had. We sat on the steps at No. 5 head 'n' tailin' them."

"Why do you sit over the road on Mrs Stebbings' steps?" Mum asked.

"'Cos there's nobody there 'n' we don't get shoved off." I told her. "Sandy and I make the boys put all the bits in the newspaper so's there's no mess 'cos the boys are so busy fillin' their gobs."

"Don't say gob, it's not a nice word for a little girl to use." Mum butted in.

"Sandy says it." But Mum told me,

"She gets it from her brothers you leave those words in their house."

"Anyway, shrimps are nice with a drink. We pass the monster bottle round for a swig between mouthfuls." Mum frowned and tutt'ed at the word 'swig'."

"Does Queenie still make her yellow green fizz drinks?" Gran asked.

"It's cheaper 'n the Fryco's, we can't afford that. Well, when we were sitting there the other day I heard this little voice coming from behind us say, 'Gis some.' Jimmy, he jerked his elbow inter Sandy's ribs."

'You got your share.' he told her, and she said,

'Stoppit. That 'urt. I'll tell Mum.' and he told her,

'Well don't be greedy then.'

'Shut up Jimmy, she didn't say that.' his pal Bob said.

'She did, I 'eard 'er.' So I said,

'No it weren't Sandy, 'er mouth didn't move.'

'Then you 'eard it too?'

'Yeah but it weren't Sandy.' Bob agreed with me. He was gobbling away at the last of his handful. Joey, squatting on the bottom step, he hadn't heard Sandy and Jimmy's little spat.

'Good ain't they?' remarked Joey as the monster bottle was handed down to him to take his turn for a drink. He choked on the bubbles down his nose making us all laugh.

'Go on. Gi's some,' said the voice again. It was a bit louder this time, so we all stopped and looked at each other. Then we looked towards Bob who was pointing up at the front door.

'Look.' he ordered in a rasping whisper, 'There's eyes inside that letter box.' His expression made us crick our heads and twist round to see.

'Shrimps are my favr'its,' said the voice – 'Gis some.' Sandy, nearest the door, said she could see the eyes of an old woman, 'An' they look sad eyes.' Without saying anything more Sandy took her last three shrimps in the tips of her fingers and held the little pink fish near the opening, but not too near just in case the flap snapped down and caught her fingers. She knew all about catching her fingers in things when her brothers played jokes on her. Two fingers and a thumb came through the letter box and gently took the offering. No 'thank you' was returned, just a murmur of satisfaction as the letter box flap slowly closed. After a bit Sandy wondered whether the old lady would like some more. I said I had some left so Sandy suggested, 'better ask.' I pushed open the letter box and looked in. It was quite light on the stairs and along the end of the hallway, a lady, not as old as I had expected, was sitting on the bottom stair slowly chewing. Her eyes were closed and the look on her face was pure bliss.

'Want some more Mrs?' I called. Whoops, I must have made her jump her eyes flew open in astonishment.

'More what?' she asked, a bit nonplussed. So I told her, 'Shrimps of course.'

'What's shrimps?' I could see a vacant look on her face. Jimmy was standing beside me an' said, 'Silly ol'e tart.' His Dad says things like that, calling ladies tarts."

"Naughty little boy." Granma said.

~O~

This odd little meeting through the letter box, brought us in halfway through, what we discovered, was a heart breaking story that started back in 1940, before I was born, and here it was, still playing itself out at the end of 1946

~O~

"The first time we met Mr Stebbings," I told Granma, "Was one evening we were playing out late. Mr Stebbings came home from work early. As he turned to walk up the steps the letter box shut with a sharp snap. I saw him look up at the door. Sandy ran over to Mr Stebbings and called to him,

'When you go out termorra Mr, will you leave the key so's we can go in an' keep your Mrs, company?' And I said,

'We'll do er shoppin'.'

'Nah, there's nobody 'ome.' Mr Stebbings fibbed, 'cos we knew there was, and Jimmy told him, 'Yes there is Mister. There's a lady locked in that house.'

Mr Stebbings looked really surprised, 'n' said, 'Oh dear – don't tell the whole street or they'll all want to know about my wife.'

'She's orlright.' Sandy told him. 'We've been keeping her company while we bin on holidays. She likes watchin' us play at hopscotch.'

'School starts again next week.' I said, 'an' she wants us to get some things in for her.' Mr S leant back against the wall. He seemed to be thinking,

'Orl right,' he said, 'just let me get out of my work clothes an' 'ave a wash, an' I'll come out to talk to you? OK, right?' We looked at each other, surprised at such language from an English man.

'Sounds like a yank.' Whispered Jimmy, who knew all about soldier talk.

As it was double summer time we were still out playing when my Dad started walking along to the Port Hall Tavern, he was surprised to see me and asked,

'Does Mum know you're still out?'

Johnny said, 'Look there's Mr Smith, it must be 9 o'clock.' Dad laughed – so did my Mum and Granma when I told them this story.

Dad was so regular in his habits, all the street knew the time by my Dad.

'Our Mum says we can tell the time by you Mr Smith. Does Mr Stebbin's go down the pub at 9 o'clock too?' Jimmy asked.

'No matey. Why? What's going on?' Dad laughed enjoying his new status. That's when Mr Stebbings came out to see us.

Dad hung back because it wasn't his business – the two men just greeted each other in the usual way.

'Evenin' Squire.' Mr Stebbings said, as my Father was an older man.

'Evening, Mr Stebbings.' Dad.replied. Mr Stebbings looked a bit upset, maybe he'd been havin' 'words' with Mrs S. He handed us a piece of paper so we moved towards him.

'Thanks for your offer kids. P'raps you'd get these bits 'n' pieces for the wife but I can't let you in.' He looked across at my Dad saying, 'Muriel might want to go out. She'd forget her way back.'

'Best be safe.' Dad agreed. He said later to Mum he could see how sad the man was about his wife."

~O~

After the strange encounter with the shrimps, there was something else I noticed while having conversations with Mrs Stebbings through her letter box. All the unusual items piled down each side of the stairs; a bag of flour and a loaf of bread, a rolling pin and a frying pan; items from the food cupboard, a sugar bowl, salt and pepper pot, a butter dish and tins of peas, beans and corned beef. It looked a real jumble. Then there was the comment Mr Stebbings made about not allowing his wife out as she might not find her way home.

The question Mum and Granma both wanted to know was...

3

What happened to Muriel in the years 1940 to 46

When Reg Stebbings came home from work the night after we children had given his wife the shrimps, he found a meal waiting for him on the kitchen table. He had been demobbed and home for three months and this was the first time his wife had made him a meal and there she was sitting quite still, at the other end of the table. The food was stone cold, but after he had reheated it over the top of a pan of boiling water the meal was perfectly acceptable. All the while Muriel Stebbings sat at the other end of the table watching her husband eat his dinner in complete silence; although he could see his wife was more content than he'd seen her for many weeks.

'Thanks love, that was really nice.' She did not respond. He realised Muriel must have used the gas to cook the food and knives to do the preparation. He thought he'd been very careful to hide anything Muriel could hurt herself with. She had obviously found his hiding places. But the gas, Oh gawd! He'd forgotten that. So he decided it better to leave her a hot drink in the morning and turn the gas off at the main before going to work. Plain tap water wouldn't hurt her to drink for the rest of the day. Reg felt relieved to see a change in his wife; she even spoke to him in the evenings and set the table, what surprised him was what she talked about. She was full of tales about playing hopscotch and fives stones, 'n' skipping games.

It was as if the life had come back to her.'

~O~

'At the outbreak of war Reg and Muriel decided to stay in Brighton, it being safer than their homes in London. Reg was one of the first to be called up. It was just at the time, early in September, that Muriel's sister, Sherry, asked to bring the family to stay in Brighton, out of London for safety, rather than let the Government evacuate her children and maybe send them to who knows where, and might even separate them, all six of them. So, when Reg left, Muriel wasn't left all alone. She had Sherry and her six kids. She was full of beans having a house full of the family she, herself, had always longed for. As Christmas came near and they'd heard from the Grandparents there hadn't been any bombs dropping around Clapham the kids wanted to go home to find their friends. Although it left Muriel alone in the house she was quite happy going back full time to her job at the tobacconists on the seafront. The owner and his male employees had been called up, that's when the women took over the men's jobs and besides Muriel wanted to earn some money of her own because next summer her parents and grandparents had said they would join her sister and the kids in Brighton for the summer holidays. Reg had a few days leave before he went overseas and was pleased to see his wife had plenty to keep her busy. Over the following months she wrote letters to her sisters and Gran and to Reg's Mum and Dad in North London. All replied full of questions about Hitler and rationing and the kids looking forward to the coming summer holidays.

Things were hotting up on the war front in 1940 but the Stebbings family still came for the summer holidays in August. Everybody mucked in together playing ball games up in Dyke Road Park or picnicking on the Downs at Tongdean or taking a long tramp as far as the Devil's Dyke to get everybody tired out; carrying picnics in old shopping bags, playing cricket and footer in the lovely soft grass. It didn't matter that the beaches were closed, the view of the sea and the air, up high behind Brighton, were better in the summer than dirty old London. Their Dad and Grandad decided to go back to Clapham earlier as they didn't want to leave the house empty for so long. When the holidays were over the children had to go back to school war or no war.

At the insistence of the boys their Mum and Grandmother relented and stayed until the last possible day to travel home.

Muriel's kitchen was chaos the morning the family were off back home, bodies running in every direction bumping the young ones sitting at the table glugging their cups of milk. Mother sighed saying they wished they could stay but Dad needs us home as well.

'Granny's looking tired,' Muriel's Mum said, 'she an' your Grandad need to get home to Glasgow next week. The house is a bit crowded when we're all there.' Sister Sherry was urging the boys to stop, "racketing about cos we've got a train ter cetch!" at the same time as she was trying to balance her baby on top of a shoulder bag, while heaving a huge case in the other hand. The boys each carried cases; girls with shopping bags, Mum with a shopping trolley and Muriel dragging a pushchair piled high with a toddler and more bags down the steps, Granny walking on behind leaning heavily on her old stag's antler walking stick.

'Leave the washing up,' Muriel said, 'I've got plenty of time to do that later.'

Instead of turning for home after waving the family off until the train disappeared she walked down Queen's road towards the sea. It was a beautiful sunny day there was nothing to go home for so she kept walking. It wasn't until the middle of the afternoon that she realised she was parched. What had stopped her was the sight of a large cut out of a tea pot on an 'A' board outside a small café. Drinking her tea Muriel noticed where a sign had been removed from the wall on the opposite side of the street. Looking down at her tea cup she saw 'Station Café' printed on the saucer. Glancing back at the blank space she wondered, 'what station?' because she didn't recognise the area. At the counter she asked the café owner the name of the station and was met with a blank stare.

'Where you from then Mrs?' he asked.

'I live in Brighton but I come from Clapham.'

'Oh I see,' the owner brightened up, 'Portslade dear, so long as you ain't a Jermin spy.' he laughed.

The walk back along the Old Shoreham road seemed interminable. Why she didn't get on the train back into Brighton station, she told Reg years later, she'll never know.

It was getting dark when she arrived home and found that in her haste she hadn't even closed the front door when they had all hurried out in the morning.

Exhausted from walking Muriel sat for a few moments in the fading light amongst the remains on the breakfast table. Taking a deep sighing breath she smiled at the memories of the busy holiday, then walked up the stairs to her bedroom where the curtains were still closed from the morning's rush.

She woke late next morning. Racing down into the kitchen she took a clean cup and drank half its contents of tap water, pulled a comb through her hair as she surveyed the result in the mirror over the sink. Then running a wet finger across each eyebrow Muriel left the house still pulling the straps of her sling back sandals onto her feet.

It was her day to open the tobacconist and the 'Mrs' had asked her to work two shifts through to late closing, saying she'd arranged to meet her husband on his short leave in London.

Back home after her long day tired and dishevelled, Muriel registered surprise there was no usual postcard she would have expected from the family to say they'd got home safe. Having returned home the night before after such a long walk she had slept so deeply that she had no idea London had been heavily bombed while she slept. Then, after this second long day she felt it was far too late to start clearing the family breakfast things away onto the draining board. Although she did pause to lay her hand on the cup her Mother had upturned on its' saucer, but had left saying there wasn't time to read the leaves. Muriel said, the irony of that unturned teacup didn't cross her mind until years later. After such a long day at the shop she was passed thinking, she was so dead beat.

One of the other part time staff had opened the shop the next day so when Muriel took over after lunch she didn't know that the Mrs hadn't returned and nobody thought to tell her.

Few male customers stopped for more than a word or two of comment about the war situation and the weather. Muriel hadn't taken a great deal of notice of those who made passing comments to one another about the heavy bombing. She closed up in the usual routine when the owner was away. Arriving back to the house, still deeply darkened by blackout curtains that had remained closed since the early hurried departure of the family two days previously, and it being a moonless night shedding no light, even into the kitchen window, Muriel walked straight up the stairs to bed pulling the clothes of her unmade double bed around her and immediately fell fast asleep.

A renewed vitality surging through her with the morning sun, Muriel was throwing a handful of soda in the enamel washing up bowl, and about to pick up the boiling kettle off the gas ring, when she heard a letter plop onto the door mat. The kettle could wait while she went through from the kitchen to where only the fan light above the front door was shedding the bright morning sunlight down onto the door mat. The letter was post marked Clapham, but the writing not in a hand she recognised. Leaning against the kitchen sink Muriel read –

'Dear Muriel. I expect you have had the awful news by now but I had to write to say how deeply sad we are that your family were caught by the dreadful bombing on the 15th. We were lucky here at our end of the street but Mr Barker was doing his rounds just passing your house and he caught it too, All our love dear, from Mrs Canning at number 42.

Muriel had to read the letter over and over to believe her eyes. She kept seeing each member of the family having their breakfast; hearing their words, the boys' yelps as they messed about at the table. Sherry telling them to behave and Billy should help with Gloria luv, 'she's spillin' 'er drink'. Gran saying, 'they're excited to see the steam engines agin, so don't go on at 'em dear.' and Mum saying she was sorry to leave but Dad needs us, 'ome luvvy, and how she kept putting Muriel off about reading the tea leaves.

Muriel stood by the sink for so long, numb in body and mind as if she were drugged, until the sun had got round to the back yard catching a pane of glass in Reg's cold frame, sending a sharp beam of light into Muriel's eyes that got through to her brain. The clock on the dresser told her it was half past twelve, waking her memory to the realisation that time had flown by and she had to be on at the tobacconist for her regular shift by half past one. Just time to get down to the seafront and take over from Stella. Stella had to be away and home to get the shopping and a meal before fetching her kids from school. Muriel walked to the Dials missing the bus stop, her distress so distracting that she walked on up over Dyke Road by the Clock Tower and down West Street, all on automatic.

Strange, the shop door was closed. It was a lovely day they would usually have the door open. The sign on the door read, CLOSED. Muriel stood staring. Stared for so long the man from the café by the bus station next door came out.

'Muriel?' he said, 'Muriel love. The 'Mrs' never came back from London. Solicitor or somebody came an' put that padlock on the door yesterday, late.' She hadn't noticed the padlock and hardly made any response to the kind café owner who was saying, 'come in an' 'av' a cuppa dear.' Later the cafe owner told the local newspaper reporter that the shop assistant at the Tobacconist seemed so shocked she just walked away in a daze.

Watching Muriel's dejected back make the slow ascent up West Street all the cafe owner could do was return inside and carry on serving his regulars and wonder how long he'd be in business with fewer and fewer people passing by.

Once inside her own front door Muriel sat down on the bottom stair, cupped her chin in hands, resting elbows on her knees she stared into the distance.

A sharp rap on the front door shook her out of silence. Opening the door a crack she was surprised to see such a short telegraph boy, his pill box hat resting on his ears, 'Telegramme Mrs.' Taking the small yellow envelope she pushed the door to close it. 'Please Mrs,' the boy's urgent voice called, 'you have to read it and tell me if yer want ter send a reply.' So dutifully Muriel opened the envelope.

"Mr and Mrs Stebbings killed in bombing. No effects retrievable. Joe Stroud neighbour."

'No reply.' She told the boy.

'Thanks Mrs, Toodleloo.' Off down the steps he skipped on to his clankety old red push bike and away back down to the Ship Street telegraph office.

Muriel went back through to the kitchen, filled the kettle and put another spoonful of soda onto the one she hadn't used twenty four hours before. Silence clung around her like cold wet cotton wool stifling her movements getting slower and slower as she worked through the breakfast plates, cups and saucers. Carefully picking her Mum's cup and saucer from the table where she had sat having her breakfast that last morning the tea leaves stuck in the bottom of the cup. Muriel's Mum would have seen signs telling about her daughter's trials ahead. She was good at reading the leaves.

'What does it say Mum?' Muriel stopped. She had spoken to the empty chair. 'You wouldn't tell me would you?' She said accusingly to the chair.

Then the floodgates opened and Muriel cried her heart out. There was nobody she could tell. All her family were gone. Reg was his parent's only child and he was away. She had never known if he had any other relations. Muriel cried until she was drained. It wasn't until the early hours when she found she was deathly cold standing at the sink finishing the washing up in cold water.

For the next five years her Mum's cup and saucer remained unwashed on the kitchen table where she had put it down, until Reg returned.

Muriel found herself a job tucked away in the back office at the wholesale meat market in Russell Street. She'd always been good at figures, now she could lose herself in columns of figures. Starting early in the day, going off in the hours of darkness before anybody else in the street was up, sometimes passing Mrs T's husband Albert on his way home from his night shift. She didn't have to start so early but she liked the busy meat market, the laughter and men only back chat. Joining the office workers when they came in later at seven as the market sales had all but finished. That's when she stuck her nose in the books toting up the sales and balancing the books. Although she could go home by lunchtime, Muriel often lost herself around the town arriving home again in the dark. When the war came to an end the men returned and Muriel wasn't needed anymore, but she got up just the same, walked down to the meat market each morning until one of the returned soldiers, who had never known her to work with, gave her a playful slap on the bottom telling her to get back to the kitchen. After that she wandered amongst the bomb damaged buildings along the streets, sometimes sitting beside bonfires with homeless people.

-O-

'Muriel. Hallo Muriel.' Reg found the front door unlocked so quite expected to find Muriel at home. The house was blackout dark, so he switched the light on at the bottom of the stairs and was surprised, let alone puzzled, to see each stair cluttered up either side with opened and unopened groceries: sugar, flour, tea, sugar bowl, salt pot, open jam pot with a spoon in, frying pan, bread board – leaving just enough space one footstep wide at the centre of each tread to use the stairs. In the kitchen he found crockery piled in the sink and the cups and saucers on the draining board covered in dust. The table was laid in a sort of readiness around one cup and saucer unwashed green mould crusted under a layer of dust.

By the time Muriel arrived home Reg had made their double bed. Looking in to the other rooms he saw the beds and camp beds rumpled as when they had last been used by the Clapham members of Muriel's family. The chamber pots under the beds were dry and dusty with a yellow rime halfway up their sides.

Although it was dusk he was out in the little lean-to greenhouse sowing seeds in pots he'd first had to clear of five year old dry soil. She didn't see his kit bag in the hall at the bottom of the stairs or notice that all the items she had left up the sides of the stairs had been cleared away or even that the kitchen light was on and the back door open. Muriel's nose wrinkled, she paused to give the air another sniff before filling the kettle and lighting the gas. Immediately he heard her movements Reg was at the back door.

'Oh hallo Reg', she said nonchalantly as if he'd just been across to the shop.

'Muriel?'

'Like a cuppa?' She asked as she went back into the hall to hang up her coat. On returning to the kitchen Reg was quietly pouring boiling water into the teapot. Muriel stopped dead in the doorway giving a startled scream,

'Who're you?' she shrieked, she looked terrified.

Reg was absolutely shocked. He grabbed hold of his wife's shoulders pulling her toward him in an effort to stop her screaming, but he could see she was truly frightened of him. She said she'd call a Policeman.

The next day Reg took Muriel to the Doctor.

He told Reg there was nothing he could give Muriel except he could commit her to a special hospital. Reg wouldn't hear of it.

That's when he decided to lock her in when he went to work each day. Some days she recognised him and some days she didn't.

BOOK THREE: 1941 – 1952

4

The outcome

A few weeks later Mr Stebbings knocked on our door. He had a parcel under his arm. He told my parents what had happened to his wife over the past five years and how watching the children playing in the street had helped her out of her depression. "If it wasn't for the children in the street – well, I don't know where we'd be." He put the box on our table saying, "My parents-in-law had been so pleased to meet your Mum that time when they were down here on holiday, and havin' that talk over old times about the Willow china. The wife 'nd I thought your mother would like to have Grandad's six blue and white cups and saucers, as a keepsake like. We've decided to go back to live in London and I think it best to leave behind all the things that might make Muriel sad again. Hope you don't mind my bringing these to you."

"Aw no," my mum replied, "Mum will be thrilled to have the Willow. We'll be sorry to see you go."

"Good luck." said Dad shaking hands, like men do.

Mum didn't take the box of Willow pattern cups and saucers to Granma; her room only had space for bare necessities.

"Well," sighed Granma, "that was a story and a half. Still I'm glad to hear Mrs. Stebbings got her husband back, even though she had long wait."

"But I wished we'd known about her family loss though Mum, we could have called in and helped her." Dolly said.

"Yes, you're right dear, but we don't like to pry into other people's lives."

"Shame we don't; sometimes a bit of nosiness can help us do a good turn. Let's hope Muriel Stebbings will start a family now. I suppose we'll never know."

"But kind of him to give me the Grandparent's Willow china, Lily ought to have them one day."

BOOK THREE: 1941 – 1952

5

Could no news be good news?

Unlike Muriel Stebbings, Doris Smith was a woman whose husband had so far, not come home; nor had she heard any word of him, so she had nothing to celebrate. In the circumstances she was glad she lived deep in the countryside well away from the noisy celebrations. She had no knowledge of her husband, whether he was alive or dead nor even that he had, in fact, been dossing on a bombsite near St Nicholas' Church in Brighton for a week since he arrived back in England.

Bud Smith could not bring himself to go home. While aboard ship on his way home from the Far East he stood leaning heavily on the railings watching the Lancashire coast come slowly into focus. After the bright harsh light above the wet steamy jungle, this dull yellow grey scene emerging before him; grey green river, dirty buildings, crushed any spirit he might have felt rising at the thought of his old life. It was six years since he and the lads had sailed out of Liverpool; they were young innocent nineteen, twenty year olds, now, glancing round at the few faces he knew from the original bunch, these men looked as if they were well into their eighties. Like himself, hardly recognisable. How he could meet Doris, he just didn't know? It wasn't so much he couldn't face her but more like, how would she see him. She'd be twenty five by now and looking forward to welcoming home a brawny twenty seven year old soldier. Instead he could pass for her grandfather – pass for – more like she'd pass him by. She'd not recognise him. He couldn't do it he couldn't expect her to welcome home a bag of bones. No hair to speak of, no energy, a wreck of a man consumed by nightmares. Bud had not let Doris know when he would be arriving home. She would still be waiting and hoping at home in Chailey, where she had stayed in their tied cottage throughout the war. At the time Bud was called up in 1939 he had been a carter on Miller's

Estate Farm and recently started training for the new tractors at the Smithy's, on their engineering apprentice scheme. The couple's hopes had been high that Bud could better himself and become an Agricultural Mechanic. Tipped off and aided by Lady M up at the Manor where Doris was personal maid to her Ladyship, he and Doris had got wed in '37, to get possession of the tied cottage that was only available to a married couple. Although they hadn't been exactly in love this opportunity offered prospects, so Doris and Bud tied the knot, maybe a little sooner than their families expected, but they liked each other enough, they got on well. Love came, but no children. He was glad of that, who'd want an old, old man to come back to a young family. Only two letters had reached him, one saying how she had kept the cottage so that she could look after the land army girls on the estate who were billeted with her; and the second letter told how she was more than Lady's maid, she had taken over as housekeeper at the Manor. Although Doris was only in her early twenties she had been given much more responsibility that kept her busy. Bud had heard the Americans were in England. On the train down to Brighton the thought went through his mind, what kind of image would he make against the Yanks?

When he arrived at Brighton Station he just couldn't cross to the Lewes line to go home and having so little energy in his wasted body he walked a short distance out of the station, aiming towards St Nicholas' Church where he had been baptized, but before he got there his strength failed him. Seeing a small group of people sitting together amongst the rubble on a bombsite he went and sat near them. Nobody spoke. After a while a friendly hand held out a half smoked cigarette toward him which he took with a grateful nod.

At dusk a small fire was lit, conversation was fairly sparse, he fell asleep but it wasn't long before he woke himself up in mid-scream. His original companions had now been joined by others all were astonished, sitting bolt upright, scared, staring at Bud.

"Don't do that again friend. The Police will move us on." But he did. Before midnight they'd told him it's you or us, and we're not moving en masse so Bud had to walk. He had to stay awake. The nightmares never would go away. He hadn't slept for months, years. That was something else he couldn't inflict on Doris.

Knowing his cousin finished work at midday on a Saturday, he sat on a gravestone in St Nicholas' Church yard watching the road and sure enough there was walking home from Cranbourne Street up over the Dyke Road. Bud knew Artie's walk, anywhere, he was a strong walker leaning slightly forward taking the weight of his plumber's bag on his back. Bud couldn't keep up he hadn't the stamina, so just followed on behind knowing he'd catch him up when he stopped to roll himself another cigarette. Artie was never without a cigarette.

The sight of his old childhood friend put a little bit of life in his step giving him the strength to walk up over the hill to the Seven Dials and on to Coventry Street. When he reached for the well remembered heavy old black door knocker Bud could see, Artie, always the proud craftsman, had been at work on his front door. He actually found himself smiling, feeling confident that some things in life; some people, never changed. He knocked. The door opened and Artie stood there looking at him – his face not quite blank.

"Hallo mate?" Artie said, still not recognising Bud.

"Art?" Bud croaked. Artie's hand fell from the door slowly he took the cigarette from his mouth. The two men looked at each other, only a few moments went by although it seemed longer.

"Who is it Art?" Dolly called from the kitchen. Then everything happened at once. Bud's legs began to buckle under him. Art flicked his fag back into the corner of his mouth and in the same instant caught Bud in his arms as he fell forward.

"Dol quick, give us a hand. It's Bud, he's come home."

Bud leaned back in the chair grateful for the cushions tucked round his back and under his skeletal legs. Dolly thought of everything.

That was the best fish and chips he'd ever eaten. It had gone down slowly. Dolly had only put a tiny amount on his plate she could easily see this man had eaten all but nothing over the last years. Artie watched with a twinkle in his eye.

"Damn it boy we're glad to see you back."

"You're all in Bud.' my Mum said, "C'mon I've made up the bed. Can you manage the stairs?" Artie gave Bud his arm so they took the stairs slowly together. Granma had vacated the room and

Dad had just finished painting the walls. It was to be my own first bedroom. But Bud's was the greater need. Mum had put a glass of water by the bed and Dad nipped back in the room with a bucket saying,

"No need to go further, use this. We'll do the rest."

"Don't close the door mate." Bud whispered.

"OK lad I'm right here. You're home now."

"He was asleep before I left the room." Dad told us when he came back down into the kitchen. Bud must have told Dad what to expect about his waking screaming so Mum soon had her coat on and mine on me. She took me to see the Mickey Mouse films at the Newsreel Cinema in North Street. I didn't witness his nightmares that Saturday afternoon neither did Bud's night time screaming often wake me while he was with us.

It is strange though, how the quietest voices travel when one's attention is attracted by unusual words. On warm evenings I often hung out of the spare bedroom window overlooking the back gardens. I watched cats stroll along the garden walls, often meeting each other with deep dark throaty snarls; Mum's may be taking washing in off the lines; a young man a few doors along, a radio ham, was always worth watching as he erected yet another arial. Further afield towards the Downs smoke rose from garden bonfires.

Below me in his small lean-to greenhouse Dad was tucking his cuttings into pots while Bud sat by the door sipping tea from a Willow pattern mug Gran had left in our kitchen. Bud commented that along with having Marmite again, the old Willow pattern china gave him a comforting feeling of home.

Overhearing, 'Bloody' and 'bastard; words my Father would never say in front of us, attracted my attention to the conversation coming from the garden below. 'The Emporer's bloody warrior subject did that. The Doc aboard the ship coming home said, 'Looks more like he used a bull's horn than a blade.'

'Jap bastard kept jabbin' that sword across 'is desk into my gut. I couldn't care less by then he just kept on – little at a time, deeper – little at a time, deeper 'n' deeper. Name and Number's all 'e got. If the infection killed me I'd be lucky and out of it. The one's that weren't lucky were those that got thrown in with the rats. They gnawed their way into a mate's guts while he was alive. At night I scream his screams. He was too weak to stop 'em see. Don't s'pose I'll ever get rid of that bloody screaming from my head.'

Although I couldn't know the reality behind what he was saying I was nevertheless riveted by the colourful emotion of the words. Bud told how sometimes the silence was a raging noise of pain, physical pain, in all parts of his body. He said the sun had no mercy, it etched the sight of broken bodies lying suppurating all around, onto the backs of his eyes.

'I felt numb, with the sun poaching me bloody brains. I can't get the vile stench out of my head.'

All these words came clipped by choking sobs until Bud had scoured out his mind and Dad was brimful of the Burma railway. I heard Dad later say to Mum he'd listened to help Bud recover. But Dad couldn't tell Mum Bud's stories they were too obscene. I know they were because truth and understanding came to me slowly along the years. Thank goodness I was too young to understand but not too young to hold the words and pictures in my memory.

Dad came home one evening saying he'd heard that the all night picture theatre was advertising for a projectionist.

"Isn't that for men in dirty raincoats?" Mum asked.

"That's not important Doll. It's somewhere Bud has to stay awake all night. Better he gets abuse from blokes in dirty macs than screaming half the neighbourhood awake every night."

Bud did go home to Chailey, but not for another 6 months; he was enjoying his job as projectionist. Dolly persuaded him to write to Doris,

"Just to let her know you're alive, Bud dear. She must be so worried."

He told Doris the situation and asked her to forgive him. So one Sunday morning, Dad went with his cousin on the number 20 Southdown bus over to Chailey. Doris was sitting waiting on the bank at the side of the cross-roads, with a little picnic basket. Bud nearly flunked it by refusing to get off the bus. Dad got off and went straight into the King's Head for a drink. When he got back onto the bus for the homeward journey he saw Doris and Bud walking hand in hand slowly along the road towards the gates of Miller's

Farm. A smiling Doris gave my Dad a wave as the bus moved off back towards Lewes.

A year later Doris wrote to say Bud had passed away in his sleep –

'He never did regain his strength. Somehow the dreadful depredation had weakened his body over the edge of return.' she wrote. *'But thanks, we've had these last twelve months together that I would never have missed. At least I was able to give him love and nursing to the end.'*

6

New plans, new life to lift our spirits

About the same time Bud's journey on the helter-skelter of human events was passing through our lives, the son of a neighbour had put his demob money towards a smallholding near West Grinstead. Our whole family were invited to have a Sunday bus ride over to visit Harry and Deirdre Greens' new home. Hopefully their journey would see them striding into a future full of happy bright heights on life's funfair ride.

Bursting with plans and hopes, the Green's showed us round the run down old house that stood in the middle of a woodland clearing. It looked like a rough field of all sorts, where chickens were penned away from ducks and a goat was tethered chewing its way further and further into deep scrub. A wind up well head in the centre of the yard provided crystal clear drinking water that Deirdre bucketed into a stone sink just inside the back door. An old cooking range, looking very down at heel, sunk into a chimney opening, intermittently belched out smoke and heat. At the far end of the kitchen the space under the wooden stairs was curtained off hiding a bucket lavatory. The property had no electricity either but as Aunty Hetty said, Harry and Dee were as happy as sand boys, "They'll put the hard graft into it, they'll make it work, you'll see."

During a heavy session of giggling adults using the bucket lav, I slunk out into the yard. After the dimly lit kitchen I had to stand for a moment to adjust my eyes, squinty against the bright sun. There had just been a sharp shower of rain and all around the foliage sparkled and danced in the sudden clear light. Wandering across the rough ground to the side of a half hidden ditch I became aware that the opposite bank was seething with little brown frogs, hundreds and hundreds of the tiny creatures, their shiny bodies slithering and sliding up and over each other scrabbling towards the light on the top of the bank and away. I crouched in the long wet grass listening to the trickling water deep in the ditch. I knew I was witnessing something secret only the silent furious struggle for life filled my conscious senses. I have no idea how long it was, I lost all sense of time. Only the echo of voices calling across the clearing between house and woodland and a hand grabbing my shoulder broke the spell. "We've been calling you for ages," a voice rasped in my ear. The family had been in a fury of their own to find me before we missed the last bus home.

The next time Mum and I visited Gran my mind was still bursting to tell what I had seen. I don't think my Mother really believed me about all those little frogs, but Granma, who had been a country child, did know exactly what I was saying, for my experience took her right back into her own childhood days.

"I remember when I was very young one spring on the Marsh watching that change from leggy tadpoles into frogs', she said. 'We children lay on the bank watching all these minute creatures starting their lives climbing up out of the water." This was the start of another Marsh story when again I was given entry into her world. We were the same age seeing the same things in that undisturbed secret place of the natural world.

It was after this outing into the countryside that I had a clear picture that one day I would leave the town and live in the country.

7

Time for new interests

For more than two years after VE day my father worked even longer hours. At least the dangers of war no longer hung over everyday life.

The men in the building trade, who had stayed on the home front, were working furiously, installing new restaurants: Still rooms, plumbing in hotel kitchens, new bathrooms and toilets. With all the men and women returning from the Forces, business and services had to expand to provide jobs and places for the survivors of war torn Europe to live. Brighton's hotels and guest houses required modern plumbing. The Council had to install new public conveniences around the town centre and seafront; large numbers of holiday visitors were expected to descend on the beaches, recently cleared of their barbed wire entanglements. On summer Saturdays and Sundays Queen's Road and West Street; the main thoroughfare from the station to the beach, became so crowded it was said you could walk on the heads of the crowd filling the road to the seafront, especially on Saturdays at midday when the trains arrived from London full of visitors.

Colleagues from before the war were returning home and young Apprentices were joining to be trained into the trade so Dad's days were made full of new stories bringing different angles on life; changed attitudes and new hope. Although the hours were long and often gruelling, he loved the variety in his job.

In 1948 I began to have my Dad home again in the long summer evenings. Now that he had time to pursue his own interests and Granma was no longer the green fingered gardener in residence, Dad took over our small back garden. By the summer the beds surrounding the tiny central patch of grass were full of magnificent blooms. Bright red and deep plumb coloured peonies; pure white peonies too, the elderly gardener who gave him the roots was surprised Dad had managed to get such blossoms in the first year of planting.

"I think you know a thing or too young Artie Smith?" I heard him say to my Dad, as he tapped the side of his nose with a questioning wink of one eye.

"Yes Mr Stevens you could say that. I always listened when you gave your gardening tips down the pub."

"Well done lad." Mr Stevens was very proud to have been of help.

But Dad did not spend all his new found leisure time on himself.

"Come on Skipper," he would call to me, "let's see what's happening on the Railway." This was the time we started watching the trains, standing together at the railings in Stanford road, above the railway lines opposite the main signal box. Dad was full of knowledge and a great companion. It was exciting having everything explained as we watched the shunting activity, hearing the sharp clacking when the trucks made contacts. Sounds I had heard from the back of Coventry Street since my earliest days. The sounds I can hear even now, 65 years later, etched on my audio memory.

Shshisst 'n'hisss, as steam was released from valve gear. High pitched squeals of brakes against steel rails when signals clanked with their metallic, CLUT. Away to our right a deep muffled rhythm wafted across the air, softly at first; thud-thud, thud-thud, thud-thud, before the engine came into view clattering as it crossed high onto the London Road viaduct and sped over the valley. Now, in the falling dusk, I was actually seeing where those long remembered sounds were coming from, even seeing the people lit up inside the glowing carriage windows, and I wondered if they knew that sparks were flying out from the engine's funnel, backwards over their heads.

Earlier in the evening, down in the deep chalk cutting below us, the thunder of a heavy locomotive urging its trucks and carriages forward vibrated up through the Chalk cliff. It was like watching your own toy layout in the backyard.

Mr Watson who lived in the last house above the railway cliff at the end of Stanford Road used to have a model railway in the corner of his front garden. From my earliest days I remember coming out of the infant school gate with my friends, each pulling at our Mother's hands to cross the road to let us look down into Mr Watson's layout of little cottages and sheds with their back gardens full of little bushes, lawns and flowers. Sometimes he would have a small train running round the lines and through the tunnel. But I liked the real thing best, because exciting sounds that came with the sights my Dad would be describing and the engines we could see, pointing out what was happening.

From a point down at the bottom of Chatham Place we could see across to the great turntable where the engines, after they emerged gleaming from the washing shed, were turned around, ready to couple on their tenders full of satin black coal. In my imagination the great long engines were huge beasts filling with steam snorting fire and smoke.

"See that little yellow engine, the one you said darts about all over the place? That's a shunting engine. It's a 0-4-0 because it's only got 4 wheels. Bigger engines that pull lots of carriages on the main lines like the long one over there have to have more wheels, four at the front, six driving and two under the cab at the back so it's called a 4-6-2. And see that goods train going over the viaduct to London Road Station," he said, looking towards the sea, "it's an 0-6-0 and it's called a tank engine because it has its water tanks either side of the long round boiler."

A sharp, 'clank clut,' sounding from a signal high on a pole warned us that a train was about to come into view on our left under the bridge at Port Hall. The engine was travelling quite fast gliding majestically, its rhythmic connection to the lines slowing rapidly towards the station. On a different line closer to the cliff another train was leaving the station gathering speed smoothly along the level track. Standing opposite our viewing point on Friday evenings, during the summer months, one of the 4-6-2 engines with its huge long boiler in front of the driver's cab, stood taking on water into its boiler from a large tank raised high on brick pillars. I wondered why it took such a long time to fill and was told the journey to the West Country was many miles to travel and that was also why behind that it pulled an enormous heaped coal tender. Our neighbour, Peter Hollamby and his fireman Bill Turner often took the West Country Express. It was an important responsibility to make sure their passengers engine would have a comfortable secure journey to their holidays.

I had fetched something for Mrs Hollamby from the shop one day and found Mr Hollamby sitting on their back doorstep polishing his boots. He knew Dad and I watched the trains so as I sat at their kitchen table drinking a glass of his wife's Lemon Barley water he told me how the Driver had to know the 'roads' well before he could become a Driver, (he referred to the railway lines as roads.) Before that, he said everyman had to be a Fireman and learn when the road was level, or when they were approaching steep or gentle gradients ready to raise the steam pressure with his fire or keep it steady, as well as being aware of when his Driver would be using the brakes.

Before even that stage Mr Hollamby explained that every man working on the foot plate had to know all the sounds of every part of an engine, and learn how to clean it inside and out. In fact get to know the engine and all the mechanical parts intimately. It was a very long apprenticeship towards a great skill and responsibility, before he was satisfied was his engine ready to go. When the great locomotive pulled all those carriages out from Brighton station along the main line below the cliff, his words always made me think of the preparation the driver and fireman carried out to take all their excited families safely on that night express to Cornwall. My Father might have had only one daughter but he talked with me like I was a pal. I enjoyed hearing the knowledge and the details of other people's jobs.

Our own next door neighbour retired in 1947 having worked on the railways for 45 years. He had been a Ganger, in charge of work gangs building and repairing the 'roads'. He told me when he was working in the single track tunnels he had to lay down flat between the lines if he felt the vibrations of a train approaching. Dad said all the rail men along our street were proud to be Railway men. I will never forget how on the day of a funeral of any Railway man his colleagues would stand in a group, at the corner outside Perry's the Bakers, hats off and heads bowed, as the hearse passed by. They were proud dedicated skilled workmen.

Although their jobs were dirty they always went to work
in beautifully polished boots. It was a regular thing to see our
neighbours sitting at their back doors, wooden box of polishes,
brushes and shining rags on the step beside them, cleaning their
boots when they got home. Even my own father, who was a
plumber, included this in his wash and shaving ritual at the end of
the day. It had been when Granma was watching Dad cleaning his
working shoes that Gran told us how, her Grandfather, the Looker
on Pevensey Levels, would always clean and hang his thigh boots to
dry as soon as he arrived home. "He had three pairs," she said, "one
pair drying, one pair waxed and one pair wearing. He needed good
dry feet at all times to do his work well."

Life wasn't all train watching. I was making quite a collection
of glass marbles. Dad said if I collected a few more we could have a
game with them when it was too cold to stand out in the evenings
watching the trains. When the girls gathered together swapping
beads in each other's houses during the winter months, there always
seem to be the odd pretty glass marble in their boxes. I think they
came from their brothers who liked to get rid of any 'pretty' item
from their bags of marbles. So I set about swapping my plainest
beads for the marbles. Dad scrounged four pegs, used in the wooden
beer barrels, from Miss Cole at the Porthall Tavern. He stood the
pegs on the floor behind the front door and we sat side by side on
the bottom stair at the opposite end of the passage and rolled the
marbles along the lino to knock the pegs down. Just like having our
own skittles alley. It gave us hours of fun.

I found a group of animal cut outs in one of my comics which
I stuck on card and Dad stood these in little wood blocks then,
made us each a catapult. We spent some evenings shooting the
cut outs down with little pellets. I made the pellets with flour and
water dough and baked them hard, when Mum was using the
oven. The only time Mum joined us was to play Ludo, which we
set up in front of the fire on cold winter evenings. It really needed
four players so we each took a turn to throw the dice for the fourth
player, calling it Chu-Chu (our cat's) turn.

Most summer Sunday afternoons, Mum would be able to
persuade Dad to walk up to Tongdean; a difficult job when he had

spent his week walking carrying heavy tools. We hardly ever walked very far but he would walk with me down the hill to the windmill with my drawing book. I still have a pencil sketch of Waterhall farm buildings. It was a pity, we couldn't sit for very long on the steep bank beside the road above the farm, it wasn't a very pleasant place as it smelled mucky, littered with all the dirty old mattresses, broken bedsteads and furniture people had dumped in amongst the scrubby hedgerow. But when one of our neighbours set up a small tea hut at Tongdean cross roads at the top of the hill, Dad was more easily persuaded, there being a relaxing cuppa on route. It was nearly always crowded with a queue waiting to be served, but it was worth the wait. Dad said the young man had set up the hut with his demob money; rather like our friends the Green's son putting his money into a small holding, but not quite like this man was all on his own, he had no helpers; a few chairs and tables outside and just enough space inside the hut for a counter; a large gas powered water urn, a couple of large brown enamel tea pots, a quantity of thick white china cups and saucers, a bowl of sugar and a teaspoon on a chain for stirring. Those summer Sundays seemed to be the hottest ever. We often wondered how that man managed all day; apart from answering, 'Coming up,' to a request for, 'Two cups please,' or 'One cup no sugar,' he never had time make any further conversation, he was concentrating hard on making pot after pot of tea and sweating so profusely behind his counter in that tiny hut, trying, but never quite managing, to keep ahead of the queue, serving cup after cup of tea to his customers. Dad said it was called, 'Enterprise and good luck to him.'

Sometimes when Dad had an easier week we walked on up to the Devil's Dyke. The story I was told about this deep cleft in the Downs was that the devil planned to dig a deep ditch, in the dead of night, to let the sea in through the Downs to flood Sussex. But he was startled by a cottager coming out of her back door to use the privy at the end of the garden; she was carrying a candle. The light was so bright that the Devil thought the dawn was coming up so he abandoned his digging and fled before he was caught. Deep wide lines of exposed chalk remained after the war, even into the 1950s, evidence of caterpillar tracks scoring the turf during tank driving practice. The steep sides of the Dyke were striped, white chalk, green turf from end to end.

Granma, a true Sussex woman, said, "The Devil should have known better, *we Sussex folks won't be druv.*"

BOOK THREE: 1941 – 1952

8

A new arrival

Roy and Mildred's first baby was due in early December.

On the morning she arrived there were great celebrations in the Levett's house.

But next morning news reached us in Coventry Street, the baby's Grandfather Jack hadn't returned from work the previous evening.

Jack was a well known figure on the Brighton scene. He boarded the bus to work at eleven each morning and caught one of the late buses from the Clock Tower after eleven most evenings. He was chief projectionist at one of the main Cinemas. The day he went missing was a surprise to many people throughout the next thirty six hours. Why? Well the story went like this.

Jack was Mildred's father and the morning Millie gave birth to her first baby, a daughter, the family raised their breakfast teacups, laced with a thimble full of whiskey, "Only a splash mind," warned Jack, "it's a working day." He laughed, his joy spilling over into a little dance round the kitchen with his wife Ruby.

Along his route that morning the regular folks gave him a wave, some noticed he was a little later than usual so was taking his stride with a bit of a jog.

"Hallo there Jack, just made it then mate?" The bus conductor joked as he clicked and handed Jack his ticket, taking the tuppence as Jack, although a bit out of breath, took the stairs up to the smoker's seats, as was his routine. What happened next was unusual, because, well before his destination, Jack started back down from the upper deck but before he reached the platform beside the conductor he appeared to trip, toppled down the last few steps, hitting his head on the steel edged platform as he fell onto the pavement. The Conductor rang the bell and shouted, so did many of the passengers, to make the driver stop. Jack lay unmoving on the pavement as one of the passengers said Jack was still breathing. Meanwhile the conductor had nipped across the road to a telephone box. The first person to arrive was a fresh faced young Police Constable, who found the bus crew and passengers all round a man lying crumpled on the pavement. Without a word the crowd parted for him and he knelt down to the prone figure, sniffed and said he could smell drink on him, "He's drunk." The bus driver and conductor objected, saying, no he couldn't be, it was only half past eleven. No pubs were open. People on the bus said Jack wasn't that sort, and anyway, he was on his way to work, "No not Jack." "No," said the conductor, "He's never. Not Jack." The Constable wasn't havin' any of it, so poor Jack; having no say in the matter, was hauled off to the Police Station. At the Station under the Town Hall, Jack was unable to stand up at the desk so he was just slung into a cell and left to 'sleep it off'. And of course he didn't. Later, in the day when the station night Sergeant came on duty, he did his rounds to look over his charges in the cells,

'You say this one's bin 'ere since midday. Still out cold, lazy 'erbert?' he said, as he gave Jack a few punches to wake 'im up. Jack only opened one eye so he was punched again and that closed the other eye, when the Sergeant took the prisoner by the front of his shirt, pulled him up to punch him again Jack's body slid straight to the floor.'

The family heard what had happened in the police cell from young Fred Saunders, another of the new police recruits, who had recently moved into our local community with his wife 'n' family; he'd had to accompany the Sergeant on his round. Now he didn't know much about the Sergeant or Jack, 'cos he was new to the area. It was also Fred who was yelled at to fetch a bucket of cold water and told to douse the drunken man down. The Sergeant shouted, 'take it outa that,' and locked the door on Jack once again.

Obviously Jack didn't come home that night, and when it was well past his time Mildred's Mum, Ruby, 'phoned through to the cinema manager, who luckily had stayed behind to tot up the night's takings, and was havin' a snifter with the manager of the nearby Ballroom.

'Nah Jack hasn't been in terday luv,' he told Ruby, 'wundered where 'ed got to. Not like Jack I'll admit. I 'ad ter do the projectors meself terday.'

'Well 'e went off ter work same time as usual, even though we'd b'in up celebratin' Millie's new babe. 'E 'ad a small tot in 'is tea ter wet the baby's 'ed then orf 'e went–.' but before she could say more the money in the 'phone box ran out and she was cut off. She got back from the 'phone box just as Tommy, Jack and Ruby's eldest boy, arrived home from visiting his fiance's parents. Close behind, coming up from the station were twin brothers Jim and John home on leave from National Service. All arrived at once to hear Ruby's worrying news about their Dad.

Tommy, no longer on active service, but not one to let things slide, suggested Mum stay put, in case Dad arrived home, while he and the twins jogged off in different directions round town where their Dad might have gone. He would get on his bike and go round the hospitals – 'out Hove too, if I don't find 'im in town.' But nobody had heard of Jack at the hospitals, even at Hove hospital. While the boys were going round town they each thought they might as well drop in at the Police Station. 'That's twins for yer, always thinkin' in tandem!'

At the Police Station they got the same answer, 'Nah, never 'eard of 'im.'

By the time they all arrived back home everybody was just going off to work. Roy caught up with Uncle Artie and told him to keep his eyes open for Jack. The three brothers couldn't sit still drinking tea in the kitchen, so while the twins got a wash 'n' shave Tom went up to the paper shop for some fags. Meanwhile Artie hopped onto the No. 38 bus and as the bus conductor was clipping him a ticket he said 'Allo Artie, know if your Jack's OK now?'

'No, what about Jack – I was going to ask you.' So Cyril Balcher quickly told Artie what happened. Then he rang his bell to stop the bus and Artie jumps off and ran back across the Seven Dials to home. All at the same time Tom was in the paper shop telling how his Dad's missing. Standing behind him was young Fred Saunders, just off duty.

'Oh my gawd, I bet that's 'im.' Fred said, spilling the beans on his Station Sergeant's actions.

'Wouldn't be surprised Tom,' the shopkeeper offered, 'we all know what he's like.'

Tom and Artie met on the pavement outside the house, at the same moment both saying,

'No, can't be Dad, 'e don't drink. Not in the mornin's anyway.' But Artie reported,

'Cyril said the Constable wouldn't call an ambulance, just hauled Jack off down the nick.' Ruby coming in from the back yard said, 'Yes 'e had.'

'Wot d'yer mean Mum?'

' 'E'd 'ad 'a nip o' whiskey in 'is tea – ter wet the baby's 'ed yesterdie morning.' Tom didn't let the conversation get any further. He was halfway out of the front door as one of the twins threw him a jacket then the boys followed.

At the Police Station nobody had heard of Jack, there was nothing recorded in the desk sergeant's night book.

'Got a bloke taken off a bus dead drunk', the desk sergeant read out when he turned the page back.

Their Father lay in a crumpled soggy mess where he fell after he had been knocked about the night before; both eyes blacked, covered in bile from being punched in the gut, not to mention bedraggled from the sluicing down. Beside him, an enamel mug full of cold tea and a chunk of dry bread. The Sergeant looked shocked, he obviously hadn't checked his cells when he came on duty and he wouldn't normally have taken the public down to the cells. It must have been Tom's demeanour now buttoned neatly in his Air Force jacket; the one Jim had thrown to him and the one with his medal ribbons. Was that it? Anyway all three of Jack's sons were standing there seething mad to find their Dad in such a state.

'He's been here for more than 24 hours hasn't he?' Tom said, not asking but telling. 'No drunk takes that long to pull out of ... Has a Doctor seen him?'

The Sergeant knew that had not happened and by now he was both pulling his professional reactions up sharp and realising this poor man needed serious attention.

'Let's get him upstairs then ...'

'No, leave him, don't touch him.' Tom had made sure his Father was breathing; he could hear an unusually gravelly sound and knew there could be a broken neck.

'Call the Doctor right now. I know it's your nick but he's my Father and he looks grim.' Tom held his ground. 'You two stay here', he told his brothers. The Sergeant called his Constable to stand by the cell door. 'Nothing must be moved' warned Tom as he followed the Sergeant back upstairs to call the Doctor.

The Doctor noted everything including all those present. His diagnosis on the patient stated. The prisoner had suffered a stroke. An ambulance took Jack away accompanied by Tom, but not before sending John to report to Jack's boss at the cinema, and Jim to hoof it up to Mum, 'Tell her we've found Dad and bring her to the hospital in a taxi'.

Jack was settled in a crisp clean bed in a side ward when the Doctor led Ruby to see her husband. She was shocked at the sight of him. She reported later that he looked like a prize fighter who'd been on the wrong end of the deal. Besides all the bruising his mouth was slurred to the side. He could recognise her but the look in his eyes as he tried to speak was of a frightened child. She'd seen it before when her own father had his stroke. Ruby could tell how bad it was. There were no flies on Ruby she knew what she was seeing.

Her three boys knew even more. Words like 'it's not going to stop here', 'somebody didn't do their duty last night'. The Doctor had said 'no alcohol did this – the man's been left too long. I can only hope your Father pulls through.' They wouldn't know the extent of the stroke for some days. 'He should have been brought into the hospital straight away.'

The officer, whose name nobody would speak, left the town rather promptly. We didn't hear where he'd been stationed. Jack never worked again. He was 56. Ruby went back to earning for them both. The Manager at the Cinema gave her a job as afternoon usherette and she made up her money working at the bar in the Ballroom evenings and weekends.

Jack's jovial character, topped off with the old war department demob issue pork pie hat; which had been donated with a plop on his head by a neighbour one day just after the war; remained as ever, his sense of humour never failed him. He was the nice bloke he'd always been. Mildred's baby saved Jack's self respect. He nursed that child like a mother hen, albeit with only one working arm because it was a necessity for him to prove his value in a busy family. Ruby asked her eldest son if he'd had a hand in Bill Standin's dismissal.

'No Mum I didn't touch him.' Tom said, 'I didn't have to. But when I saw Dad's blood and the vomit splattered down those ugly shiny bottle green cell walls; well, if he had been standing instead of that Station Sergeant stood beside me, I'd have given him a dose of what he gave our Dad.'

'I feel sorry for his wife, 'cos neighbours have heard what 'appened. You can see she's so ashamed.'

'She's probably better without 'im.' Tom announced.

'Well, she 'asn't followed 'im to his new job so they say.'

It was Old Miss Turk, Roy's Great Gran, who told Clara all about Jack's do.

The two old friends still had a game of cards together in Clara's room. Mrs Turk helped Ruby no end in massaging Jack's good arm and leg,

'Keep what's left of his circulation going.' Granma Turk said. The old nurse had witnessed many a Stroke victim in her day.

Jack's plight did not only go deep amongst the residents in our streets; what happened to him reverberated through the wider Brighton community, so many knew, and liked Jack.

On Christmas Eve when Mum and I stood beside aunty Ruby in the queue, waiting to collect our Christmas drinks orders at Findlater's, the Off Licence at the Seven Dials, people were going out of their way to touch Ruby's arm asking,

"How's Jack?" and making their feelings known with,

"Sorry to hear about Jack." Passing on their support to Ruby,

"How you going on love?" or, "How's the new baby, Granma?"

Christmas Eve was the only day Mum and I went shopping in the dark.

By the time the lights came on at six o clock, when the Off Licence was allowed to open, frost had already spread across the other darkened shop windows around the Seven Dials. Shoulders shivered in the cold air; people stamped their boots on the pavement, but the atmosphere was bright with laughter and cheeky joking in the patiently waiting gathering crowd.

While most customers walked out of the Off Licence carrying a bottle of Findlater's own, Mountain Blend of Scotch Whiskey, my Mum's order was the same every year; one bottle of Cockburn's Ruby Port to go with the Christmas pudding and if she had been able to save enough money, she bought her own favourite drink, a bottle of Dubonnet. When I was old enough I had a bottle of non-alcoholic ginger wine. I remember I didn't like it very much because it burnt my tongue. I would have preferred Ginger beer, that fizzed in my nose, but that was only sold in the summer. After collecting the alcoholic drinks we went next door to another queue at the Tobacconist to buy Dad's, 'surprise,' packet of Mannikin cigars. Going from one queue to another was all down to the fact that, in those days, the local shops kept rigidly to their own wares. After all that waiting in queues, Christmas Day usually saw me sitting on one of the hard Rexene covered coal boxes beside the fireplace sipping my ginger, waiting to hear what the King had to tell us over the wireless; while Mum, Dad and whoever aunts and uncles had joined us, sat dozing and waking to ask me guiltily if I was, *"enjoying myself". "*

The previous summer there had been quite a set to when the Grocer on the corner of Coventry Street put bags of flour on his shelves. The Baker's shop on the other corner sent a man to remonstrate with the owner of the Grocer's shop, saying it wasn't playing fair to take trade away from fellow shop keepers.

Earlier in the year the shop workers at the Co-Op and other provisions stores went on strike when goods, like sugar and rice, started coming in to their storerooms ready packed and sealed in 1lb and ½lb bags, instead of in sacks like they had always been in the past. The shop counter assistants said they were trained to package goods and now their time was being knocked down because it didn't take so long to serve customers consequently, they complained, that their wages went down.

More surprising changes were in the air. Even the Misses Cole and Wood at the Porthall Tavern placed a glass jar of big round Arrowroot biscuits on the counter in the Private bar. When my Dad brought me a biscuit with my new non alcoholic drink, called a Muscado, onto the step where I stood outside the pub he told me the biscuits were being sold for the ladies to nibble along with their drinks. Mum told me the landladies thought the biscuits were more ladylike than Smith's crisps. As for pickled eggs! Well, they were only tolerated on the Public bar counter and never served in the Private or Saloon bars.

9

A visit to the past

My ears pricked up when I heard Granma say, 'I think I will take a train ride over to see Albert at Westham. "I haven't heard from him since before the war."

"But how are you going to know they'll be there?" Mum asked, "You said his wife has never answered your letters."

"I've written to say I'm coming." So I quickly asked,

"Can we come on the train with you too Granny?"

"Yes," Mum said, "we'll come with you. Summer holidays start next week so no school dinners to serve." It would be the first time I had been over the London Road viaduct and for Gran it would be the first time she had been out of Brighton Town in ten years.

It was a beautiful day to see the view from the Viaduct looking down the valley towards the Palace Pier and the sea from way up high and so exciting to look on the view of my home town from high above at that different curving angle. Most of all feeling what it was like to travel behind one of the steam engines I had so often watched gliding cross that high bridge.

The train went through Lewes without us seeing anything of the town at all. Rounding beneath Mount Caburn along through Glynde village, Granma said the fields looked healthy and well on their way to a good harvest. As we neared Polegate the skies changed to a lowering dull grey under heavy clouds, so when the train arrived at the halt at West Ham, drizzle was putting a damp look over everything.

"Has Uncle Albert got any children?" I asked hopefully as we walked away from the station.

"No dear, so far as I know he and Ivy never had a family."

"This is the house." Granma said. We were standing at the foot of three steep steps going up to a door set flush into a flint fronted row of five cottages; each had two diamond pane leaded windows, one up one down, all shut tight at each house. No porch for shelter.

"Are you sure?" asked Mum.

"Yes quite sure." Gran answered stretching up to lift the small rusty iron door knocker. Nothing happened. All was quiet except for the sound of the knocker echoing away along the blank flint walls. There seemed to be nobody around. Granma lifted the knocker and let it fall again. The whole world sounded hollow and the drizzle was becoming a steady gentle rain. Having started off on a bright sunny morning my elders had not thought we might need an umbrella. Suddenly the door opened and the three of us looked up expectant and smiling.

"Hallo Ivy," Gran said, "Is Albert in?"

"He's out." A woman with a vinegar face told us, making no move to invite us in out of the rain.

"When will he be home?" Gran asked hopefully.

"Later." And the door shut in our faces. I caught the look on my Mum's face – astonishment mixed with concern for her Mother. Granma just turned away and we followed her slowly back along the lane to the main road where the sight and sound of a motor bus made Gran's step break into a trot.

"Come on Dolly." she called. The single Decker bus coming towards us had, 'Battle,' on its destination board. "This one must go through Hooe village." Gran already had her hand out to stop the driver. "Let's visit Grandfather's grave." she told us as the bus splashed to a halt beside her.

Through the steamy windows I had a view onto the high flint and red lined brick walls of Pevensey Castle as the road ran the half circle close round into Pevensey Village. "Over there, l ook." Granma pointed almost behind us to a grey tower just visible on the skyline through the cloudy air. "There's Aunt Hetta's windmill."

"Lilian's and her husband's now isn't it Mum?" Mum asked. But Gran was already telling me that the Manor House, whose roof we could only just glimpse above a high wall was where the Anderson's used to live. Round in the main street Gran said the old timber building on our left was called the Mint House.

"I lived and worked there for a while when I was very young, and this building with the steps at the side, on the right, that's the Courthouse." As the bus went over a low bridge Granma gave a half strangled cry of shocked surprise. The bus had turned sharp left looking inland over the Marsh and Gran had fallen back in her seat staring. "Oh no, look at those huge ugly pylons." Three great tall towers like giants dominated the land and sky. They seemed to be watching us wherever we directed our gaze. Over the bridge we had come to a junction where the bus turned right onto a wide concrete road running ahead giving a long curved clear view. "This used to be a narrow winding lane Dolly. Oh my, what sad changes ..." before she could finish the conductor, who had noticed Granma's exclamations of astonishment said, "Had ter' 'ave a road in, ter get about quick durin' the war, lady."

Reeds waved in the wind either side as the bus sped along the straight road. Again Gran was drawing our attention towards the sea, this time where she said the old waterways cut through the marsh carrying salt barges in earlier times.

"Look, those big lumpy looking blocks way across there, those are Martello towers built to stop old Boney from coming in to land."

"Nasty things 'appen in wars." the conductor commented.

It wasn't until he turned to walk back down the bus that I noticed the skin on his face to one side was oddly pink and stretched tight. He had one face one side and a different one on the other side.

"Oh dear little halfway bridge has gone." I heard Gran say under her breath, her voice trailing to nothing for a long silence. Mum took my hand directing my thoughts across the white dots smudging the flat landscape, "Look, what a lot of sheep." She said. Waterways glinted here and there between the reeds and low stands of blue-grey willow trees. The bus lurched off the concrete to the left taking a low rise. Gran came to life once again. "There's the Inn." My Mum gave a little jerk, trying to twist round to see, "Oh!" she had never seen the Lamb Inn before and like me she was surprised to come upon it without prior warning. But before we could take in the view, the bus conductor shouted, "Sewers Bridge, anybody want to get off?"

"Let's go on to the Church. I want to go to Grandfather's grave first." So the bus carried on up the winding lane.

"You ladies going up to the village?" the conductor enquired.

"No thank you. We'll get off for the Church." Gran said.

Walking down the cool lane darkened by high hedges I could see a haze of steam rising in the air above. Droplets of rain twinkled in the sunlight on the sharp hawthorns. Great heads in clusters of tiny white flowers swayed gently on tall stalks along the edges either side. One or two early poppies bright red nosed their faces up to the clearing sky.

"I've always loved those pretty white flowers. It's called Queen Ann's Lace." Gran said. "No good picking it though my sweet." She told me. "It soon wilts."

The lane was steep, the view opened out in front of us and the sun shone hot into our faces making our first sight of the Church a dark mauve silhouette across the little valley. Out into full sunlight up an incline to the Church gate and Granma flopped herself down on the grassy bank among buttercups and spread her arms wide gathering a thick strand of yellow eyed daises towards her face.

"Just smell," she breathed, "their warmth is so beautiful."

Mum sank down beside Gran and I did too, copying Gran who was lying back almost hidden in the long grass, "I didn't realise how much I've missed the smell of the earth." She said in a sighing breath.

"It's rather damp Mum do be careful," cautioned my Mother.

"Oh we'll soon get dry – look how high the sun is – we'll soon dry out." Gran never went anywhere without a bag full of juicy apples. Biting deep she said, "Ah, my reviver." Granma had all her own teeth even into her seventies they made her smile look younger than her years.

"He died thirty seven years ago and this is the first time I've visited his grave." She said kneeling to pull away clumps of tall grass better to read his name. "They said he died in the same room he was born in 87 years before. He must have heard the Church bells that were tolling muffled to mourn the death of old King Edward. I read that in the papers and I didn't even know my Grandfather had died until a few days later." She gave a big sigh as she held up her hand for Mum to give her a steady as she stood up. "We used to be able to see the sea shining over there across the fields but those ash trees have grown far too high there's not even a glimpse."

The fields on the hillsides all around the old grey stone church were just beginning to turn pale gold scattered with Daisies trying to keep their heads above the fast growing wheat and corn.

Inside the Church was cool. Light streaming through the windows picked out the silver and plate on the altar. Deep ruby and plum coloured pads lined the pews all in neat order.

"I can just see Grandfather's father and brothers singing along with the violin and squeeze box." Granma mused, "Oh, yes, he did enjoy his singing."

Mum smiled, adding, "And their great dogs lying by their feet smelling to high heaven."

"That's right," Gran laughed, "Great Grandfather wouldn't allow his workers to be shut out in the porch. If they couldn't come in he wouldn't come to Church. They were all part of the family those hounds."

Although my mum Dolly was a town girl she was quite at home steeped in the stories of her Mothers' life on the Marsh.

We walked in silence, only the sound of our shoes crunching on the sandy soil back down the lane to the Inn. Gran wondered if they would serve us a drink.

"It's nearly dinner time," she said, "'corse Grandfather served travellers at any time, none of these drinking hours in those days."

"Looks a bit bare out in the yard not much life about." Mum observed.

The door was ajar so Gran walked in.

"C'mon." Gran said. So Mum and I snuck in behind her because it seemed so dark inside. Glancing down at the dusty stone flagged floor Gran stood still looking round the room she had last seen in 1888. Her gaze moved across to the big inglenook fireplace, "That's where Grandfather's high back chair was, that side of the fire and that's where the Grandfather clock stood, in that corner – hmm – his portrait hung over there on the wall at the end of the bar."

Being summer there was no fire but the fire basket was full of ashes and rubbish and the bracket on the wall to the side looked very rusty. "Spit's gone." Gran was saying when a voice rang out,

"We're closed." Gran didn't move. A grubby looking woman with a scarf knotted on top of her head came from the back. "You shouldn't be in here – and get that child outside – we're not open."

"Then that's alright," Gran said firmly, "we're visitors not customers, just visitin'."

"Oh." was the glum reply as the woman marched over to the door holding it well back for us to leave. No time to say more. No time to ask questions. The door closed behind us, the sun had gone behind a cloud. "That floor would have been washed and dried by this time of the morning. Ah well." With a big sigh Gran stood with her back to the Inn looking across the Marsh towards the Mill way over on a rise. I could see she was breathing in the warm air feeling a light breeze. Perhaps she was brushing a hair away from her face but maybe it was a tear. Without looking back she moved slowly towards the road.

"Sad to see this ugly straight concrete road, s'pose they must have built it when they put those horrible pylons over there. Our little lanes were lovely and cool when they wound their way round with the waterways."

It wasn't long before a bus rumbled towards us, its tyres thumping over the concrete slabs. Gran looked wistfully at the landscape open and flat to our right and hazy across to the sea on the left.

"The tide must be out," she said, "difficult to see much where that high banking is now. More than fifty years since I last saw this sight. Fifty years." she repeated under her breath. By the time we reached West Ham the drizzle had set in once again. Granma wasn't one to be put off saying she would like to try again.

"Maybe Albert's come home for his dinner." Back along the soggy lane we trudged heads down against the rain. This time her knock was answered promptly.

"Is he back?" Gran asked.

"No 'e's not." The woman looked astonished to see us again. Nevertheless, without a hesitation, she shut the door on us for a second time.

"Oh Mum!" My Mother couldn't stop herself and taking Gran's elbow as she steered my speechless Grandmother away from the door.

We had only gone a few steps when thumping footfalls behind made us all three turn to see Albert's wife was running towards Granma thrusting something into her hands, and shouting,

"Ere, 'e's bin wittering on about this for years wouldn't let me throw the dirty old thing out. Says he knew you would want it. There, take it – be glad to see the back of it, clutterin' up my cupboard." These last words flung over her shoulder as she stalked back in her door shutting it so firmly we could hear the windows rattle. It was certainly meant to be final. Gran had almost dropped the thing, in surprise as much as anything. Mum stared at the, 'dirty thing,' as Gran turned it over in her hands a smile of recognition beginning to widen across her face.

"Well I'm blessed! It's the old cat dish we used to put up on the beam in the barn for the cats when the yard was full of terriers." As we returned along the lane Granma hugged that dirty crazed old blue and white Willow pattern pie dish to her chest saying it was full of memories of farm kittens.

There wouldn't be another train for an hour. The station only had a tiny ticket office, nowhere for us to sit and wait so Mum suggested we go to the Public House on the corner for a drink while we waited.

"I'll ask the publican if there's a room where Lily can sit," Gran suggested."We can't leave the child out on the step in the rain." Reluctantly I was taken into the billiard room out the back and sat down on a wooden chair with a glass of orange squash.

"Don't touch anything." The man told me as he shut the door behind him. I heard him tell Mum and Gran he would serve them a half pint of Guinness, "But only in the bar. You can't take drinks in there with the child." So I sat there alone for half an hour sipping at a glass of watered down weak orange squash in that cold dreary wooden walled billiard room watching a big black beetle scurrying around the edge of the stone slabbed floor. The happenings of that day have been etched on my mind ever since. Naturally I could feel my Gran's sadness at the time but only at my age now do I understand fully the depth of the unwarranted bitterness that was meted out on her.

Before we got on the train Mum had nipped into the village Bakery. As it was after mid-day she only managed to get a day old loaf. In the Green Grocers she bought some tomatoes. Food rationing was still on so we couldn't get cheese or butter. The lady in the Baker's was kind enough to cut the loaf for us making it easier for us to eat a sort of picnic on the train.

Getting herself comfortable beside the window facing the engine Gran told us how Grandmother Annie often wondered where the dish had disappeared to. "Cat dish, that's what we called it, lovely to see it again. There now, that fits just nicely in my ol' crocheted shopping bag. Home we go little Cat dish." Digging a bit deeper into her bag, she said, "Ah, here we are I knew I'd saved this tucked away." Out of a pocket inside the bag she brought a small blue paper twist of salt, "Kept this from a bag of Smith's crisps Jimmie bought me in the Lewes Road Arms last week, just what we want on these tomatoes." From the tips of our fingers we sprinkled salt on our tomatoes and bread slices, "Lovely." pronounced Gran as she dabbed her lips and fingers with her handkerchief.

"Yes, wasn't it?" Mum agreed. The expedition wasn't the complete wash out it had looked like being.

Some days later a postcard arrived at our house for Granma. It was a short scribbled note from Gran's 'little brother' Albert. He'd obviously been surprised to see the cat dish was no longer on the kitchen shelf, Ivy had owned up to where it had gone.

'So pleased you've got the old cat dish at last. Found it that day in 1919 when Ed. and I marched back from Brighton to see Ma and Pa at St Leonards, Love Albert.'

10

The Trembleur

It was a deeply dull afternoon when Mum and I arrived at Granma's bedsitting room, "Come on," she said, "we'll get comfy and I'll show you what's in this box." She and I propped ourselves up on Granma's bed and leaned against the wall.

"Oh good," Granma sighed, "and you tell us the story just like, 'Worker's Playtime,' on the Wireless. I like Wilfred Pickles." That made them both laugh. Clara lay back in her old basket armchair, shutting her eyes ready to enjoy reliving happy times.

"I'd forgotten I had this." Mum said, pulling open a double layer of yellowing tissue, revealing a blue and white cup and saucer. The clinking sound of china prompted Gran to open her eyes. "It belonged to Madam's son Toby. He gave it to me to look after when he went off back to school. He said the chaps would think him a sissy if they saw a lady's cup and saucer it in his luggage. It was in my case when we all had to leave Madam's employ, in such a hurry."

"Oh dear, then he was killed." Granma added.

"Yes and Madam is, no longer--. So I've still got it, the diary and her miniature too. I remember the morning this arrived in the post, Madam was sitting up in bed, smoking her fancy smelling ciggies; that's what she called her special Turkish brand; the long holder in one hand and marmalade toast in the other. There's me nipping round hanging up clothes and laying out what she wanted to wear that morning; and all the time quickly sliding a big ashtray in place to catch the ash from dropping on her beautiful Japanese yellow silk counterpane." Mum stopped and looked at me sighing,

"Ah those were the days I was Lady's Maid to Madam at Ocean Breeze, back in the 20s. She used to wear the lovely sequined dresses, feathers and powder puffs you like to see in my memory boxes on top of the wardrobe. Well, Peggy, she was the parlour maid at Ocean Breeze, came in with the post, it was this box with a letter inside, it was from Madam's father, saying the contents had belonged to her mother." Mum opened the box and eased out a rather unusual cup and saucer; unusual because the saucer had an extra deep recess for a tall cup.

"What a lovely set." Gran exclaimed. Any blue and white Willow pattern china took her eye. This was far more sophisticated than the poor old cat dish.

"Madam wasn't very interested in the china, she told me to put it up on the tallboy. There was also an old diary in the box that caught her attention and she read bits out to me."

"Who did it belong to?" Gran asked.

"The name on the first page read Suzannah, with an address, Moat Mount, near Canterbury. She was Madam's three times back great Grandmother, known in their family as Carlotta; and the owner of the Trembleur. It seems when she was young, she had a very exciting time as a trapeze artist in a circus in France. In her diary she records how the circus was staying on the outskirts of Paris, just for the winter months, while they were not touring; to earn extra money she joined the clowns who went out to entertain certain ladies who were living in the capital while their husbands were away fighting with Napolean's army. Well, the way the writer explained, she had performed a dance that enchanted one old lady so much, she offered Carlotta, '*anything you would like to take as a keepsake*,' and she chose the cup and saucer the lady had been served a chocolate drink. This set here. Unusual shape, isn't it?"

"I can tell you the reason for that." Granma said.

"Oh, can you Mum. How do you know that?"

"You called it a Trembleur?" my Mother nodded yes, "doesn't that give you a clue? Granma Annie used to say that an old friend of the family, in fact Amy's life-long friend, Aunt Martha, loved her little tipple in the evenings. Ale was very strong in those days; back in the very early 1800s, but what Martha drank, on high days and holidays, was even stronger. She took a glass of laqueur, thick and syrupy, followed by hot chocolate or coffee. Her hands shook so much after the strong alcohol that she needed her drink in a cup with a deep saucer. Annie told us it was called a Trembleur."

"Ah, I see, tremble. What a sensible idea."

"I met Martha when I was a small child."Gran said.

"Really, she must have been very old."

"Yes, she was. It was at my Great great grandmother Amy's funeral, she was 107 when she died in 1872 and I was four years old. Aunt Martha was over a hundred. She had known Amy well. Showing us the diary reminded me of that day.

"Heavens Mother," my Mum said, "what a memory you have."

"Well, it left a big impression on my mind. You see, Carlotta, who wrote that diary, was there. She was a striking figure. She made quite an impact on the company with her shimmering eye patch. You say there's a miniature in that box? Let's have a look at it." The miniature showed a head and shoulders of a young beautiful woman. "Ah yes, you see she isn't wearing her eye patch, so this must have been painted for her husband. I remember thinking what a strange eye she had,

"That's why she always wore the patch over her eye."

This was the first time I saw the Trembleur.

I didn't hear the story of where this piece of china comes into the family, until years later. I would have been too young to understand. When I did hear the full story of where it came from I discovered it included dark events that a family would not speak of openly.

11

Something new on the wireless

"Come on hurry up." Mum pulled me along faster than my legs would go.

"Why?" That was my usual reply.

"Because there's a new programme on the wireless this afternoon and it's just for Women. Come on I don't want to miss the beginning."

Before I started school I had my own programme straight after lunch that Mum switched on the wireless just for me, it was called, 'Listen with Mother.' It used to send me to sleep.

All I can remember about the new 'Woman's Hour,' was the sound of the narrator's voice talking down in such a superior way like the ladies who ran the Mother's Union at the Church hall in Exeter Street. When those women invited our Mothers to tea in their Dyke road gardens they talked from high up down to our Mums. There was nothing for us children to do, it was all don't touch this, don't touch that and keep out of the bushes. The gardens were for adults.

Later it was my turn to say I had to get to school on time on Monday morning. "There's a new school's programme," I told Mum, "and we've got a wireless in our classroom." The 'Radio Times' listed Programmes for Schools and showed our programme was called, 'How Things Began'. I loved that half an hour on Monday mornings, it made me visualise such wonderful pictures of what would have been happening on the earth before human beings arrived.

12

Long held attitudes had to change

The clock spun round on one foot as its wheezing old bell rung at seven o'clock every morning. Most mornings Dad shot his arm out of the bedclothes and caught the falling clock in mid-flight but not this morning.

"Damn and blast!" heralded the day as the poor old red tin alarm clock hit the floor, "I'll see to that when I come home," he sighed laying the tinkling instrument back on the table. Things were still hard to get in the late 1940's and anyway Dad was determined not to be beaten. His old clock was old back in 1939. Now the numbers were hard to see, its face brown, soaked with constant oiling, its back had been off so many times only one clip remained to hold it all together. Dad treated his clock like a sad old pet animal, sometimes it worked best laying on its back or on its face or propped at an angle. Mum had even sewn a soft pad for it to lie on, especially to stop it dancing round on its three little feet across the slippery table top. But she was now threatening to throw the, 'leaky ugly thing' away.

Down in the kitchen jogging on one foot as he hauled his boiler suite overalls over his trousers Dad asked,

"So it's Mum's 80th in two months?"

"I told you last night." Mum answered, handing him his cup of tea.

"Right, if I get going there's time for the smell of paint to clear." Pulling on his old sports jacket, hitching his knapsack, holding the bag of cheese sandwiches on one shoulder, throwing the rope of the heavy carpet bag of tools onto his back he grabbed up the last of his usual bread and butter breakfast, he waved 'cheerio,' as he took the stairs two at a time up from the kitchen and off along the hallway.

"So I'll throw the clock away?" Mum called, half in humour.

"No you won't." He called back as the front door banged shut behind him. Dad hated being late for work so I can imagine him hoofing it off along Coventry Street and down Stanford Road toward the Seven Dials to catch the number 38 bus up over Dyke Road to the work's yard in Cranbourne Street, or to wherever the day's job needed him.

Dad left us full of excitement that morning because his turn had come to have the leftover paint from finished jobs. The Painting and Decorating department at Bostal Brother's, was now getting a lot more work since rebuilding was at a stage of paintwork completion. The Colourman, who made up the customer's colour choices, had a system of collecting all leftover paint from jobs, mixing it all together, then allotting each employee a free tin of paint when it became available. Now Dad's name had come to the top of the list in the Plumbers' department. When he came home with his allotment of paint he said there would be enough to do the front room and the hall and all up the stairs. It seems the mixture of leftovers had produced a bit of a funny colour none of the other men's wives liked.

"It's very good gloss paint." announced Dad. He wouldn't start the job tonight. There's plenty of rubbing down to be done before we paint he'd said. The house hadn't seen a lick of paint since well before my parents moved in during 1938. Apart from the fact paint wasn't' easily available during the war, Dad said he'd never spend money on anything in a landlord's house since Mum refused to let him buy the new house in Patcham. Things were changing and Mum was agitating to have the house throw off the drab years, so to keep her happy he had to change his long held attitudes; he even said he would bring the book of wallpapers home from work because, he said, he couldn't paint the woodwork without putting up fresh wallpaper. Mum and I couldn't wait for Dad to get home on the following Saturday midday. He was bringing the book of wallpapers for us to look through; one for the front room and a different one for the hall and staircase.

We had a whole twenty different patterns to choose from, the colours were pale green; apricoty pink and bluey cream. To me, all seemed to be varieties of nothing. Anyway Mum liked one for the front room because, as she pointed out that had a pearly silvery shine, Dad came back with a quick remark,

"Must be real silver at 12/6 (65p), twelve and six a roll."

"Oh." Mum muttered.

"The other ones are 8/- (40p), eight shillings a roll."

"Oh, that's good then." Mum mollified.

Dad worked out how many rolls he needed to do the front room with the pinky silver at twelve and six a roll and how many in the eight shilling beigey pinky grey for the hall. He took the book back to work on Monday saying we would have to wait until the next batch of customer's orders were delivered.

Meanwhile Dad soaked and stripped the walls back to the plaster revealing layers of ever greyer coal smoked wallpapers. When the original bare plaster walls were exposed in the front room and the hall, we could see the first paper hanger had written his name in pencil, 'Albert Pierce 1888,' in beautiful handwriting on the new plaster surface.

Before Dad hung the new paper he too wrote his name and the date in pencil, 'Arthur Smith 1948.' His handwriting was in Copperplate script just like he wrote out his plumbing Time Sheets every Monday evening.

The skirting boards, window frames and doors had been rubbed down to a fine tooth, even the old black marble fireplace that had for all my young life stood in heavy judgment over the whole room, that too was carefully washed down ready to be painted. The original electric bell beside the fireplace, that our neighbour told us had not been used to summon a maid since the 1920's, and the huge two pin electric sockets, long in disuse, were removed and the wall re-plastered. Once stirred, the funny colour paint was a biscuit pinky cream and wasn't as funny as Mum and I had expected. Only Dad could do the paintwork, he told us, as he didn't want any drips or splashes on the stained floorboards. It took a long time. Mum asked if he would be done before Christmas. He didn't answer. He was enjoying himself.

When it came to the wallpaper he set up a long pasting table in the front room and let me help him trim all down the register mark on either side of the pattern. I had to cut accurately straight as each drop of wallpaper needed to butt together perfectly. I was even allowed to paste the strips. We nearly had a disaster with the first strip finding the paper to be rather flimsier than expected. The front room done we stood back to view the lovely bright room before Mum cleaned the whitening off the windows and hung her newly washed curtains.

My Father was not a tall man so the ladders and planks arrangement he erected to paper the stairwell was quite a comprehensive structure, having to be moved along to allow a two storey drop from bedroom ceiling height down to the ground floor at the base of the staircase. But he did it all on his own, it was a marvel to see him paste up and fold that great long first drop, climb the ladders and planks, position and press the top edge, then let it unfold smoothly without a crease or ripple down to the bottom floor. When the whole job was finished the neighbours came in to admire and comment on how light it made the house feel. Gone were all the dirty greys of the 1930's they said, whilst others commented that he had cleaned the war time out of our lives.

13

Granma's 80ᵗʰ birthday tea

When the day arrived the strong smell of new paint had almost
gone. Mum made a cake; on its top she stood a number 80 that
she cut out of cardboard and painted with gold paint. It was Gran's
regular Sunday to come to tea at our house and unbeknown to her
it was planned that the rest of the family living in Brighton were
dropping in for tea and cake to wish her happy birthday.

The bus from outside Gran's lodgings brought her across town
to the bottom of Highcroft Villas. Taking her time she walked
slowly up to Coventry Street. When she lived with us she would
have stopped to talk to various neighbours, then along the way
call in the little shop, but being Sunday the shop was closed and
there was nobody about on a dull February afternoon. Although
her ankles hadn't swollen too much Mum soon had her parked in
a comfy chair in the back room with her feet up and a restorative
dish of tea. When Dad started taking the dining chairs out of the
room she wondered what all the fuss was about. Using our front
room was a rare thing. The door was usually closed on all the
best furniture, including Dad's wind up gramophone majestically
standing in the corner; tall in its red wood cabinet, its numerous
doors on front and sides opened onto wide shiny black interiors
where sound volume was controlled. Being February Dad had lit
a fire; amid much cussing and sheets of the Sunday paper held
against the in the fire place, he finally got the fire to draw. What
with all the extra furniture brought in to supplement the two soft
armchairs, the room now felt cluttered and through long disuse,
began to steam. Faintly, but none the less obviously, the atmosphere
took on an odd smell that wasn't the new paint. The sideboard was
full of nick-nacks; like my old horizontal feeding bottle in its ugly
box describing, *'How to administer,'* stood alongside a half used
tablet of stinky black soap which the school nurse had given to

me when I caught nits, and Mum had refused to throw away, in case we couldn't get anymore. I was surprised my parents hadn't noticed the funny smell wafting from the black soap in the highly polished 1930's sideboard cupboard. Maybe I noticed it the more because I was the one who had intimate experience of it, having had the smelly old stuff administered to my head. As the room filled with uncles, aunts and cousins the density of the fug rose, the fire blazed and although it was February the front room door had to be propped open.

Gran was ushered in to the front room to gentle applause and settled, stately fashion, in the bay with her back to the window.

"It's so nice to see a cheerful little fire crackling in the grate." Gran commented. I noticed Mum give Dad a sly wink. The low swearing from the front room and Dad emerging all sweaty and irritable not long before Gran arrived, had not passed her notice. Just as the company were raising their cups to Gran around the softly lop sliding number '80' on the cake, a taxi pulled up outside our house.

"Mummy, a lady's getting out of that car and coming to our house." I squealed. Mum held her finger to her mouth. Gran had her attention on her tea dish.

"Oh good," Mum said quietly to Dad. It seems she had read in one of Leslie's regular letters that Aunty Fanny would soon be home from Paris having cleared up Pierre's estate following his recent death. So she had sent a note to Fanny's son Peter just to say Gran's 80th was in February and we were having a little tea party for her.

It wasn't until Fanny's head appeared around the front room door bringing with it a waft of French fragrance, that Gran, jumping to her feet like a school girl almost tipped her tea into her son Jim's lap – thank goodness he was a good fielder - she had no idea Fanny was home.

"Fanny! Oh Fanny my sweeting, I'm so glad to see you." The pair fell into each other's arms. Nobody in the family had seen Aunt Fanny since early 1939 when she had taken her regular trip to visit Pierre. Paris fell to the Germans so she stayed to look after her old friend because she thought he hadn't got long in this world. With her care, and the luck that a high ranking officer had commandeered the elegant apartments on the lower floors of their block, did they have some measure of security, and Pierre had lived on for more years than expected, only passing away just a few months previously.

Fanny told us how in 1940 a German Officer had walked over the whole building turning out residents from the lower apartments but when he discovered Fanny's small workroom at the top of the building where she was making hats for the most well known fashion houses, he let the pair stay, ordering the latest hat creations for his wife and daughters, to send back to his home in Germany for the rest of the time he was in Paris. He was also instrumental in obtaining the medicaments Pierre required. However the officer had no knowledge that Pierre was actually his landlord.

"Did the Germans know you were English Fanny?" Clara asked.

"Who'er no dear, that would never have done. Pierre had his paperwork – I was just 'Madam Pierre' to them. That's all."

"Pretty much a nonentity then Fan." laughed Aunt Hetty.

"Hah," Fanny grunted with a little laugh. "Except for the hats – it seemed they were too appreciative of those to bother us with officialdom."

When Pierre died, Fanny's son Peter inherited the building and Fanny was left very comfortably off.

With all the family stories to hear the talking went on well after the buses had stopped so it was Clara's turn to share a ride in a taxi along with Fanny, Jim and Hilda on their way home.

As Uncle Arthur left to walk with Aunty Hetty back to their house round the corner in Upper Hamilton he took my Dad aside saying,

"This afternoon's done my pocket no good. Now I'll have to get the wife some of that French scent or I'll never 'ear the end of it!"

"Oh heck, that is gonna cost yer a packet Arthur, 'cos she'll want enough to bath in." Dad chuckled.

So, funny smells left unmentioned, everybody had a lovely time leaving our house laughing their ways back home.

On my next visit to Granma I told her how we had discovered who had hung the first wallpaper in our front room in Coventry Street because he had written his name and the date on the plaster.

"There now, that's the year I was nineteen." Granma said, then after a long pause, "I can see myself standing under a darkening sky watching the stars." She paused again. Having heard her paint so many pictures for me, I waited patiently for I knew she could make the moon glitter on the sea and sounds come from afar on the still air.

This time Mum and I were a little stunned into expectancy at the intensity of her words. "I could hear the horse's hooves straining heavily against the coach's harness, up, up over the hill by the Mill. Frank, my Frank, was going away, further and further, 'til I could no longer hear the metal horse shoes on the hard road." Taking a long deep sigh she released us. "That's where I was in 1887. It was the last time I saw him."

Each time her memories were triggered, I heard her voice tell more turning of events in her young life. Letters from Frank still came to Gran from another continent. Mum often read them out loud as Gran's eyesight was becoming very weak. She was only just managing to read with the aid of a small oval bone framed magnifying glass. It was obvious to me, although I only had a child's experience, that Franks' letters kept his memory very much alive. He really was there in the room with her as she bent to her pans and kettles, going about her domestic chores and little bits of cooking on the fire in the small grate, surrounded in the hearth by the world of her youth.

How I remember Granma's hearth

14

The old neighbours

Mr and Mrs P next door, known to us as Uncle Bert and Aunty Peerless, had come to Coventry Street as a young married couple back in1890s, not long after my Grandmother came to Brighton. The couple had never had a family. He was a retired Ganger on the railway and his wife, who by the 1940s, was confined to the house by her bad legs; a house so calm, only the sound of the clock chiming the quarter hours in the downstairs front room penetrated the quiet. Like many of the houses in the street they only had gas lighting. Their two ground floor rooms each had an ornately etched glass hanging central ceiling lantern, while the kitchen had one wall bracket gas lamp. As the winter evenings drew in I liked to watch Uncle P lift the glass chimney, pull the chain down on one side to release the gas, hold the flame of a burning spill to the little white clay beehive shaped mantel and with a soft sounding pop the room was filled with a bright white glow. Well, more of a yellow white glow. From that moment on the hiss of burning gas gave a background sound to the kitchen. It wasn't until Mr and Mrs P got a small wireless in their kitchen the hissing sound faded into the background.

Although the wireless came in to being in 1928 it only arrived in Mr and Mrs P's home in 1946 where it stayed firmly in the kitchen, as to them, it was a new invention so never allowed entry into the best front room where the elegant decorated glass gas lantern was always the proud centre piece, made to look even more delicate by the black marble fireplace that presided heavily over the grey brown upholstered chairs. Pristine white lace curtains shielded the windows from prying eyes. Eyes that knew every house, still occupied by its elderly tenants, had a green china pot holding an aspidistra behind those curtains. Aunty P, new bride in Victoria's reign, had placed hers there the day she moved in and Uncle P never changed it when Aunty P died.

She had been bed-ridden for some years in their downstairs back room, doing huge puzzles on a tray resting over her bed. As a small child I helped, or so I thought. Mum told me I should play very quietly and leave the room if I saw Aunty falling asleep. Aunty P spent hours making the finest hand sewn underwear, petticoats, pinafores and pretty lacy edged caps, their stitching hardly discernable amongst the frills and all worked beneath one wall bracket gas light. She made underware for her little nieces, who lived two doors away, and for many others along the street. I had sets of knickers and petticoats and always accompanied by a matching set for my china doll.

Every new baby in the street received a beautiful layette including pretty covers for the pram. Her legacy showed a woman for whom movement was curtailed by what she called 'bad legs'. But her hands and fingers travelled up and down the street in lovingly made personal garments.

Uncle Bert in his kitchen

Uncle P was an ace wine maker. While our cellar smelled of coal dust and cats Uncle P's contained a heady aroma of homemade wines. Big stone crocks and flagons stood around the walls and on sturdy tables and shelves, the jam he made lined shelves in his kitchen cupboards. Although I never joined him in the evenings I knew from my parents that Uncle P sat in his high backed Windsor chair in front of a glowing coal fire in his cooking range, listening to his wireless with a glass of parsnip wine, or damson, elderberry or maybe dandelion. The white yellow glow from the gas bracket on the wall beside the back door giving off its gentle hiss.

His front door was always open to neighbours, who, for two raps on his highly polished brass door knocker would be met with a welcoming, 'yoo hoo,' from the kitchen and later, as his visitor left through the front hall he would call out 'toodle-loo' – always the same.

Every Saturday morning Uncle P gave me a threepenny Joey (3d – approximately 2 new pence) that I put into my pocket and skipped along to Queenie's to spend. My purchase was never an ice cream because Queenie, like Uncle P, had lived in the street since before the First World War, and had no electricity. Queenie's stock was limited to dry goods and items that came in sacks, jars and tins. Her shop took up the space the same as every other front room in the street. An L-shaped counter fronted with boxes of biscuits faced you as you came in the door while to the right a curved glass counter cabinet topped with a line of glass sweety jars formed the shorter side of the L. On entering a bell tinkled above the door to tell Queenie she had a customer and if there wasn't a group of women and children all talking and choosing you were left in a lonely gloom. Sometimes the frosty patterned glass door to Queenie's private domain was closed making time seem to slow down, so you had to call out your presence. I felt silly calling out on my own because so often Queenie, Miss Noakes, as my mum said I should call her, would suddenly appear at the counter from behind the barrier of glass jars. In whispers I chose my 2ozs of liquorice allsorts, aniseed balls or later on when they came into the shops, lemon sherbets. Sometimes I bought a Mars bar and kept the ½ penny change towards next week's sweeties or to save towards a

Mother's Day present. Miss Noakes didn't waste words. My order fulfilled I said, 'Thank you.' With a little smile she replied, 'Thank you', and I knew I was dismissed.

I didn't like being in the shop on my own. It was dark. The only time the one hanging gas light with its big overhead disk was lit would be on dim winter afternoons. On Fridays Mum and I chose ½lb of biscuits from the glass topped tins along the front of the counter, with Queenie handing a bag over the counter to put our chosen biscuits into. Then Mum handed back her choice for weighing. Miss Noakes talked to the adults with a little high lilting voice, her animated rosey face surrounded by a well ordered froth of hair held up on either temple with pretty little girl slides.

"Would you like to try the new sliced bread Mrs Smith?" she asked, "A man will be bringing it on Wednesdays and Saturdays?" Bread hadn't been offered before in Queenie's little shop because the Co-Op baker delivered along the street every other day but this, she told Mum, was something new. It was bread that didn't go stale. It was already sliced and it didn't go stale? Well that was something we really did have to try. Dad's sandwiches were always dry and stale by the time he got round to eating them at midday. So yes please, Mum was enthusiastic, "Save me one to try this coming Saturday." Our name was added to the list. The bread came in a white and blue printed waxy covering and was called, Wonderloaf. And it *didn't go stale*. Even on the following Monday Dad's sandwiches were soft and moist and not only that, Mum wrapped them in the Wonderloaf waxy packaging making doubly sure the freshness was retained. Wonderloaf was a great success. It was the first fresh item Queenie ever offered and every delivery sold out.

The only time Miss Noakes moved fast around her cramped shop and talked anything above her soft lilt was in the school term time when the shop would fill with children all wanting serving at once with penny drinks and sticky sweets. Queenie made the penny drinks herself each day by dropping a flavoured tablet into bottles of water screwing the stoppers on tight and lining them all up ready.

"What do you want?" Queenie would ask,

"What have you got?" So often came the reply, knowing quite well Queenie would say,

"Red, yellow or green?"

"Green, no red." This answer invariably received no movement behind the counter.

"Please." Then a bottle would be picked up tipped and shaken, the tablet would fizz, the stopper unscrewed and handed over with the words,

"Drink it in here."

"Why?"

"I'm not having broken bottles left outside on the pavement. That's why."

"Come on hurry up." Boys would urge from the back of the queue. Especially when yet another child in the front asked, "What colours?"

An hour of turmoil at midday and another at four o'clock was a bit too much for Queenie alone. Later, one of her relatives from up the street popped in to help serve and shout at the kids, while watching in the half dark where the boys huddling in the corner up turning their penny bottles to drink were also slipping their fingers under the glass tin lids to pinch the biscuits.

Like my Uncle Arthur's newspaper shop window, Queenie's shop window display was changed once or twice a year by the tobacco company. Myriads of cigarette packets or Navy Cut pictures showed satisfied old seamen puffing happily on their pipes. In front and surrounding the jolly faces were animals, fashioned out of folded cigarette packets. The whole vista presented a boring pale grey blue blur to us children and no doubt the adults as well. In consequence their heavy handiwork obscured any morsel of light penetrating inside the shop.

BOOK THREE: 1941 – 1952

15

School Music

Although I saw Granma less often we still exchanged our stories when I visited her lodgings. She always asked what I had been doing, being as good a listener as she was a storyteller.

"We're singing about Hiawatha's wedding feast for the Music Festival this year Gran." I told her, to which she replied.

"Ah, I remember the night the Whiteside's returned to Adelaide Cresent from a visit to London. They'd heard young Mr Coleridge Taylor's Hiawatha's Wedding Feast performed at the College of Music. They were so impressed. Of course none of the rest of the household ever heard the music except for the parts Mrs Whiteside played on her grand piano and she made it sound so romantic, her touch was always so full of emotion. Down in my kitchen Colleen and Madge, the two housemaids, and I listened quite overcome by the lovely sound. It was always such a treat to hear the music coming from that big room when the windows onto the balcony were open."

It was thrilling to me that my Gran and I seemed to have so many interests in common. Then Gran said, "I did eventually hear the whole of the Hiawatha music when Mr. Algernon gave Frankie and me two tickets – Now then, that would have been about 1924. Oh it was so lovely."

I was thoroughly enjoying the music we learned at Stanford Road Juniors. And I know Gran enjoyed hearing all about the Music Festivals we took part in each year; all the Brighton Junior schools came together to perform their pieces at the Dome. There were acts from plays or operas that the pupils had performed for their parents the previous Christmas. I told my Mum and Gran all about St Bartholomew's Junior's, because that was Mum and Uncle Jimmie's old school. This particular year their performance was part of the Mikado. The boy who played the Mikado was really tall with bright ginger hair – ooh ever so tall.

"Was he a teacher?" Gran asked, "Because it's a very big part to play."

"Oh no," I was adamant, "only children were allowed to perform."

The year our school did Hiawatha's Wedding I was in the choral speaking group. When I recited Longfellow's poem for Gran tears came into her eyes. But it was the music to Hiawatha I loved best. The chorus behind our voices sounded like our voices were being lifted into the huge domed roof.

Mum made me an Indian girl's costume out of an old brown coat lining. I had a jacket and trousers with fringing round the hems and Mum painted bright patterns with poster paints around the hem of the jacket and across the shoulders and down the trouser legs. The patterns represented Indian beading she said. I had my long hair plated into one thick plait, and a painted band tied round my head with a fancy feather at the back.

"Wherever did you get that feather?" my teacher asked. "I want that for another play I'm doing." I overheard Mum tell Dad,

"That teacher doesn't ask nicely and never says please."

"Was he the one who wanted the children to address him as, 'Captain,' when he first came to the school?" Dad asked.

"Yes that's him. Head Master refused. He said the war's over now. He's one of those six month trained teachers." Mum added.

"Sounds like he thought a bit too much of himself, thank goodness they're not all like that."

Well Mum wouldn't let him have it because she said it was part of my costume and anyway she would like as not ever get it back. The feather came from a neat little felt hat Madam had given her back in the 1920's. Over the years I had loved it when Mum allowed me to see in the cardboard boxes she kept on the top shelf in her wardrobe. They were the keepsakes she treasured from her days as Madam's personal maid. There were gorgeously coloured feathers; soft powder puffs; and a beautiful pink silk Chrysanthemum flower that Madam had worn in her hair to a Carnival dance.

The following year I was a fairy in a school play Mum made me a dress using another of Madam's throw outs.

The teacher asked again, "Where do you get all these fancy things?" I was wearing a white frothy skirt with a shiny silver bodice and sparkling sequined shoulder straps, another dress from Madam's wardrobe. Mum told me they all came from a time in her life they called the, "Roaring Twenties."

"Might as well make use of these bits 'n' pieces now," Mum said, "I won't ever use them again." I know she didn't respond to the teacher's request to have these little touches of the authentic items for his own productions because his manner was so demanding.

I was quite happy in the choral speaking line up or the choir, I never performed alone in a play. Just to be part of it all each year was so exciting for me. The Dome was filled with pupils from the Junior Schools in Brighton. We sat all day in the darkened auditorium watching each other's performances until it was our own turn to perform. Then a man named Dr Grayson (the adjudicator) spoke into a microphone from the centre of the stalls, telling us what he thought of our performances and announcing the winners of each play and chorus. Throughout the following year around the town we would see children we had met at the Dome and know what schools they came from. Sometimes I saw them in the Public Library, down in Church Street. Mum had taken me to join the Children's library room where I could choose my two books to take home, while she went into the adults section, a place we children were not allowed to enter. Once I did wander in unnoticed. On the wall just inside the door, book jackets were on display along the wall, one had a photo of a lady's breast showing a far advanced cancer growth. I imagined it was like an Italian sculpture I had seen called, 'The Young David', but this lady had a bunch of grapes held against her chest. It was some years before I knew what I had seen. I had seen it without fear because I hadn't known what it was and nobody had chased me away. The sight had just been filed away in my memory until the time coincided with understanding.

I was really enjoying school. There was so much to do; writing and drawing; geography and history and making things like aquariums with rocks and coloured fish. I even designed a little garden on one of Granma's blue and white meat dishes. It had real grass from our back garden, a small mirror from Mum's handbag for a lake and a bridge I made from Plasticine.

The following year went by in a horrible haze. I used to enjoy all the lessons but now I didn't like arithmetic because the teacher smacked your legs every time you got a sum wrong. When arithmetic lessons came round my brain shut down, I couldn't think, especially when the teacher shouted out for answers to mental arithmetic questions. I went blank and had my legs slapped. When he called round the room for us to make up sentences with Nouns and Verbs or Adjectives and Adverbs I got them right. I told about the colours of a Crested Newt, gaining his surly comment, "How on earth do you know about that subject?"

The afternoon I came home from school on the last day of that summer term I said,

"I've just come out of a nightmare." Granma was sitting at the end of the kitchen table.

"Well, I'm blessed, and the child's only nine years old."

16

Health comes through many aspects

On my ninth birthday I went into the Royal Alexandra Children's Hospital to have an operation to have the persistent cyst on my collar bone removed. After seven years of Doctor's visits and a small operation when I was five, it still erupted every few weeks. My parents had great hopes for everybody's future health needs now the National Health Service had come into existence.

Dad said he didn't want us going back to the miserable 1930s unequal health care.

Now it was my turn to be treated by the new health service. At the Royal Alexandra Children's Hospital Mum had to sign a consent form for me to be given an anaesthetic. The lady who explained the details on the form wore a brooch on her chest with the word, 'Almoner,' written on it. A strange word I thought. Not as strange as her manner, I now know it as 'plummy;' but it was more the way she talked down to my Mum, as if she were a silly child. In fact her voice and manner was the same as the ladies who ran the Mother's Union and the WVS.

Hospital visiting times, for parents was in the afternoons of Wednesday and Sunday for one hour only. Mum and Gran had already visited on the Wednesday and were upset to find the comics and books were taken away from them at the ward doorway; visitors were told that paper items had to be baked in an oven before the children could have them. Sweeties and fruit had to be placed on a tray on the staff nurse's table so that it could be distributed amongst all the children in the ward. When my Father visited with Mum on the Sunday he brought my dolly tucked down in his raincoat pocket. As he stood beside my bed I felt the dolly pushed under my pillow. Nurse Eustace, who gave me a kiss from my Mum each evening before I went to sleep, noticed my dolly but didn't give me away.

Nurse Eustace

I wrote a letter to my parents every day and one or two to Granma. Mum kept these letters for many years. One letter told of my excitement when I was recognised by one of the Mr Box twins whose garden we children had been on a school visit to the previous summer. I could hardly believe he meant it. Anyway he signed the autograph book I had been given for my birthday. His page shows a horse's head drawn in shorthand. The Mr Box twins were film makers who came round the wards at the Children's Hospital giving out books and games. It was all very quiet so as not to disturb the really ill children, but it was such a change to see happy chirrupy faces. Gran reminded me how indignant I was when I heard we were being taken on an outing to the Mr Box's garden in the country because we, town children, were described as being, 'Deprived.' She said, "Those two gentlemen know more about children than you think. They like to see you happy."

I always wanted to go out on to the hospital balcony to see the view across to the piers and the sea but I was told that area was special for other ill children. Hooray for the National Health, I got completely well after my operation thanks to the little brown greasy tubes of yellow penicillin cream the hospital gave me to take home. I hadn't liked the tin plates they served our food on, but that was all forgotten, with my small skin graft healing so unexpectedly quickly.

All the paraphernalia that had gathered over the years; 'Kaolin Poultice,' in its rusting soggy paper labelled tin, standing in a little old saucepan always at the ready to boil the water for heating the poultice; packets of lint and rolls of elastic bandage, thick sticky plaster strip and horrible spirit that was supposed to soak sticking plaster off the skin without causing pain, could finally be thrown away.

Something else, or rather somebody else went missing from my life after this operation. Somebody who I hadn't realised meant so much to me; our lovely motherly lady doctor, Grace Vance. Since as early as I can remember my mother used to take me to the surgery in the doctor's family house in Richmond Terrace, opposite the Level, where we waited, in the front room, sitting on dark brown hard dining room chairs, until the patient who came from seeing the doctor put their head round the waiting room door and said, 'Next please.' There was no such person as a receptionist in a doctor's family practice in the nineteen forties. We walked along the ground floor passage, passing the door to the family kitchen on our left, through to a small conservatory where, a lush overgrown garden pressed against the windows behind our doctor who sat at a low desk facing us, comfortably surrounded by a large heap of soft cushions. Doctor Grace had such a sweet welcoming smile. Mum put her arm round me as I stood beside her. She knew I wanted to go round the desk and sit on doctor Grace's lap. But she wouldn't let me, saying, 'If all the children did that the poor doctor would pick up all sorts of illnesses.' Nevertheless when I did go to stand in front of her to be examined, she always gave me a little kiss on the top of my head when she finished. I grew up expecting this was how all doctors would be.

On my arrival home from the hospital I found Dad had bought an upright piano and Gran had been down to St George's Mews to look up Alfred Moffat to come and tune the instrument for us.

By the time Mr Moffat came to Coventry Street he was totally blind, but nevertheless, although he could not see his way, he walked unaided along the London Road and up Hamilton Road to our house. Like him, my Granma and my mother he knew Brighton streets intimately. I overheard the three of them laughing that they could find their way anywhere in Brighton, even in the pitch dark.

He spent a day renewing the felting in the piano, bringing it back to life. In the kitchen at midday they talked and laughed over old times Mum reminding him how he showed her the keys on the piano using an imitation keyboard he made for the local children. My piano had two fancy brass brackets to hold candles and shining bright red brown woodwork. The keys were not quite white but ivory cream. Dad said the black keys were made of ebony. I was looking forward to learning lots of tunes like Aunty Hetty played. Dad found a piano stool he re-polished and Mum re-padded the seat. Aunty gave me sheet music with lovely pictures on the covers like, 'Pretty Kitty Blue Eyes', 'Daisy Daisy' and 'It's a Grand Night for Singing'.

Grandad Smith dug out the old Community Songbook he used when he was in a Mandolin band as a young man. I was all set up. (I still have that sheet music and the Community Songbook).

Mum heard about a piano teacher who lived nearby and learned through meeting his wife at the school gate that her husband charged two pounds a term for an hour lesson once a week.

I learned the names of the keys and the values of the notes. My teacher, Mr T gave me a book of short tunes and I was shown how to exercise my fingers and do the scales. All seemed to go well but I never told my family how short tempered my teacher was when he quizzed me about listening to 'Grand Hotel' on the wireless on Sunday evening. And why had I not listened? "So I expect your parents take 'The Daily Mirror.' too?" Clearly inferring my parentage was too low class. When he saw I had the sheet music my Aunty had given me tucked into my new leather music case, he ripped them out as a handful and flung them across the room, telling me they were trash. The trouble was once or twice I had referred to my piano as my, "Joanna," copying Uncle Arthur and his down to earth humour. My family often joked about 'Aunty's ol' Joanna,' and that did not go down well with the piano teacher

My parents did everything they could to make the front room warm for me to practice my scales and short pieces the teacher gave me. Then Mr T started slamming his hand on mine to correct me shouting louder and louder. I began to miss my lessons by going for a long walk so that I arrived home about the time my parents expected me. The music lessons were worse than the arithmetic lessons that had been accompanied by slapped legs.

When Christmas day came I knew I would be expected to play a piece for the family, when they gathered round the piano so I left my music at home. Dad went home to fetch it and while he was gone I locked myself in the lavatory and was violently sick.

Nobody made any comment.

Finally I poured out the whole story to my Gran because I felt so embarrassed to hurt my parents.

"You've tried your best." She told me. "No good making yourself so unhappy. I'm sure you're going to be really good at something perhaps playing the piano is not to be."

I felt relieved because I had tried, tried hard for two years. I still loved music but this man had put the kybosh on me making music.

Gran said, "Go home and tell Mum and Dad what you've told me but don't say you've been to me first."

I waited until Mum and Dad finished their meal before I started. "I don't want to go to any more piano lessons." I said, in a quiet firm voice like Granma told me. I explained how it had been and said I didn't want to find another teacher. I didn't want to learn the piano at all. They weren't surprised. They were sad for me and sorry they had given me a bad start. That wasn't their fault. Maybe not seeing it for themselves sooner would have been a help but neither were musical, they just thought one had to practice to make perfect and that often proved hard. Being forced to count and remember sequences of movements stopped me in my tracks.

I did feel bad as I knew money was tight and my parents had to make sacrifices to pay for the lessons. I had seen Mum collecting up jam jars and rags to take down town to sell for a few coppers.

Sometimes you just have to walk away from something and leave it behind to move on, and above all, not feel guilty.

Granma gave me a two shilling piece saying, "Next time you go with mum when she collects her wages in Ship Street, turn down the road that goes to the seafront and you'll find a shop that sells all sorts of Artist's materials. Buy yourself a nice drawing book.

Nobody will slap your hands for drawing pictures." (I still have that first drawing book too.)

Now I began to develop my own interests, taking my new sketch book with me when I stood outside the pub. I drew what I could see in the distance across the railway bridge. The Chatry, a memorial to the Indians who died in the First World War, shone white far away in a rise on the Downs. In the foreground the square Church tower was the tallest building across the valley in the Drove, beyond Preston Park. Customers at the pub laughed at me for including all the cracks on the walls of the bridge. They didn't get away with that because when I turned to look inside the pub I drew their portraits as they stood at the bar. One old man's face I drew made my mum annoyed because she said he wasn't a very nice man. Like any artist I was only interested in recording what I saw – maybe what she disliked showed in my interpretation, but I never knew what it was. During the winter I nipped into the unoccupied saloon bar, unseen, to draw the furnishings.

"Well you won't have many people to draw if you only draw the nice ones." Gran told me. "I recognise that lady's face but you've made her look happy but she and her husband always look so glum."

"I think she's happy inside, walking along with her husband." I said.

"Yes, I would be if I had my husband so close." Granma replied.

Granma, old Mrs Turk and Aunt Fanny were all ladies who had no husbands. Aunt Fanny hadn't got any grandchildren. Mrs Turk's grand and great grandchildren were mostly all grown up. My Gran had me and Uncle Jimmie's little girl Kathy, and Don the eldest, who was now a busy apprentice mechanic with little time for Granma's.

17

Some things don't change

Three elderly ladies, Gran; Fanny and Mrs Turk were still wearing long skirts in the late 1940s. Granma's skirts only cleared the floor by three to four inches; pure white hair framed her face in a shiny wavy swathe. Her eyes smiled even when she wasn't smiling, a warm voice always on the verge of a chuckle and cool soft hands of a confident cook. Granma Clara remained a strong minded independent character; setting her little close fitting hats at a slightly rakish angle.

No less independent a character was her younger sister Fanny – slimmer and very chic she wore her skirts a little shorter; usually cut on the cross giving the fabric a swing in the French style, whilst scarves of silk flowed across her neckline and furs round the collar of her coats and always elbow length gloves. Fanny looked just like the fashion I was copying, from Woman magazine into my drawing book. It was called the New Look. Skirts were synched in at the waist swinging wide at the hem. Hats were bigger, heels were higher and long gloves had to be worn.

Mrs Turk on the other hand was a down to earth older lady whose skirts almost always touched the ground, whose ankles were always covered by her side buttoned boots. No furs for her. Cloth coat, high collar and a small felt hat sat straight on her head. Her strong character had never changed, if anything she had become the more so; still hale and hearty well into her nineties. Being the eldest of the trio she was able to remember the shock that went through the household when Victoria's Prince Albert died.

The ladies met regularly for a chat and a game of cards. When Granma started coming back to her lodgings by taxi, paid for by Aunt Fanny, the landlord kept giving all sorts of reasons why her rent was being put up.

'Just smile', advised Aunt Fanny. 'Don't let him get you down dear.'

When mum and I dropped in to see Gran on one of our regular afternoon visits Mrs Turk was saying,

"Such a wonderful thing this National Health Service, I've never been able to afford glasses, now I can see ter read the paper."

"Talking about health care; Mr Algenon was such a loss."

"Who's that you're talking about now Clara?" Mrs T. asked.

"AHP, you know, the Dental Surgeon I worked for out Hove, back in the twenties. I don't think I ever mentioned what he did when he was away in London those two or three days a week. I didn't know myself until after he died. It was when his chauffeur took me over to catch the boat at Newhaven. James told me AHP had a special Clinic in London where he rebuilt men's faces."

"What do you mean, faces?" Fanny queried.

"Men who came back from the trenches who'd had parts of their faces shot away. AHP remodelled their bone, some in metal and some in Bakelite and rebuilt their faces, while another surgeon worked on the skin. James said Algenon had set the Clinic up himself and gave his time for free. Oh dear what a loss. He was such a nice man. It was James who told me why Mr Algenon asked me to make my soft cakes to take with him they were for those poor men with their damaged faces."

Fanny perked the company up by saying,

"Yes I remember now he gave you the job because you had such a nice smile, didn't he Clara?"

Then it was my turn to tell the three about when mum and I visited the Pantomime at the Grand Theatre in North Road.

"Ah! The dear old Grand." sighed Gran. Mrs Turk's laugh burst forth as she recalled how, one night she delivered a baby out in the backyard at the Grand Theatre. A young woman lived in a decrepid old caravan parked behind the big scenery doors. We were all ears. "It was a bit of a squeeze," she said, cackling with laughter again, "Aw the baby was more like a bloomin' toddler, 12½lbs, an' tall. I think 'e must've bi'n the son of Jack 'n' the Beanstalk." Oh dear we all joined her laughter. When my mum nipped out to the Dairy shop at the bottom of the road with a jug for some more milk, I said,

"Granny, when we go to the Grand, mummy always leans against the wall when we stand in the queue waiting to go in. I want to see the pictures on the wall but she never lets me." The Aunties and Gran looked at each other – Old Mrs Turk asked me who was in the Panto? "Charlie Chester." I told her.

"Hmph he's a bit of a naughty boy." Aunt Fanny couldn't hold her giggles back any longer. "Oh, stoppit you're making my tummy hurt." she was laughing so much, "You know who's on at the Grand next week don't you?" And I saw her wink.

"Aww, yes." Mrs Turk guffawed. Gran raised her eyebrows trying not to laugh.

"That's Phyllis Diller and her all girl Band." Fanny informed us.

"Oh dear me," Gran said, "Well you might as well know luvey your mum is standing in front of photos of a group of ladies who play in a band." It was easy to lip read Granny Turk's overacted mouthed words, "an' wearing next to nothing while they're at it!" ending with a decisive nod coupled with a cheeky grin.

When mum came back in she asked what all the mirth was about, I piped up.

"Phyllis Diller, she plays a trumpet. Gran's told me about her!"

"Your Gran's full of stories." Mum laughed.

"Aunty Hetty told me you said that about Gran after she'd taken me up to Granma's bed when I was first born." I answered putting mum on the spot this time.

"Told you what?" Mum looked puzzled.

"You said Gran told stories right back to 1065." And that made Aunty Fanny laugh all over again.

"Oh well, better ask your Gran, she'll tell you that story, won't you mother?"

"Is this another family saga?" asked Mrs Turk, all ears.

"I haven't heard this one," Fanny queried, "1065, that's a long time back Clara?"

"Grandfather John told us. You may have been too young to remember Fan. Granfer said, he was a small boy at the time when he was out Looking with his Pa and brothers. Well, Granfer said he could see something different happening way across past Aunt Hetta's mill on Stone Cross hill."

"Hm, that's a bloomin' long way away." Fanny remarked.

"Yes, it is," agreed Granma, "and that's what reminded Granfer's Pa of how they had an ancestor whose eyesight was long, just like John's. The story he told has been passed down in the family about this ancestor, who they called, 'Young Long-sight', his given name was Eldred."

Granfer's Pa, told how the young boy could see across very long distances, just like John could. It is said that Eldred saw men watching the coast from out at sea. He told the village elder what he had noticed and the elder included the information in his report at the next area moot (meeting). Eldred came from a village at the back of East Dean. His job, as a small lad, was to watch over the sheep up on the cliff top high above the Head (Beachy Head), to stop them venturing too near the edge. Anyway, during the summer months in 1065 he'd noticed fishing boats, French ones like those his Uncles did barter with; but the people on these boats weren't fishing, what he saw were tall figures standing still and looking towards our coast while the boats drifted free up Channel towards Dover. The figures were much taller than the usual fishermen and that's what attracted the boy's attention. He noticed his sightings always occurred on one day in the middle of every week. The boats came in closer all that summer.

Granfer's father said the young boys living along the coast had always been watchers. Even when he was a lad just around 1800, they had to keep their eyes skinned in case 'Old Boney' was coming!'

"Well I'm blessed." Fanny sighed. "The tales from Grandfather's Inn are never ending. How do you remember them all Clara?"

"They just come back to mind when I'm asked."

"It's what I meant when Hetty said you were already telling Lily your stories." Mum explained, to which Granma replied,

"That's right. Now Lily's got them hasn't she?" Gran sounded almost relieved.

"And now you can forget." joked Fanny.

"Don't s'pose that'll ever happen." Gran smiled, "The characters will always be close by me."

"I know, I know," I piped up, in a hurry to ask another question before they all went home, "but why did Uncle Barney call that

man, 'Americany,' before he walked out on him Granma?' Gran
looked puzzled and Mrs Turk, "Ooh are'd?" in great anticipation,
"There she goes again. Come on then Clara, wot's this one all
about?"

"Blessed if I know," Gran admitted. Then a smile lit up her face
as the penny dropped, "Are yes, I know what you're getting at, I
had to ask Grandfather the same question. It was when that young
reporter from the local paper came to the Inn. He walked straight
across to Uncle Barney, put his hand out and asked, could he 'shake
the hand of a man who had taken part in Mr Tennyson's famous
Charge of the Light Brigade."

"Another one I haven't heard of," Fanny murmered under her
breath, "what's odd about that?'

"Ah, I know," chortled old Granny Turk, Gran smiled at Mrs
T and she smiled back, "Funny how everyday practices change over
the years is'nt it Clara?"

"Well, go on then," Fanny was frustrated with the delay, "are
you two going to tell us or have we got to guess?"

"Barney had met people from all over the world and he didn't
hold with some of the new American ways, so when a complete
stranger expected to take hold of his hand, he got up and walked
out." and Granny Turk added,

"People in England didn't shake hands. Aw no, especially not a
working man touching hands with a man in a collar and tie. Sounds
odd these days now, though don't it?"

"I thought you were going to say Barney wasn't one of Mr
Tennyson's Light Brigade." Here Granma's story telling mood was
on her once again because she replied,

"Yes, you're right, there but the young man was a journalist so
I expect he knew more about the poet's vivid writing than the man
who sent those young riders, who were Barney's comrades, to their
horrible end."

"I don't know how you do it Clara," Fanny sighed, "that story
must have happened a good seventy years ago."

"Mm,' mused Gran, 'no, I can't have been more 'n ten year old."

These conversations were often the way I learned the little tit
bits about life as it was in their younger days. During another time

of their reminiscing I heard Gran telling how Grandfather John's father, Robert had warned him, when he took over as licensee of the Inn, not to let anybody draw or scratch a ship on the walls, especially opposite the front door. He said it was a Smuggler's sign to show this was one of their meeting places and a venue for hiding contraband. Aunty Fanny said, wouldn't Smugglers bring in valuable extra money and Gran replied that was true, but they often caused fights and could be very cruel. It was best to avoid their business so not to put the family and local village people into danger.

18

New Experiences

Ever since I started school Aunty Hetty had sent me the colourful
Mickey Mouse comic with my parents' newspaper delivery
each week. On my eighth birthday Dad changed my weekly
Mickey Mouse to the Beano and the Dandy. I could read well
and understood the knockabout language. From the big bundles
of American comic papers Uncle Arthur acquired through his
newspaper trade, I also followed Dagwood and Blondie and got
to know Flash Gordon and Popeye, well before I was old enough
to join the group of children along the street who, shepherded by
the older girls, went to Saturday morning children's Pictures at the
Odean Hove. We caught the bus at the Seven Dials, at nine am;
the return journey cost a penny happenny and the entry ticket was
ninepence. It was a bit scary at first because the older boys in the
audience shouted, 'Hallaballoo'd,' and threw lighted matches into
the air when the baddies came off worse. I soon got used to all the
noise surrounded by friends.

Life was full of exciting new experiences. At a cost of eight
shillings (8/-) each, our class was taken to London by coach. In the
morning we went to the Science Museum where we saw Stevenson's
Rocket and other engineering models. The coach took us through
central London so we could see famous buildings like Westminster
Abbey, the Houses of Parliament and Nelson's Column. In the
afternoon we went to the Zoo to visit the new born Polar Bear,
Brumas, named after his two keepers Bruce and Max. More than
sixty years later I still have the picture book about little Brumas,
the story of his birth had been in all the newspapers so we were
especially keen to see the little bear. We were allowed to roam round
the cages without teachers or parents. The lions and tigers looked a
bit scruffy to me, their cages were small and the lion just lay against
the back wall looking out at us looking in at him. I thought, could

an animal really look so bored? Our cat at home looked much happier. Rhino's had a big space and elephants walked around outside the cages giving rides to children so did a couple of camels. Sea lions had a big pond; all sorts of colourful birds flew about in cages and in a dark corridor we looked through windows at snakes and lizards. On the way back home in the coach we sang at the tops of our voices until most of us fell asleep. It had been such an exciting busy day.

This last year at junior school was by far the most interesting. As part of the Brighton Schools Music Festival we were taken to the Theatre Royal to see Benjamin Britain's 'Let's Make an Opera.' I enjoyed it very much but it wasn't as good as actually joining in and taking part, like we did the weekend the Pageant was put on in Preston Park. Friends and neighbours dressed up in costume performing historical events through the hundred years from the Great Exhibition in 1851.

During the same year we were taken to see the Festival of Britain Exhibition on the South Bank. By then we thought we were old hands knowing London well, checking our whereabouts on maps as we went. The Dome of Discovery was full to bursting with a huge array of items but there was nobody there to tell you anything about the exhibits. All I can remember seeing was a big stuffed brown bear and a huge electric light bulb. Whatever the Skylon was for I never found out. Later we were taken to see the Shot Tower instead of an expected visit to the Battersea Fun Fair. We were all disappointed. I understood what the Shot Tower was for but it was a poor substitute for the Fun Fair. My Mum heard that the teachers thought they might lose some of us in Battersea Park's large open space so that visit was cancelled.

Following our visits to London our class teacher set us a project to learn more about people from other countries. I remembered seeing, 'South Africa House,' written across the front of a building near Admiralty Arch, when our coach driver took us round Trafalgar Square, so I wrote to tell them what I wanted to learn and by return post I received a lovely large book of photographs and text titled, 'The Peoples of South Africa.' (I still have that book.) It told a little of the history of how the white civilisation in South Africa was founded by Jan van Riebeck and, for administration purposes, the main racial groups; European; Native; Coloured (mixed); Asiatic and Cape Malays that had been recorded in their 1951 census. The following pages pictured the life styles of a population that included a wide variety of racial types looking free happy and healthy. To my young eyes, used to the bombsites and dirty beaches, the black and white photos showed a fresh air life in a wonderfully sunny warm country.

Granma said Uncle Frankie had recently written to say his son, my cousin, had taken a job in Africa so we looked back at my school atlas and found where he was headed, and that's when I learned there were many countries in the continent of Africa.

Dad came home from work with a collection of books given to him by a lady in whose house he had been working. He had spoken of my school project and she said her husband took groups of people on World Tours so gathered together a small collection of his tour books. They were about the railways in Japan; Maori people in New Zealand and the jungle covered buildings of Ankor Watt. I was so excited to learn about these countries through those guide books. One book on Japan had pages of faces but, couldn't read the language to find out why there were so many portraits, it certainly made me look harder at all the faces around me. I can't remember what became of the actual project however, all the books that came from that project still remain on my bookshelves.

"Well what a coincidence." Granma remarked, when I showed her the World Tour books, she went straight to her old tin Bowler hat box and brought out another copy from the same Company that offered a World Tour that explained that the tour described, would be returning, 'In time for the Coronation,' I was astonished; how did she come to have her copy?

"That was in 1938," she said, "my employer, Mrs Hunter had persuaded, her daughter Miss Helen, to go on this Tour hoping she would find a nice Gentleman friend. This guide book was left down in my kitchen after Helen had been telling me about her adventure. She was so sad to come back later in the year to learn king, Edward viii, had abdicated so there wouldn't be any Coronation after all."

BOOK THREE: 1941 – 1952

19

Childhood Adventures

In the late 1940's, early 1950's, we children wandered freely finding exciting places to play all across Brighton; sometimes out all day ranging alone to Queens Park and high up on the Race Course and over to the huge Municipal Cemeteries at the top of Bear road; where sitting very still and silent we watched snakes and other wild life until the grave diggers chased us away. But then just a penny each would take us on a Trolley Bus ride down Elm Grove and swiftly up New England Hill, dropping us off close to home territory once again.

Our home territory was at Tongdean's deep chalk pits, we spent hours there, arranging large flints to make camps, finding fossils, bits of bone and broken slivers of flint under the shallow soil, among the tight stands of small trees. Out on the open down-land there were no Park-Keepers to spoil our play, like in Dyke Road Park, where a school friend's lovely Aunty Evelyn ran the little tea room providing rock buns for us to eat in our secret camp. Until a loud voice shouted, 'Come outa there you young rascals,' ended the secret that was our hidey hole down inside a bank of thick shrubbery.

Along the Preston Road, in the Rockery gardens, that sprawled down the railway embankment snuggled a little thatched cottage which made a good pretend house to play in during the weekdays. At weekends it was occupied by couples who crossed the bridge over the lily pond and climbed the rocks to canoodle in our little house. On the opposite side of the road Preston Park's lovely wide open space is where I first saw Bertram Mills colourful Circus. The band played soft music as the Elephants balanced their great bodies on one leg; drums rolled ominous noises while we squeezed our arms round each other in dread anticipation when the Lions growled at their Tamer. I held my breath till I was almost sick, craning my neck to watch the trapeze artists throwing their bodies across the roof in the Big Top.

On wet days the Museum in Church Street was a good place to count the legs on a centipede and a millipede. That was a huge disappointment because I discovered a centipede had only thirty-four legs. It was difficult to see the legs on a millipede but I did manage it to about seventy-two. When there were no adults about we could still stroke the stuffed lion and big brown bear and look inside King George the fourth's Coronation Carriage that stood on a landing. The paintwork was chipped and peeling revealing the Coach was all carved out of wood.

The exhibits in the Booth Bird Museum in the Dyke Road were fascinating, even better, was if the keeper would pull open some of the hundreds of drawers to let us see the magnificently colourful butterflies, many with huge spread wings or minute fine lacy specimens that made me hold my breath, just in case they blew away, even though they were covered by glass.

Our mother's didn't know just how far we ventured unless we came home with tales of what we had seen or, as sometimes happened, older brothers and sisters caught sight of us around the town.

A regular event we watched with glee on Saturdays, was the barrow boys taking to their heels and running when their lookouts signalled a, 'Rozzer,' was getting too close to their pitches. They parked their flat barrows, loaded with cheap fruit and vegetables, just up the side streets, usually off the Western Road. As they paid no rent for pitches, the shopkeepers and market traders were against their kind of trading. Lookouts stood watching, further away along the road, you could see their arms waving signs like the Bookies on the race course. The Barrow boys called out their wares, everyone was on their toes. When the tip off came, 'Rozzers,' squawked a nearby lookout, all hell broke out. It was fun to watch their antics. They'd turn tail and run like hell, their barrows bouncing and rumbling over rough side roads, often shedding fruit as they made their getaway, leaving half served customers without their change, shouting abuse after the fleeing salesmen. We often picked up items from their fruity trails.

A few steps away from home one of the Aunties who served bread in Perry's the Bakers on the corner of Coventry Street sometimes let us have a bag of yesterday's stale buns for a penny, we called this, 'our feast,' together with a 'Monster' bottle of fizzy lemonade. I will never forget walking, into the kitchen where two of our friends lived, with our bag of buns. Their Mum was standing leaning against the table (a door laid over an old tin bath) she was sloshing butter out of its paper wrapper onto a piece of bread her face a study in bliss. Her children chorused together,

"Whor! Mum, can we have some bread'n'butter?" Her immediate answer,

"Yeah, get the marg out." Even at my young age – probably about 8 or 9 years old – I found her reply ironically funny.

A little girl whose family of six lived in a two roomed basement flat across the other side of the Seven Dials asked her Mum if I could stay for dinner one Sunday. Her brothers and sister had said, their Mum 'did smashin' Sundie dinner.' They didn't wait until the pubs shut at 2 o'clock for their Dad to come home like we did. When the food was ready their Mum spread newspaper on the kitchen table and gave us each a fork then brought a big black roasting pan out of the oven putting it on the centre of the table. Before the pan hardly touched the newspaper all four children were digging their forks into huge crispy golden brown/black potatoes pulling them out of the still seething hot bubbling lard. Aw! They were lovely we ate them like toffee apples. My friend's younger brother mopped up all the last diggings, including the hot fat, in great hand and spoonfuls. When I told Granma about the lovely Sunday dinner I had eaten she said,

"Ooh yum, that sounds lovely." Unlike my Mum, who raised her eyebrows and discouraged me when I was invited to go again.

I didn't tell anyone at home about the day another friend and I thought we would do cheese on toast at her basement home in Chatham Place.

"Wo't we gonna make it in?" she asked. I suggested a saucepan because I had seen a cheese sauce made in a pan. My friend got the family cheese ration out of the cupboard and put the whole lump of Cheddar Cheese, (mousetrap,) in a saucepan turning the gas up high under the pan. I said I hadn't seen it done like that. "Oh it'll be quicker." she replied, as she tried to stir the bubbling gluey lump around in the pan. In no time the pan refused to release its contents so we abandoned it in the sink and went back out to play.

At school the next morning my friend looked decidedly dishevelled. From then on, whatever the weather, she and her young brother had to wait outside their front door under the ground floor steps, where the bins were kept, until their Mother got back from work. It was a long time before they were trusted with their front door key again and it wasn't even left on a string hanging behind the door like most people had, easy to retrieve through the letter box. If my Mum was going to be out I had to collect the key from our next door neighbour, or I had to carry our huge heavy front door key in a purse hung across my shoulders.

Before we had time to get into further misadventures the youth club at the Clifton road Congregational Church allowed us 10 year olds to join their athletics evening. We were taught how to climb wall bars and vault over padded boxes, under the watchful eye of a muscle-bound young man who looked like Max Bygraves. He was as kind and patient with us younger children as he was firm and friendly with the older boys. I say, older boys because I had not heard them called teenagers in the late 1940s. On one memorable evening we were taken on a Youth Club outing to see the latest equipment in use at the Post Office's main Sorting Office in North Road. The elderly church member, himself a retired Postman, was like a tall gangly kind Granfather and very proud to tell us that Brighton was the first Sorting Office in the country to have this advanced machinery. He reminded me of the railway men in our street who had the same proud manner about their work on the Railway. Learning about other people's lives and work; seeing where they came from in the school 'Pictorial Atlas.' I couldn't get enough of these wonders.

20

The cheek of it!

As I have told you, our street was a long street where the children played outside; chalking hopscotch on the pavement, throwing tab cards against garden walls. The girls swung their skipping ropes across the road, the boys ran races or shot at each other round corners. Few, if any, vehicles passed along the road; vans delivering milk and bread were expected in the mornings, but in the afternoon and evenings the space was ours; if a car should enter the street, interrupting our play, we moved slowly away to the pavement with, 'Well, the cheek of it!' written all over our faces as we stared at its passing. The adults took little notice of us, while we kept ourselves busy.

Inevitably, there always came a time for mischief in the long school holidays when the need for extra fun prompted the old idea of tying door knockers together. Unless one of us little girls could be persuaded into taking the end of a string and getting caught activating a door knocker, it was a game I could only watch; the door knockers being too high for me to reach were no problem for the older boys. The houses were built in two long terraces facing each other on either side of the road; all the houses had the same front doors with long heavy door knockers; the porches to every pair of next door houses, side by side, made it easy to tie a length of string from one knocker to its counterpart in the next door neighbour's porch. One result of this prank remains in my memory.

Snuck safely, waiting in giggling groups behind gateposts, we onlookers watched for the thrilling results. The cheeky boys knew how to get the fun started; they knew who was at home.

Two knockers tied and ready, one boy lifted a knocker to give a good loud bang swinging him-self quickly away down the steps and out of sight. When the door was opened the tug on next door's knocker got the expected result, but with a slow response. When it did come, the first knocker worked again bringing the occupant to a swift return and closure when it was obvious nobody was there. This caused the next door knocker to make a second loud bang, its door reopening so violently that the string snapped almost trapping the first neighbour's fingers in her door. A dishevelled man, dressed only in vest and braces raced out onto his step, shouting,

"Little Buggers!" his neighbour, out in full view out on her step said,

"Now then Mr T, mind the language, there's little children present," adding,

"You used to be a little bugger yerself." To which he called back,

"Yeah but this little bugger's bin up all night on the ambulances, Mrs." The verbal argy-bargy just made the mischief even more fun, besides revealing that grumpy old Mr T used to be a mischievous little boy.

21

The wheeze

Thirty miles away, over in the East Sussex countryside, two little boys hid quietly on a sloping bank behind the hedge bordering the lane outside their farmhouse home. One held the end of a piece of string that ran under the hedge and across the grassy verge to a box wrapped in brown paper to look like a parcel. A passer-by walking up the lane to the village spotted the parcel lying in the grass and bent to take a closer look. As he reached out to pick it up the parcel moved slightly aside; causing him to stretch his arm further before he realised the parcel had moved on its own. Looking confused and seeing nobody about, he tried again. This time the parcel flicked up in the air toward the hedge. A smile crossed his face and he walked on.

The boys spluttered laughter into their hands; the wheeze was working.

Although theirs was a fairly quiet country lane, minutes later another passerby, seeing something lying on the side of the road, stopped and stared down at the stamped and addressed parcel. Shaking each other to, 'Sshh, don't let him know we're here,' their shivering expectancy turned to deflation, as the man walked on by. Deep breath, keep still, 'Quick, here's another.' Curiosity got the better of this lone walker who appeared to check behind to see if anybody was in sight before making a grab for the parcel, 'Agh,' he exploded when it disappeared through the hedge. His reaction left the two scheming eight year old Forshaw boys, holding their aching tummies with unsuppressed laughter. Their holiday jape gathered further hapless victims most seeing the fun of being caught out. Until a man, riding a small two stroke motor bike, caught sight of the parcel on the grass verge, stopped on the side of the road, turned his engine off, pulled the bike up onto its stand and walked across to pick the parcel up. It moved gently out of his reach, for a second he stopped, bewildered; then straightened up with a puff and walked back to his bike. Pulling it off its stand he kicked it over. The engine wouldn't start. After trying a second and a third time he gave up and carried on up the lane pushing his bike.

Two little boys Paul and Peter

22

Little incidences that mean a lot

Yet another event took the family to London for a second wedding.
Again we travelled, all dressed up in our finery. Boarding a double-
decker bus in the Preston Road at the bottom of Lover's walk, and
as before, we climbed up onto the top deck. I loved watching the
passing scene from high above the road. Granddad Smith always
said the approach roads into Brighton were some of the most
colourful in England and he knew about that because he had been
all over the country on his Union activities.

In Brixton High Street we had to change buses. As we were
walking to the next bus stop a man came towards us along the
pavement. He was black. I was about to say I had seen pictures of
black people in the book sent to me from South Africa House, when
I noticed my Aunty Hetty walking out on the road making a wide
detour around the man. Uncle called out to her, "You'll get run over
out there Hett." But she took no notice, as she appeared to be intent
on keeping well away from the black man.

I don't think he was the first black person I had ever seen;
he was certainly the only black person in sight and I couldn't
fathom why she was treating this oncoming pedestrian as if he was
contagious or something. It puzzled me. Apart from wishing him,
'Good morning,' as my Uncle would have greeted any passer-by, had
he been in Brighton, nobody else in the family was acting so oddly
or even made more comment to Aunty, than Uncle Arthur.

Apart from learning that the bridegroom's surname was
Pilbeam, the same as my great great Grandfather's name, the other
clear memory was the dish of little pastry swans filled with cream
cheese. I was told it was choux pastry.

On the journey home I overheard Aunty crying, "But Arthur,"
she was saying, "all I saw was a figure in a light mackintosh and he
had no head. It was so frightening." It took her a long time to get

over the shock. Aunty Hetty wore glasses as thick as pebbles and frequently her misinterpretation of what she thought she saw often sent us into chuckles, she even laughed at herself, but this time her reaction caused no laughter, leaving her distraught in case she'd hurt the man's feelings. It has stayed in my memory all these years because I wrote about the incident on the following Monday in my school Diary. Oh yes, including those delicious cream filled little choux pastry swans we ate at the wedding breakfast.

23

Family changes

One morning we had just started our first lesson when we were told to leave our books where they were and line up to go into the assembly hall. We were all quiet as our very serious faced Headmaster told us King George the sixth, had died. After saying a prayer we solemnly marched back to our classrooms to get on with our lessons.

The following day the newspapers had pictures of the Royal ladies wearing long black veils. Adult conversation sounded glum; voices and music on the wireless sounded quiet and sad; we wondered what was coming next.

A few days later Granma received a letter. It had a black edge. Postmarked, London, she wondered who it could have come from. It was Peter.

His mother, our Aunty Fanny, had died in her sleep while she was spending the weekend with him. The shock was almost too much for Granma to bear, knowing she would not see her sister again. She already knew that her brother Jack in Lewes was none too well. Her younger sister Nancy had always written regularly and though she only had the rare letter from her brother's wives she knew how they were all keeping, except Albert. But Fanny, well, that was a shock, she was the first to go naturally unlike Rose who was killed in the war. But Fanny, she had seemed so well. Peter wrote that the strain of nursing Pierre throughout the war years in Paris, besides keeping their German officers supplied with hats for their wives. It had all taken its toll on her strength. He had tried to make the blow easier for his Aunt Clara, by writing about some of the funny things that had happened to Fanny during her days in the Milliner's trade. It was a loving thoughtful letter.

On top of that, now Gran's landlord wanted the room, so she had to get out. As with her previous moves, Mum and Dad received

a note from Gran to say she was moving, this time to St Martin's
Place off the Lewes road. Mum came home in tears saying what a
dark old dismal back room Gran had got. She had tried to get her
to come to live with us but Gran said, 'no,' she was nearer Jim and
his family and Mr Simons, Hilda's 80 year old Dad who lived with
them; he would be somebody of her own age to chat to and it was
only a short walk up to Jim's house. She said she couldn't afford any
of the rooms advertised in the Dyke Road area. This little room
would be more convenient she said, 'and I'll not turn Lily out of her
own bedroom.'

"But this room is so dark." Mum countered.

"That doesn't matter. I don't need light." Gran answered. Her
eyesight was now very poor and her ankles were swelling. The
Doctor said it was her age.

Not long after Gran moved in to her new room, a letter came,
re directed from her previous address. It was from Frank. As mum
and I arrived to see if she needed anything, we found Hilda reading
it out to Gran. The letter said he probably would not be writing for
a while, but hoped she was well. Post marked from somewhere in
Canada; this letter wasn't as full of news as all his other letters had
been, but those last words did sound oddly final.

The mantelpiece in that little backroom wasn't very deep, in
fact so narrow Gran's little keepsakes were constantly in danger
of falling off into the grate, nevertheless, she stood Frank's letter
between the Edward the eighth's egg cup and her little glass sugar
bowl.

As time went by Clara didn't go to see Hilda's father very often,
she said the walk up the hill to have tea with the family on a Sunday
was about all she could do. 'And I can't walk all the way from the
bus stop at the Seven Dials up to Dolly's home anymore.'

A day rarely went by that Dolly or Hilda didn't call in to see
Clara.

Granma never seemed to get lonely she had her little kettle on
the fire and the wireless Jimmie had rented for her. She told me she
heard the BBC announcer say there would be an orchestra and choir
in the studio performing Hiawatha's Wedding Feast. 'I had a lovely
afternoon, listening to that music again. It brought back such good

memories.' Gran never sounded gloomy. We still told each other our stories, while she sipped her tea, and chuckled at the funny side of life.

Dad on the putting green at a works outing

24

Uncle Artie,

I could not have written about my father earlier in these memories because then, I was in the hazy, lazy days of very young childhood, when I only knew him as my Daddy who skipped along the street beside me; carried me up the steep stairs to bed to keep my toes warm, gently changed the dressings on my neck; showed me, with great patience, how to cut rubber washers when he was reseating a tap or WC ball cock valve. He even explained how to be sick without it making my tummy feel horrible.

On discovering a large pair of earphones on a low shelf in Dad's wardrobe, I learned that in the 1920s he was an enthusiast for the wireless, then the latest invention, and taught himself to build a Crystal set. His sister said he spent hours in his bedroom listening to music through that huge pair of earphones. Those earphones stayed on the shelf, next to the hat I never saw him wear, for the rest of his life. When he could afford it, in the 1930s, he bought a gramophone. It was a tall imposing piece of furniture; cabinet built in highly polished rose pink wood. It stood in the corner of the front room in Coventry Street. The top lid opened upwards held in place by a chrome stay; inside, the immaculately clean brown felt turntable and chrome fittings were surrounded by small tins; each tin lid had a picture of a white dog, who's name dad told me was Nipper, looking into the wide end of a large trumpet with the legend that read, His Masters Voice. The tins were full of small shiny sharp needles. Father explained a needle had to be sharp and clean before inserting it into the playing head, adding, that if you want to hear clear sound you had to treat your equipment and records with respect. Beside the tins sat a red velvet pad with a varnished wood handle. That also had His Masters Voice printed on its top. He had gathered a large collection of shellac 78rpm records that were stored in a separate oak cupboard; each record in a paper sleeve stood on its edge, like books in a shelf supported to keep them standing up straight. Using only two fingers to hold its edge, he would carefully slide a record out of its sleeve, but before he lowered the record onto the turntable, he gently swept the velvet pad in a circular movement round the surface of the record, 'to remove any dust.' 'Never touch the velvet pad,' he told me, because you may leave grease on the surface. Next job was to insert the winding handle and wind up the turntable mechanism, stopping before it felt too tight. He knew how many turns that should be. With one finger he moved the chrome pointer from zero to 78rpm to start the turntable revolving, then lifting the curved playing arm he carefully placed the tip of the needle into the most outer groove. The sound was very loud. The volume could not be lowered but could be regulated to sound even louder by opening the doors to horns beneath the turntable. The music he played for me to dance around the room to, were Russell of Spring and The Skaters Waltz. On family occasions he played Paul Robeson, but I liked The Laughing Policeman best. As with everything else he always explained how to do things, in this case it was not so that I could play his gramophone myself. Nobody was allowed to do that. By the time I was tall enough to lift the heavy lid, records were long players and EPs played on an electric record player.

Listening to him telling mum and me where he had been and who he'd met at work each day took me into a wider world, a world of other people's lives; as I stood outside the pub door I overheard the talk, laughter mingling with other men's attitudes. Of course there was much I didn't understand but I knew if I asked questions on our walk home, he would answer my questions. There were the times his young apprenticed plumber's would call in at our home to see him, so by their conversation and laughter, I came to know how much he was liked and how carefully he listened and respected people and relished their views and stories.

Rarely seen without a cigarette; which he made with great dexterity almost always before the previous one disappeared; Dad was known in the family with affection, as Uncle Artie; full of life and good humour, he held strong views, was never seen to lose his temper; although, I have known him to be, 'like a bear with a sore head,' as my Mother would say, if he had run out of his favourite Old Holbourne tobacco, to make his next cigarette. He had begun smoking when, aged eighteen he started his plumbing apprenticeship days, with the building firm Bostal Brothers. His mate, the man who was his first trainer, Arthur Bundy, advised him to light up, saying, "Ours is a smelly old job son, having a cig covers the worst of it." And that was it, he'd smoked ever since. "Ah! And there's another thing. **Never swear in a customer's house**." Dad told me he had just caught his thumb in his new pair of pliers and said, 'Bugger!' "Well it didn't harf hurt." he remarked. That's when Mr Bundy said, "Think up something, unexpected, to relieve the pain and clear the air lad, something like, 'DISTRICT NURSE!' you can say that as loud as yer like." Then each time he had his own new apprentice mates, he gave them the same two pieces of advice.

Since the war ended the lads who started their working lives in the plumbing trade soon went off to do their National Service, sadly, many good workers did not return to the trade after their two years away. When they came back on leave they always came in to see Dad. I heard one of his best mates, Johnny Robinson say, 'Artie Smith was a good teacher, he praised you when you did a good job.' Others said he was well liked, they said he was a man easy to work with, who could always see the funny side of life. I heard these young lads laugh when they remembered how, 'Art took the stairs two at a time, and his walk was so distinctive, you knew who it was, if he was walking way on ahead, because he walked at a measured pace even when carrying his heavy bag, made of carpet, full of plumbing tools, thrown across his back to one side and his shiny brass blow lamp on the other.

Dad was as good a story teller as Granma. Life, for him was full of interest, full of happenings; he could hardly wait to tell what he had seen and done each day when he got home in the evenings. "I was standing at the kerb waiting, to cross the road at the top of West Street this afternoon, when a young woman came along side me pushing a big pram. She stopped at the edge of the kerb herself, but carried on pushing the pram off the kerb into the road; and there she stood. I just managed to grab the pram back onto the pavement before a lorry ran into it." Recalling the picture he'd just described, made him stop, as he was pulling off his boiler suit, and give a shudder, "My Gawd, gave me a fright, poor baby could have been flattened"

Turning away from the stew she was stirring Mum asked, "What did she say, wasn't she frightened?"

"No, didn't seem to notice. She just said, 'oh ta,' and carried on across the road." While Dad sharpened his razor with even sweeps up and down the leather strop that hung on the back of the kitchen door, Mum filled the enamel bowl in the sink with water from the kettle.

"You haven't called in to Emanuel's to book a hair do Doll." The thought caused him to stop as he brushed white foam from a stick of shaving soap on his chin, "I've been putting new wash basin units in there today; the salon is looking really smart now they've changed it and got rid of all those old curtained cubicles."

"Oh so it's all open plan as they call it then?" Mum said, carefully ladling the stew into a large shallow serving dish and arranging the dumplings around the edge. Dad ignored the question as he guessed she wouldn't like anyone seeing her hair just in case the alopecia had returned, "Old Mr Emanuel says he needs models for his apprentices. You'd get a free hair do."

"I know but I don't want some apprentice turning my hair green or making me look a fright."

"No they wouldn't let you leave their salon like that. They've got a reputation to keep up Dolly." But she never would take up the offer.

By the time he had washed and shaved, with his bone handled cut throat razor, he would have related other sights and scenes. Mum would have taken the dishes of stew and vegetables into the dining room and started serving out portions onto hot plates. As we ate our dinner we heard more about people he'd met on the bus and maybe described a beautiful house he had worked in that day, installing the latest coloured ceramic ware. He would be finished and laying his knife and fork together tidily, pushing his plate away, when Mum and I were still halfway through our meal, having so often halted in mid forkful to take in all the twists and turns of his day. A man of regularity he always expressed his appreciation saying, "Thank you that was lovely Doll." He said he didn't need puddings. The only time he ate pudding was Christmas pudding. He never ate any kind of fruit; he wouldn't go into a room where there were bananas, he said he couldn't bare the smell.

Father wouldn't eat out in a restaurant. His work had taken him into so many eating places in and around the town, from the lowliest greasy spoon to the top hotel restaurant kitchens. The only place where he said you could even eat your dinner off the floor was Divall's eating house in Middle Street. 'Everywhere there was as clean as a whistle,' he told us.

"Johnny Robinson and I were sitting outside in the sunshine eating our lunch at the back of that National Restaurant, when a lad comes out into the yard and starts searching through the rubbish bins. He saw us looking at him and he says, 'we've run out of lettuce, the manager sent me out to see if there were any decent outer leaves bi'n chucked away that shouldn't a bi'n.' Young John said he'd remember not to go there for a meal."

"Dear oh dear, you never know what goes on behind the scenes do you?" Mum commented, but as she could never afford anything more than a cup of tea in Lyon's Tea shop, she still wondered, 'they couldn't make a mess of that, could they?'

"I nearly got into a tight corner today," Dad said, "I'd just finished setting up some pipe work at the back of the Princes News Theatre in North Street and stopped to have a smoke out in the yard. I heard the music for the big picture start so I stepped back in and stood by the side of the stage to see what was on. I got so engrossed in the film I didn't notice my smoke was drifting across the screen."

"Aw dear Artie," Mum asked, full of concern, "whatever happened?"

"Well somebody in the audience shouted, 'fire.' And young Johnny said, 'Blimey, you'll be for it!' So I left him flapping the back door open and closed to get rid of the smoke, and buzzed off round to the box office to find the Manager."

"Oh Artie whatever did he say?"

"'Well, I suppose that shows one of our customers is still awake,' then he laughed and carried on counting what he'd been adding up."

Just another story in Dad's ever changing daily repertoire that usually ended with us all laughing as we cleared away the dirty dishes; but there were some stories he didn't tell while we were eating, such as the time he had been to unblock the drains at a new Chinese restaurant.

"New Chinese Restaurant?" Mum queried, "The Nanking's been there years."

"No, not that one, this place opened a couple of weeks ago and we've been called in four times already. I went in through their back entrance and caught a bloke peeing into a saucepan, when he saw me he poured it down the sink. Well, I couldn't believe my eyes."

"What did you do?" Mum had a look of on her face that said, Yuck!

"I just carried on through the kitchen like usual. I hadn't seen anything." I had heard him say that before when he told how he had knocked on a customer's bathroom door before going in, just in case there was somebody in there. "Nobody answered, so in I went to test the radiator and bother me there was this woman laying in the bath. 'Oh don't mind me plumber.' She said. I just turned tail and walked out as if I hadn't seen anything." Mum had stopped asking, 'What did you say?' because she knew by now he'd told her, that if he responded that showed he *had* seen.

One spring day he and his mate were taking a short cut down through from the top of Bear Road cemetery, to their next job, when the heavens opened and the rain absolutely fell out of the sky. It was a long trek down the bleak treeless hillside to the small arched chapel and seeing there was a half dug grave by the pathway, they both jumped down into it and pulled the tarpaulin over their heads. Artie said they were standing there smoking, chatting and laughing, when they realised the rain had stopped, so, without thinking they climbed out of the grave and almost bumped in to a couple of old dears carrying bunches of flowers who, both stood rooted to the spot, staring in disbelief. You won't believe who they were?"

"No Who?" Mum asked.

"The two ladies Arthur Levett call Miss North and South. You remember the two old dears who collect for the church. Well, the little one screamed; so I said, 'Sorry ladies.' And the tall one said, 'Thilly thods, you scared my thithter out of our wits.' then she bent double laughing her head off."

Dad told us that story on a Saturday lunch time when Granma was with us.

"Oh Dolly," Granma wheezed, she couldn't go on for a moment, as she was laughing so much, "I've always said your Artie will get into trouble one day with all that smoking."

Yes, my Dad Artie was fun to be with but he also retained an air of his father's pre 1914 generation upright good manners. Grandad Sam wore the gold watch and chain, given to him for long service to his Union, hanging across his waist-coated front. My father wore his silver pocket watch, given to him for his twenty first birthday; hanging from the lapel and top pocket of his sports jacket, as was the fashion in his generation. Like his father he only wore his watch and chain when dressed for leisure in their best clothes; both stood erect, as if to attention, when each, very carefully took the watch out of its pocket, to be referred to for the time. Like Father and son, each was a reliable character who, between them, they created a strong safe life for all the family.

On Monday evenings Father sat down with a large file of green coloured duplicated pages, took up a pencil, he kept standing in a vase originally designed to hold cigarettes, and wrote out his weekly time sheets, in a neat copperplate hand. This delivered into the firm's office on Tuesday morning raised his pay in cash on a Thursday evening. Dad never had a bank account. Banks only opened on weekdays from 10am and closed by 3.30 in the afternoon. They were no use to him, because his working day did not allow him time to get to a bank. A tin box for savings was at his convenience.

The photo of him on the putting green was taken at the last works outing he went to. He stopped going because he couldn't take my Mum, because he said, the men used bad language and told stories women shouldn't hear. Dad never swore in front of women and children.

BOOK THREE: 1941 – 1952

Part Five

1

Was Granma's last move, design or coincidence?

"Put your Mother away in a home I hear." A woman's raised voice came from behind Mum and me as we walked through the Regent Arcade heading for the bus stop in the Dyke Road. We both looked round to see who it was. Mum had already recognised the voice and groaned a quiet little, "Oh dear, now what."

I saw a beautifully groomed lady with piles of carefully arranged tight curly grey hair. As she came towards us she was still talking at the top of her voice. Mum stopped and turned to face her, saying, in a firm voice,

"No Ethel. I don't know where you got that story from but it's not true." I could see Mum was very upset but the woman didn't stop.

"Yes you have," she said, "who'd put their Mother in an old people's home. You've got plenty of room in your house haven't you Dolly?"

It was useless bothering to answer the women. After a few moments Mum turned and took my hand.

"Come on we'll miss our bus." Mum didn't look back so I didn't either. On the bus I asked, "Who was that lady Mum?" Her answer was short,

"My step-sister."

"She smelled lovely." I said

"Yes, when I was your age I used to admire how she always looked so beautiful. I thought she smelled wonderful in her perfume and cosmetics."

"What did she mean? Why was she so noisy?" I learned that Ethel was well known for being a busybody. Always poking her nose in, loud with criticism but never turning a hand to help out.

A month previously Granma had taken advantage of an offer of a place in one of the Council's new Homes for the Elderly. A card had come in the early morning post from Gran. It just said, "Have place in Home," with the address and date when she would be there, "Love, Mum." My Mother could hardly read it, the writing sprawled two words a line. That afternoon, as soon as she left work, Mum hot-footed over to Gran's lodgings to find her mother packing the last of her possessions into boxes.

"These two boxes can go home with you." Gran said to Mum without looking up as if her daughter had been in the room all the time.

Apparently Granny had been collecting her pension at the Post Office in the Lewes Road, when the lady behind the counter pushed a leaflet inside her pension book.

"What's this dear?" Granma asked, "Will you read it to me?" The leaflet told of a new home especially for elderly people being opened by the Council.

"Thought you might like to put your name down for a place, Mrs Cowley," the Post Mistress suggested, "you not being able to see so well nowadays."

So that's just what Gran did. No question of her son or daughter having any say in the matter. "I'll never be a burden." I had heard her say those words over the years.

The Home was in a large Edwardian red brick family house. Visitors were only allowed on Wednesday, Saturday and Sunday afternoons. The first time we were able to see Granma, the Matron met Mum in the front hall and took her aside whilst I was ordered to, "– stand still just inside the front door while I speak to your Mother." Later I heard Mum tell Dad, 'she said would I ask my Mother to stop slopping her tea into the saucer to drink.'

"Mother has always been used to taking her tea from a dish." Mum replied.

"What dish?" asked the Matron, seemingly nonplussed.

"She has her tea from a dish. That's the way she was brought up. It's always the way she's taken her tea. I've never seen her slop her tea, ever."

"Mrs Smith, it is Mrs Smith isn't it?" But she didn't give Mum a chance to answer. "Nevertheless perhaps you'd speak to your Mother." The Matron's wishes sounded imperative as if an important Inspector might come through the door at any minute.

Looking very small in a rather high backed arm chair Gran was sitting staring into a smoking fire looking very small in a rather high backed chair surrounded by warm ruby velvet cushions. As soon as she saw us her face brimmed with her lovely happy smile. We all three pulled our chairs up close together as we had always done. It must have looked rather a huddle in that great high ceilinged room. Gran told us she had packed her cup and tea dish, she called Laura and Bea, away in the box she had sent to Coventry Street to be stored. She hadn't wanted to have her cup and dish in the home because she thought they might get broken in the washing up.

When our tea was served Mum could see the saucers used in the Home were very shallow with hardly any lip so it must be why it looked like the tea was being slopped. Mum got it all sorted out by asking the lady who served the tea to take great care of Gran's own cup and tea dish if she brought them in.

"They're old friends and Mum wouldn't want them chipped." She told the helper.

It seemed to work, the helpers were themselves daughters like my Mum and had respect for the things that were dear to their own mothers. That's what I heard Mum tell Dad.

I think Granma felt a relief that she didn't have to go out to the shops in bad weather if she didn't feel like it, or search for a shilling for the electric meter. The rooms were spacious and warm, but Mum was shocked to see Gran slept in a room with three other ladies, sharing washing basins in an adjoining room, where there was a cubicle with one lavatory. Gran never complained about that. We visited at weekends and as the weather warmed we found Gran in the gardens. She told us she often sat in the garden listening to the Rooks arguing high in the tree tops, saying she could smell the earth, and asking were there antirrhinums close by?

"Bring me a packet of night scented Stocks will you." asked Gran. Turning to me she said, "You and I will scatter them along the border. It'll be our secret, they won't know till they come up."

We did sow her seeds and later that summer, when she lingered in the garden one evening, Gran told us she smiled at the Matron's words.

"Come along now Mrs Cowley, it's about time you came in, you'll catch cold in the evening air." Taking hold of Gran's elbow she said, "I don't know what's come over Mr Scanlon sowing flower seeds half onto the edge of the grass here."

Gran had asked the Gardner not to remove the lovely smelling little blooms. He knew what she had done alright, he wasn't silly. He was just kind. He told my Mum that Gran sat on a seat he had placed to catch the afternoon sun. She was humming that song she told him she had heard on the wireless, 'You know,' he said, 'Those two 'oo sing together, Anne Ziegler and that Webster Booth chap, something about love and my heart and I. Your Mother said it reminded her of young love. Lovely aint it thinking about young love an' she's over eighty 'int she?'

Some months later the Matron had another request. Would Mum persuade her Mother not to wear a pinafore, it makes her look like one of the sewing ladies. She should realise she is now a lady of leisure she told Mum. We knew Gran liked her wrap around pinafore because she was comfortable wearing it and she kept little items in the pockets. This time Mum didn't complain, knowing her Co-Op divi had just come due she went straight down the Co-Op in the London road to find a wool cardigan with pockets.

"Look Mum I've found this lovely cardigan in the Co-Op. Winter's coming so it will be just right. Got pockets in it too, look here."

Feeling the soft wool Gran said, "Oh Dolly you shouldn't have spent your money on me, I'm old, I've got enough clothes to last me out."

"Don't worry the divi paid for it. Anyway I remember the time you came home with two dresses for me."

"Ah yes," Gran giggled a bit. "I couldn't resist them. Just the right time wasn't it though?" My Mum didn't answer immediately.

"Yes, I know what you mean between that horrible man trying it on with me and losing my job. You were always so thoughtful of people's feelings."

Gran smiled. "Thank you," she said, "The pockets are just what I need."

It worked; wearing the pinafore over the top of the cardigan would have been too bulky, so finally Mrs Clara Cowley fitted in to Matron's view of her world.

"That's a pretty bonnet. Did Mummy make it?" Gran gently laid a hand on my head. The shaped bonnets made of four black felted wool squares stitched together with bright red blanket stitch were all the fashion. Mum had embroidered the sides and back with flowers, poppies and leaves in embroidery wools.

"Keeps your head nice and warm my sweeting." I thought Gran couldn't see at all, but no, she had little chinks of vision she told me. "Nice warm feel too, now the weather's closing in." She said, repeating the story of her own Grandparents knitting bonnets and socks to make sure the Grandchildren kept their heads and feet warm in the low misty months on the Marsh.

"Frankie's written to say sorry he couldn't come to see me in the summer, he says Marjorie wanted to go to Skye and Iona, but he's coming after they've done with all the hotel's Christmas Festivities." She looked so pleased and relieved to know she would be seeing him. Mum had heard from her half brother too. He told her his plans in a few words on a card with a picture of the Abbey on the Island of Iona where he explained Christianity first came to the British Isles.

2

A gentleman is taking
too much interest

After Christmas we noticed there were more chairs occupied around the large sitting room. One of the helpers said a further six bedrooms had been refurbished and six new residents had begun to arrive.

Again the Matron took my Mum aside as soon as we arrived for our regular visit. As before she told me stay in the hall while she spoke to Mum. By then I knew where Granma sat in the now heavily draped sitting room, so I sidled up to the curtained doorway and peeped through. Normally Gran had some idea when Mum and I would be coming and would be positioned in her chair where I knew, if she was looking straight ahead, she could just see me. This time things were different. Somebody was sitting with their back to me obscuring her view – in fact obscuring her altogether. I didn't hear what Matron had said until Mum told Dad that evening.

"Matron said a gentleman was taking too much interest in Mother and she felt it very unseemly."

"What did you say?" Dad asked.

"Well, I was a bit taken aback. She talked as if it was Mum's fault."

"Mum's fault, how?"

"If you had heard the Matron's opinion, you would have thought Mum was acting like a flighty youngster to get the man's attention." Dad laughed at the thought. "Surely it's her place to have a word with the gentleman if she thinks he is giving one of her lady residents too much attention, not blame my Mother."

"Granny looked extra happy today, Mummy," I commented to Mum, "and a gentleman had been talking to her."

My parents turned to gape at me as if I had no ears and eyes. Then Mum carried on telling Dad, "The Matron said it wasn't right for people of their age, she said, the Gentleman was actually holding Mum's hand."

"Oh dear." mimicked my Dad.

When I saw Mum coming out of the Matron's office I skipped across the room to Gran just as the gentleman was kissing her hand, whispering, 'Clara Ann,' before he moved to a chair across the room. When Mum walked in to the sitting room, Gran looked warm and happy and there wasn't anybody with her, except me. I could see Mum wondered what all the fuss was about. But I noticed how Gran's cheeks were flushed and she was smiling in a rather special way.

3

My 10th birthday gift

The following weekend was my birthday. Mum was sitting next to Gran, and I was cuddled up beside her in a big old armchair, when she turned to Mum and said,

"Kettle's boiling make the tea dear, I'm too comfy to get up." Just as if we were in her bedsitter. For a split second Mum and I looked at each other and immediately decided not to show anything was unusual.

"Yes," said my Mother, and straightaway bent down beside the fire and performed all the movements of making the tea as she would have done back when Gran lived in her rented rooms; where her kettle would have sat on the trivet down in the fender by the fire, the tray holding the tea pot and a jug of milk, alongside Laura and Bea, Gran's cup and tea dish, were ready on the chair-side table. The sugar bowl, that had been a wedding present to Granma and Granddad Tom in 1902, was always kept to hand, on the mantelpiece above the fire.

Unlike Gran's little bedsitter this huge room was subdued by the light ruby coloured velvet drapes now pulled across the tall windows to keep out the winter cold. Fires popped and crackled, burning deep and mellow in the spacious fireplaces, one each end of the room. Tea was being brought round and a tray set beside us just in time before Gran asked Mum to pour the imaginary tea. After Gran had taken a few sips from her dish she suddenly seemed to remember she had something for my Birthday. From her cardigan pocket she handed me a small bundle wrapped in a fine but ageing cotton handkerchief, inside I found a little Willow pattern plate.

"This is Mispah," she said with a smile, "keep it safe and give it to your own daughter one day." perhaps we both knew something about the future. Her next words did seem a bit odd, for she said, "Now Mispah is yours to watch over you."

I loved the dear little dish cupped in the palms of my hands, and I couldn't wait to find out why it had such a strange sounding name. Where had she got it because I hadn't seen it before, and I thought I knew everything about my Granma, we had always been so close. But Mum said yes, the little Willow plate had sat on Gran's mantelpiece. I thought about it and decided it must have been hidden behind Leslie's silk card and the egg cup with the man's face on. The face that had a rather a blank stare, but then I found all faces interesting. Gran had once told me the man on the egg cup should have been king but his brother became king instead; now it was that brother who had just died – that's where my thoughts wandered. What now!

Gran, Mum and I talked for longer than usual, getting ourselves a stare of disapproval from Matron. It was my birthday after all.

The story Gran told me about Mispah's travels was so wonderful but she couldn't tell me the whole story, it was too long and I wouldn't understand it all. "Mummy will tell you more when you're older," she said, "I'm just a bit tired now."

Mum whispered in my ear, "We must go home to get Dad's tea." So while she had a last few words with Gran I wandered across the room towards a gentleman who was beckoning. I thought he wanted me to pick up his newspaper, instead he asked if it was my birthday. I told him my Grandmother had given me this little Willow pattern plate to look after. He held out his hand and I laid it on his palm.

"Gran said it would look after me." I told him and he said,

"So it will, so it will." It seemed odd that he knew all about it; I tucked Mispah inside my glove, gave Gran a kiss, waved to the old gentleman and went home to my Dad.

As we scrunched down the pebbled drive, out to the Preston Road, Mum asked,

"What did the gentleman want?"

"To see my birthday present," I told her. "Mummy, why did he call Granma Clara Ann?" she stopped walking.

"Are you sure," she asked, I assured her that he had. "The only person who still refers to her by that name is – surely not." she said, partly under her breath. Then she went on walking.

4

Granma's 84ᵗʰ Birthday

Uncle Frank came the first weekend in February to see Gran on her birthday. He said he'd left Glasgow deep in snow. It wasn't much better in Brighton, although the snow wasn't so deep that we couldn't walk down Lover's Walk steps and along the Preston Road to visit Gran. Mum on one side and Uncle Frank on the other we skipped and laughed as we walked together. Gran was so pleased to see Uncle Frank. She always called him Frankie. He brought her a lovely warm soft curly wool lavender coloured scarf and shortbreads in a tartan tin. I was eager to show her the Fair-Isle cardigan and Tam o' Shanter he brought me from Scotland.

"Don't tell yer Mum. Aunty Marjorie bought that for you." Uncle had whispered when he helped me on with the beautiful cardigan, in our warm kitchen back in Coventry Street.

Granma listened and laughed as Frankie described his kitchen where he was head Chef. Oh my, did she giggle over the funny situations his staff got themselves into. How proud she looked when he told us he was setting up a kitchen in the new hotel, planned to open in Edinburgh by the end of the year. Granma had that 'extra happy look' again and Frankie called her, 'his little Mother.'

Noticing a disapproving look blazing from the other side of the room, Mum touched Uncle Frank's elbow, warning him,

"Oye, oye, time's up."

"You're right." Uncle Frank agreed. "We've tired Mum out."

I went across the room to say goodbye to the old gentlemen, he was beaming from ear to ear as we had a little chat. A lady with a pinny tied round her ample middle padded towards us pushing an elegant tea trolley collecting tea cups.

"Is the little girl a relative?" she asked the gentleman. He looked at me and smiled. Slowly he replied,

"Yes, I think you could say we are related by Willow."

Granma and me

5

In the days that followed

From the conversation between Uncle Frank and Mum on our walk home I heard he had asked to visit Gran the following morning; although visiting wasn't usually allowed on a Sunday morning, he explained to the Matron that he was taking the train back to Glasgow in the afternoon. Then he described how, 'the Matron said, meltingly, "Of course Mr Dann." Meltingly! Even at ten years old I thought Uncle's description suited the woman.

When Mum and I visited Granma on the Sunday afternoon we found her asleep with a broad smile on her face, her chair was now angled slightly away from the fire. As she became aware of our presence her eyes opened but her gaze was straight ahead to the chair on the opposite side of the fireplace where the gentleman sat. Somehow, that afternoon I thought she had a look of warm contentment.

6

A bunch of Snow Drops

The first thing I asked Mum when I arrived home from school on Monday afternoon was why wasn't she in the school canteen at lunchtime.

"Granma died this morning," she told me, "The Matron 'phoned up the school and the Head came and said I'd better pop off down the Home. He even called a taxi for me. Always thought he was a kind chap. You never know till the time comes do you?" Mum seemed to go on talking, she couldn't stop.

Later that evening, at the dinner table, she told Dad what had happened and went on to say, "When the Matron took me in to see Mum, I said, how lovely. Thank you. There was a sweet little bunch of snowdrops laid in Granma's hands. The Matron looked really surprised, she said, 'Who put those flowers there?' Just as if somebody had done something wrong. It sounded so unfeeling, so I had to say, it must have been somebody very loving. After a few moments the matron whispered, 'Yes, you're right, it was a loving gestured, your Mother was a sweet lady Mrs Smith. We'll miss her.' Well that filled me up." Mum said, and burst into tears. I felt so sad for my poor Mum, she was full of sadness that Gran would never come to live in our house so she could take care of her Mother. "Mum's always done so much for us kiddies when she had so little herself. I suppose when all your contemporaries have gone, life must feel empty; old Mrs Turk gone and Fanny too. Mum said she hadn't received a letter from her friend Maud Sinden in Australia, for a long time.

"She did things the way she wanted to Doll, and she had a lot of nice people around her in the Home didn't she?" Dad replied,

"I know, I know." Mum sniffed, "You're right. Funny really, she looked so, so, well, fulfilled, when we saw her yesterday. Look here," Mum held out a tissue wrapped bundle, "one of the tea ladies gave me Mum's cup and tea dish as I came away. She said she had given Mum a cup of hot chocolate at bedtime last night. Wasn't that thoughtful of her Artie? And do you know what else she told me? She said, 'Your Mother told me, 'Thank you, it is lovely being served, so kindly, after I have been the one serving others all my life.'" Mum turned to look at me and said, "It's almost as if she knew?" Knowing my Gran, I'm sure she did.

7

Little Mother

Frankie didn't return for Granma's funeral. He said in his letter to Mum that he'd 'been with his 'Little Mother' at the right time, when she was alive.' Mum organised the funeral, bought herself a black coat and hat, borrowing a pair of black shoes from a neighbour. Dad couldn't go because he wasn't allowed time off work, his contribution was to wear a black arm band. I went to school and the family went to a funeral. It wasn't thought I needed to be there. It didn't worry me. Adults did a lot of things where we children had no inclusion. I don't even know who attended only that Mum had tea that afternoon with her brother Jim, sister-in-law Edith and their cousin Leslie.

Gran's life insurance policy paid out £39 for which she had paid in, one penny a week since 1900.

I knew my Granma was happy when she died in February 1952. She had lived for 84 years and two days. I have carried her life stories in my memory, ever growing in details passed on through my Mother, her daughter Dolly.

BOOK THREE: 1941 – 1952

After I finished writing the first draft of 'Arrival' –

Snow, snow and more snow had come storming in with the year 2010. It kept us completely snowed in for almost a month, only the third time it has happened in the forty years we have lived here at Deerfold cottage. A real treat for me as it gave me the space to write these final chapters. We usually have very mild winters here in Sussex.

Outside everywhere was peaceful under a deep blanket of perfect dry snow. Great branches on the beech trees hung low, nearly touching the ground so heavy with duvets of white along their branches. Fir trees dipped to the earth under flowing feathery cloaks looking like a crowd of monks trudging along on their way to Chapel. Through the still cold air raised voices could be heard clearly from half a mile across the valley, sharply followed by the sudden roar of a tractor engine firing up, sending a puff of grey smoke lazily smudging the air. No bird sounds; sometimes a fox's bark, but that's rare, for who's going to let on where they are and let a meal get away. At dusk owls hooted conversing at the outset of a night's hunting. In the morning it was plain to see there had been plenty of night movement by the fox prints; one single line of footfalls close to the double thump of rabbit hind legs flat in the snow, two dots of front paws hurrying across our human pathways back to their burrows. This winter should mean less rabbits to ravage vegetable patches in the spring, but above all this hard winter will have been good for the land in breaking down the old and weak to make room for strong new growth.

Groups of fallow deer range over our garden, soundlessly in their seasonal migrations. This extra silence has sparked a greater vigilance among the dogs in the area. Farm dogs rarely bark, now, when their warning voices sound it reminds me of Clara's Great Grandfather James waiting in the dunes, in 1802, listening for the approach of an ailing ship along the channel coast, its position dogged by barking shoreline sentinels.

Inside, the house is quiet, just the snap and crackle of logs in the fire basket. For forty autumns we have prepared for a hard winter, although few have kept us enclosed like this one. We've certainly had to burn more wood. An old ash tree, we reluctantly had to cut down last year, has already proved a blessing. The tree was very close to the house and like an old friend we had noticed it had not been thriving recently. When the felling process started it was obvious why. An insect nest, made high up in a cleft had allowed water to seep down through the trunk, starting a deep vein of black rot. Had it come down in the autumn storms it could have caused a lot of damage. Being so near the house careful plans were made to avoid any damage. It took three days to debranch and fell, then a week to clear; all the while three buzzards soared high on the thirmals above, against a brilliant clear blue sky watching the human progress disturbing the wildlife below. The ash's life wasn't wasted as it has provided us with the extra logs we needed. Its demise was well timed. Ash to ash and dust to earth again, it had parented many new trees in its eighty years.

Children's piping voices and the thump of wet boots in the back lobby heralds clear roads. The door burst open and a little hand comes slowly round the heavy curtain that has shrouded the doorway for the last three months, before the whole drape is thrust aside letting in a shock of cold air. Unable to wait to pull slippers on our first grandson scampers across the kitchen calling, "Grandad, Grandad." He's two and a half and we are both Grandad until he can get round another syllable. His progress is a delight to witness for us as it is for all Grandparents. Since I started telling Clara's family stories he has been joined by a brother now seven months old his little face bright fresh from the cold air snuggling a red nose against his Mum, the pair closely followed by their Aunty, our daughter Galia, unfurling her long scarf she could hardly contain the question,

"Was it him?"

"Well, was it?" I couldn't keep them in suspense any longer.

"Yes, it was." Did I hear a great sigh of relief from the Willow china on the dresser shelves, or maybe it was just my imagination?

"How did you know, for sure I mean?" Galia asked.

"Simply because when the tea lady was collecting the old gentleman's cup Uncle Frank came across the room to say he and Mum were ready to leave, he reached down for my hand and his eyes met the old gentleman's. I saw his face reflected a mixture of shock and recognition."

"'Father?' it was barely a whisper as the pair shook hands, the old man gently clasped both his hands round Frankie's. No words passed between them – we just turned, and walked away, Uncle stopping to give Gran one last kiss."

"And did Frankie go back the next day?"

"Oh, yes, and I know he stayed all morning."

"Gran died a couple of days later you said?"

"No, it was the very next day."

"It must have been Frank who put the snowdrops in her hands."

"Yes, must've been." But I couldn't say anymore – not at that moment. Later, I suggested we might have a family picnic in June, near the village church where Great Great Grandfather John Pilbeam was buried in June 1910. Granma would like that and I thought I would take with us, Big Pol, the jug that sat on the end of the bar at the Lamb Inn for so many years.'

On a sunny summer afternoon in June we all met at the church with a picnic tea, sitting on a grassy bank among the gravestones. Swathes of tall daisies bobbing and waving their heads around us in the warm breeze, just like the reporter wrote in his Obituary for The Bexhill Observer, describing the scene on the day 'The Great Man was buried.'

A hundred years on we raised our teacups to, "Johnny Pilbeam, Innkeeper."

Johnny Pilbeam at the wheel of a car

Epilogue

These stories have been gathering in my memory for more than 65 years. It wasn't until the delivery man saying our old Willow pattern china "must have some stories to tell," that I had the link I needed to bring the collection into a book.

The Willow pattern pieces of china tell most of their stories in book one, when their lives were more often in use. Through the days of book two Granma and my Mum were both in service having little opportunity to use the Willow China; in book three, only Granma's cup and tea dish and chamber stick stayed with her. All the other willows were packed away during those war years

Granma and Mum had so often told their own stories and passed on more from other Grannies and Aunty's, going back three further generations. What I tell also includes gleanings from family conversations, members telling their own experiences or re-telling and passing on the happenings told by others often corroborating truths. I've woven their medley through with entries from diaries and the information I read in painted portraits and photographs. I've always been fascinated by more than one person telling their experience of the same happening. As an only child I grew up listening to table talk among the adults, especially my Dad's daily tales of his doings and as I have said Granma has told me stories from the very day of my birth, recalled many times by my Aunt Hetty. Even more arresting for an only child was to hear my husband and his twin brother telling their versions of the same happening.

A population of comforting familiar characters, full of curious tradition left within the pieces of Willow pattern china, still exist on my dresser shelves. I lift the cup and dish down to wash knowing my Granma and her Grandmother used it before me; I fill a big jug and know it stood on the bar at an Inn on the Marsh witness to the world of my great-great-grandparents, who, everyday gave wayfarers hearty welcome with good food and drink at their Inn; also showed genuine compassion by never allowing a local orphaned child to go homeless and unwanted. All enjoyed a song or four.

I still have Clara Ann's treasured copy of the local Bexhill newspaper published in June 1910 with Grandfather John's obituary. In her husband's old frayed wallet are gathered postcards showing Johnny Pilbeam at Hailsham Market including a newspaper cutting photo of him sitting high at the wheel of a car; his first time.

I knew from the diary handed down to mum's employer, Petronella, by her great great grandmother Carlotta, that Sophie, the Willow pattern Trembleur, must have witnessed, first a joyful life in France, followed many years later by the turbulent life her great great granddaughter experienced in the 1920s and 30s, recalled by my Mother. I have written that down in book two. 'All Change 1919-1940' Carlotta's story is entwined with Clara's great great Grandmother Amy who was born in 1765. I tell this story in my Prequel, 'The Last Box'

Whilst bringing all these stories together, coupled with the usually unheard voices of these old family friends living in our midst, I discovered the life of an ordinary woman can be, in truth, so extra-ordinary.

I know Granma loved exchanging tales with me, she rocking with laughter or shedding a tear at the stories I told her in my childhood naivety. Those times were a joy in the memory of my first ten years. Her last ten years.

Lilian Forshaw, August 2010

PS: The Love Token, Mispah, still sits among its Willow pattern family on our Dresser here at Deerfold Cottage. Thank you Granma.

Author's Notes

The incident that really made me feel I had to write about my Gran's
life was when I heard how callously she was told to vacate her home
on the day her husband died. At the time a woman could not hold
a rent book. It shocked me that in the twentieth century women
still had little or no control over their lives. Of course it didn't
happen entirely like that, but it would have if it hadn't been for an
older more experienced neighbour who reminded Clara that Tom
had paid a whole week's rent only two days previously, on his way
home from work on the Friday evening. It was lucky Jenny Starr
was prepared to stand up to the bully of a rent collector on Clara's
behalf.

~~~

Few people, amongst them some acknowledged food historians, do
not know and don't believe, that there were such places as second
hand food shops. Just you think. Factual history records the heavy
late night meals taken by some of the wealthier families in Victorian
times and the numbers of courses served at Lunches and Dinners in
the Edwardian period. Gran often said many dishes never even got
touched, and yes it was the case that House keepers were ordered
to throw away leftover food and untouched dishes rather than
servants have it, 'in case they got a taste for the superior upstairs
diet.' Second hand food dealers got to know when a kitchen was
making preparations for special guests and would be ready to collect
leftovers. They might even be the regular local bone collector and
know the Cook and kitchen staff. Gran's cook mentor Mrs Charlish
told her about the secondhand food shop in the Vauxhall Bridge
road that collected from the establishment where she was resident in
London.

Here are a few of Granma's little tips for you

- If you are going out and haven't had time to wash your hair. Give your hair a vigorous rub all over with a real silk scarf.

- Always look after your feet – you are on them all your life. Treat yourself like you are an athlete. Keep your feet dry. Cream and massage them, including your ankles, as often as you can. Try to do that every night as you get older.

- Take a spoonful of cod liver oil every day. It's good for your bones and joints.

- To avoid cramp, take a glass of Indian tonic water regularly for the Quinine

List of characters in order of appearance in this book. No.3 of the trilogy.

Clara Ann Cowley nee Dann – *Lily's grandmother*

Frankie and Marjorie – *Clara's eldest son and his wife*

Jimmie – *Clara's youngest son*

Hilda – *Jimmie's wife*

Violet May (Dolly) – *Clara's daughter, Lily's mother*

Arthur William Smith (Artie) – *Dolly's husband*

Fanny – *Clara's 2nd sister*

Dr John Vance and his wife Dr Grace family GPs

Hetty and Arthur Levett – *Artie's sister, Arthur Levett was Frankie's WW1 pal*

Frank Anderson – *Clara's first sweetheart*

Petronella Marshall Wilson (Madam) – *Niece to Frank, and Dolly's employer*

Toby Marshall – *Petronella's son*

John and Annie Pilbeam – *Clara's Grandparents, owners of the Lamb Inn*

Robert Pilbeam – *John's father*

James Hartshorn – *Annie Pilbeam's father*

Granny Hartshorn – *(Amy Cakebred nee Mortain) James's mother Clara's Gt Gt Gran*

Aunt Hetta – *Annie Pilbeam's life-long friend*

Mrs. Charlish – *Clara's cooking mentor*

Rose – *Clara's first sister*

Leslie – *Rose's son*

Uncle Barney – *Robert Pilbeam's brother*

Elizabeth (Lizzie) – *John and Annie Pilbeam's eldest daughter*

Gracie – *Lizzie's daughter*

Charlotte (Lottie) – *John and Annie's second daughter*

Lilian – *Lottie's daughter*

Emily – *John and Annie Pilbeam's youngest daughter, Clara's mother*

Bill Tidy – *potman at the Lamb Inn*

Nancy – *Clara's third sister married to Valentino Prestigiafore (an Italian family spoken of as conjurors with food) their son, shortened his name when standing in a queue waiting to sign up in 1914 and became known as -*

Bill Pretty, and his story appears in the Sequel book 5

Ruth – *Bill's wife*

Uncle Bert Peerless (Uncle of respect) – *next door neighbour in Coventry Street*

Alex and Joyce Forshaw – *Lily's future parents in law*

Uncle Fred – *Artie's brother*

Roy – *Hetty and Arthur Levett's son*

Mildred – *Roy's girlfriend, later his wife*

Miss Cole and Mrs Wood – *Owners of the Porthall Tavern*

Mrs Volks – *wife of Volks's Railway owner*

Betty – *Aunty Hetty's daily*

Bud Smith – *Arties cousin*

Miss Noakes (Queenie) – *kept the little shop halfway along Coventry Street*

Mrs Turk – *Arthur Levett's mother, midwife to Clara's son Frankie*

Eldred (Known in the family as Young Longsight) – *distant Pilbeam relative*

Ethel – *Clara's husband Tom's daughter from his first marriage*

Jack and Ruby – *Mildred's parents*

The Willow Pattern China characters

Mizpah

Big Pol

Tubby night
stick

Old Po

Laura and Bea cup
and tea dish

Big Tureen

Josephine
ring tree

Little Jug

Cruet Triplets

Hannah hat
pin pot

Mrs P

Sophie Trembleur

Dolly

Bessie

Uncle Bert

Here is a taste of book four
Lilian Forshaw

BOOK THREE: 1941 – 1952

1765 – 1889

Granma's final story
Christmas 1951

A Cameo Prequal to the 'Clara' trilogy

"I may not see another Christmas." Granma Clara announced, as if this was a sudden thought. Then she added, "I've just remembered a story that I should tell you all." The room went quiet. The family had been sitting around the fire in conversation long after a pleasant Christmas tea, so it was quite late in the evening. Lifting the handle of the old copper coal bucket my Dad asked,

"Is it going to be a one bucket or two bucket story Clara?"

"Don't be so cheeky Artie." His sister Hetty said. Granma laughed,

"You won't change him Het. I'll try to keep it to a one bucket."

While Dad built up the fire, Uncle Arthur topped up the glasses and my Mum and Hilda, her sister in-law, Jimmie's wife, went to cut a few sandwiches.

"If Clara says it's something she should tell us I'd say it is gonna be two buckets worth!" whispered Hilda as she cut and buttered bread on the kitchen table.

Meanwhile Granma Clara had been up to her room and was sitting with an old bowler hat box down beside her chair.

Granma's story telling was legend in the family. Everybody sat back getting themselves comfortable in anticipation of, what my dad Artie, called a good yarn.

"I was 4 years old when I heard a hint of this story." Clara began, "It was when my mother took me to old granny Hartshorn's funeral tea. Mm, let me think now, that would have been in 1872. I had no idea what a funeral was, but I thought it must be a special tea party, because mum dressed herself all in black and tied a black bow in my hair." Clara paused to take a sip of her warmed ginger wine. "I can see that darkened room and hear the voices as if it were yesterday.

There was a little old lady sitting just inside the door, she had a lacy cap on her head. Mum had to stoop down really low to kiss the lady's cheek.

'Clara, this is Aunt Martha.' Mum said.

'Hallo child.' The lady spoke in a voice that sounded like a chirping bird.

I stood tucked in beside my Mother's knee watching lots of people coming into the room. The gathering bodies appeared to rise all around me; glum faced women sat on straight backed chairs surrounded by volumes of black stiff layered skirts. Men stood behind the lady's chairs holding their top hats sedately on their arms, leaving their uncovered bald heads shining white in the candle light, like the summits of mountains bobbing up against the ceiling. The only sound and colour in the room was the genteel plink of Granny's blue and white teacups and saucers. Somebody told my mother to lift me up above a long box, 'to take a last look at the dear departed,' I was surprised to see a face I recognised, although I couldn't understand why my Gan gan Amy was laying there in the box, so still." Granma paused, " I can just feel the times when I was cradled on her lap, she smelled sweetly of rosemary or tangy of mint. But most of all I remember her rocking with laughter in a way that made me happy. Oh, and I was sure the face smiled at me.

'Mummy, why ...?' Mum shushed away my question. A gruff voice from deep in a bonnet said,

'I heard she had a hard start.' Heads nodded in agreement. The lady topped with a little lace cap added firmly,

'Amy was a lovely girl.' quickly clipped by the gruff like woman, adding,

'But he was a beastly ma- .' a sharp intake of breath through many sets of clenched teeth cut the speaker's flow. In the lull, a thud on the polished floorboards turned glances, lingering with distain, towards a large mothball; I had seen it fall from the folds of a skirt. Eyes followed as it rolled across the floor and when it stopped under the coffin, well then, I was certain Grandmother Amy Hartshorn really had smiled at me.

Silence again descended shrouding sad looks. A stomach rumbled.

'Sounds like you've left room for the bean feast Lottie?' my Mother said under her breath, loud enough to be heard.

'Oh don't be so course Emily.' Her sister snapped.

A waft of cold air turned all heads. In the doorway stood a tall majestic old lady; her dress filling the space ablaze with marigold orange and pansy blue flowers; a grey fur edged short mauve coloured jacket shaped her body. Even more surprising was that she had one eye hidden by a shimmering silver patch. And, she was hatless. Shock vibrated through the company, the visitor's apparel was obviously so inappropriate to the occasion.

'That's the French woman.' Came a hiss, followed by,

'Hmph! a la mode I suppose?' a reply containing more than a hinted sneer.

With a cheeky wink from her visible eye and a nod to those that breathed, the lady walked unbidden across to the coffin followed by stern looks from the women and surreptitious smiles from the men. The air seemed to prickle with expectation.

'Hallo Mother.' The visitor addressed Gran as if she was lying in her bed. For a long while the woman's faraway look filled time before she patted Gran's folded hands, whispering, 'Thank you for Sally. Sleep well.' To my surprise my own Grandmother Annie, stood up and held out her hand,

'Carlotta?' she asked. The lady turned with such a graceful movement.

'Annie?' she replied. The two women went out of the room into the hallway where I saw them embrace then move away talking and out of my sight.

'Now that's how they used to treat funerals in my youth,' the lady with the lace cap said, 'gay colours and thanks for your company.'

'Aunt Martha how can you be so disrespectful.'

'Quite easily Lizzie, Amy would have laughed at all this heavy black sentimentality. We were close friends all our lives, I know she was happy and fulfilled.' Martha wasn't a blood relative but being Amy's friend she was our Aunt of respect. Gruffy face hadn't given up and interrupting once again, blurting out,

'But what about the first one, they say he was a ....?'

'A head turner, oh yes he was that alright, and more.' Martha announced,

'What more could there be? Tch! we all have our bad experiences.'

'It was more than a bad experience, Martha added, 'There's murder too.' In that instance a lady stood up saying briskly,

'Oh, come away George we're not listening to any more of this.' My mother's cousin by marriage, Amelia's imperious voice dropped to a whisper, 'Martha's always telling tall stories.'

'This is no tall story; perhaps now the time is right to reveal this episode of family history; I'm the last one left who can tell you.' Martha may have been 105 but her hearing was still sharp. Just as sharp came back the retort.

'Haw! But not murder, we don't have murders in our family.' proclaimed Amelia.

'That's what she thinks!' Martha shot back under her breath.

'What would the neighbours say?' My Mother mimicked behind her hand. Amelia gave Mother such a look, while tugging hard at her husband's coat sleeve.

'Amy was my Grandmother too you know, 'melia.' George reminded his wife. Nevertheless he allowed her to drag him away; not before my mum caught his eye lifting a drinking motion to her lips as she mouthed, 'Come back later, new barrel.' George winked as his wife pushed him through the door in front of her, saying,

'A funeral is no place for this kind of talk, especially with the box still open.

'Oh close the box then.' Martha said with a brisk finality. 'My turn next.' And she laughed, a laugh tinged with sadness.

Then somebody noticed me.

'Hush the child in the room.' And I was swiftly hustled out and into the perfumed wake left by the beautiful woman with the eye patch.

'Hush the child,' Clara repeated. "At the time I did not like being hustled out of the room, but I've never let a good story pass me by.

After the funeral Aunt Martha was staying with my Grandparents, John and Annie Pilbeam at their Inn, The Lamb on Pevensey Levels in East Sussex; and it was there she told the story of Amy's life as only she could, because the pair had been close friends all their lives."

In the firelight a cheeky grin spread across Clara's face.

"I know what you're thinking." She said, "How could a four year old remember all that adult conversation?" Chuckles and grunts of assent came from the company, "Well I didn't of course. This is what I meant about hearing just a hint of a story at the funeral. No, I didn't hear the full story until the summer of 1910, after great Grandfather died when I joined my Mum clearing out the old family home before the Inn was sold."

Clara took a long pull at her now cooling ginger wine. "It was one of those odd coincidences that got us onto reminiscing about Granny Amy's funeral.

Mother and I thought we had finished the clearing when a voice from above called out, 'Right ho, here we are folks, I'm bringing down the last box.' followed by a hand descending from the loft holding and old tin bowler hat box.

'Oh, I know who that belonged to,' Mother said, 'it was Amy Hartshorn's. Aunt Martha had it in the evening when we met after the funeral. Wait a minute,' Mum said. Setting the box on the table she started to ease open the heavy brass fastening. 'I wonder if -?' The lid was stuck tight but finally opened with a sigh like puff. The smell of rosemary was unmistakable, 'that's Amy's surely.' And there I was again, a little babe, sitting on her lap.

'You're right. No mistaking that perfume. And look, here 're all the rolls of letters and a diary Martha showed us that night. The night Martha told us the story dear old pompous Amelia didn't want to hear.'

'Right then it's time we sat down for a rest and a cuppa,' I said, 'come on Mum, tell me what Martha said.

We went into the back kitchen, I put the kettle on the old range and Mum settled herself at the table.

'It's a long story.' my Mother sighed. So rapping my hands round my cup of tea, I waited for her to begin. 'Well, to start off Martha said something I will never forget, she told us,'

'In every generation there is somebody who passes on family stories, and I warn you, some of this tale I have to tell will be painful to hear, and for me to recall. But as far as the family is concerned, it IS something you need to know.'

1

Head Turner

"Oh yes, Abel Cakebread was a charmer, he certainly turned heads, there's no mistaking that." Martha recalled. "He could charm the socks of your cat. My father Bernie, who was the village butcher, said those who thought themselves anybody wanted to be associated with Cakebread. The man so obviously had money but nobody knew how he got so much. All the locals knew his father had kept a boat for fishing and a bit of smuggling down across the Channel in the early 1770's.

After old man Cakebread died, word got back through the grape vine that young Able took a modest, but beautiful house some distance from where the family grew up, – humph! He had more than just the one. In another luxuriously furnished house, he kept his two sisters, dressing them in elegant expensive clothes. Folks nearby sometimes caught sight of them on the odd occasion they came and went from the house; the pair smiled but never spoke and nobody ever met them socially. It was the local women who Cakebread employed to look after his sisters who whispered of the fashions and appointments in the house.

Cakebread was known to pay well and in gold. Although he had got himself a second boat and kept it in constant use from the harbour, two fishing boats wouldn't have brought in all that wealth. The benefits gained by the few who knew his activities kept their mouths shut tight; besides all those that he slipped a penny or two. They thought him a good chap and although they called him 'Sir,' he seemed just like one of them.

Yes, he was seen around in Society, people thought they knew him but no man could actually say they'd had a conversation with him. Women openly made a play for him. His very aloofness drew them on. He was so damnably good looking. He wore no wig, although it was the fashion of the day, with his glossy raven hair he didn't need one. Coupled with shapely eyebrows and long dark lashes, to some, he was overwhelming – and blast the man, he could have worn anything – and he did. From fashionable town dashing, to fisherman's rough; with a body like his he cut a deuced fine figure. The women found him irresistible.

One lady was heard to comment, 'Have you felt his hands dear? He's no fisherman.' It made some men sick 'don't cher know. People either loved him or hated him there were no grey areas with Abel Cakebread.

"The very thought of him makes my blood curdle." Martha shuddered.

The Town Council received substantial gifts of money, 'for their good deeds,' from this elegantly dressed man who stood so well, so well to be seen in his cut steel buckled shoes. Nobody local had ever received him at their table nor had they been at his, he didn't live in any town, and no town Mayor could, or would, say he knew Cakebread, but his money was readily accepted no questions asked.

Ah! But who bought the neat elegant Merchant's house in the same cobble paved carriageway near to his sisters?' Somebody was in there preparing its readiness. Furnishings were delivered. Then it was locked up and left.

The two boats "The Lucky Maid" and "The Abel" went out regularly, making good hauls of fish and lobsters, the catches sold and his men were well paid. When his shoreline sales were completed, Cakebread mounted his horse that was always at the ready in a hostelry by the harbour, and rode away to nobody knew where.

It seemed he was accepted for his very presence; he was an enigma, even a Cameleon.